INTERNATIONAL SERIES OF MONOGRAPHS ON
PURE AND APPLIED BIOLOGY

Division: **ZOOLOGY**

GENERAL EDITOR: G. A. KERKUT

VOLUME 7

THE CILIATED PROTOZOA

OTHER TITLES IN THE SERIES ON PURE AND APPLIED BIOLOGY

ALFRED KAHL (1877–1946), producer of great monographs on ciliate systematics during the period 1926–1935. His keys to the ciliated protozoa of the world, profusely illustrated with figures of many of the species, have never been equalled in modern times and thus remain indispensable to the taxonomist today.

EMMANUEL FAURÉ-FREMIET (1883–   ), ciliate cytologist, ecologist, morphogeneticist, and systematist who has been making significant contributions to the literature since 1904. His recent revision of the scheme of ciliate classification represents the first major change since the time of Friedrich Stein (1818–1885).

Twentieth century leaders in the study of ciliates
[also see Pl. XXII]

The Ciliated Protozoa:

CHARACTERIZATION, CLASSIFICATION, AND GUIDE TO THE LITERATURE

by

JOHN O. CORLISS

Associate Professor of Zoology
University of Illinois
Urbana, Illinois

PERGAMON PRESS

OXFORD · LONDON · NEW YORK · PARIS

1961

PERGAMON PRESS LTD.
Headington Hill Hall, Oxford
4 & 5 Fitzroy Square, London W.1

PERGAMON PRESS INC.
122 East 55th Street, New York 22, N.Y.
1404 New York Avenue N.W., Washington 5 D.C.
Statler Center 640, 900 Wilshire Boulevard
Los Angeles 17, California

, PERGAMON PRESS S.A.R.L.
24 Rue des Écoles, Paris Vᵉ

PERGAMON PRESS G.m.b.H.
Kaiserstrasse 75, Frankfurt am Main

Library of Congress Card Number 61-9777

Set in Imprint 11 on 12 pt. and printed in Great Britain by
THE BAY TREE PRESS, STEVENAGE, HERTS.

CONTENTS

ILLUSTRATIONS

Acknowledgments—Grateful acknowledgment is made to the following persons or journals for permission to include various figures (as specified below) in the present publication. Original sources of figures which have been modified to a greater or lesser extent in my redrawing of them, however, are not listed here, but are acknowledged in the figure explanations accompanying each plate.

Prof. E. Fauré-Fremiet, for his photograph in the Frontispiece.

Dr. B. M. Klein, for his photograph in Pl. XXII.

Dr. A. Lwoff, for his photograph and that of the late Dr. É. Chatton in Pl. XXII.

Drs. B. Párducz and M. Müller, for the photograph of the late Dr. J. von Gelei in Pl. XXII.

Drs. L. Provasoli and L. E. Noland, for the photograph of the late Dr. A. Kahl in the Frontispiece.

The Journal of Protozoology, for Figs. 1–8, Pl. I; Figs. 1–6, Pl. III; Figs. 3, 4, Pl. IV; Fig. 3, Pl. VIII; Figs. 1–8, Pl. IX; Figs. 1, 3, 4, Pl. XIII; Figs. 1–3, Pl. XIV; Figs. 1, 2, Pl. XV; Fig. 4, Pl. XVI; Fig. 4, Pl. XVII; Fig. 1, Pl. XVIII; Fig. 3, Pl. XIX, Fig. 1; Pl. XX.

Systematic Zoology, for Figs. 1–4, 6, Pl. VII; Figs. 2,4, Pl. VIII; Figs. 1, 2, Pl. XII; Fig. 2, Pl. XIII; Fig. 4, Pl. XIV; Figs. 1, 2, Pl. XVI; Fig. 2, Pl. XVII; Figs. 2, 4, Pl. XVIII; Figs. 2, 4, Pl. XIX; Fig. 2, Pl. XX; Pl. XXI.

PREFACE

THE ciliated protozoa have not been treated monographically, within the confines of a single study, since the encyclopedic works of Bütschli (1887–1889) and Kahl (1930–1935). Even the more recent of these, the invaluable keys and diagnoses by Kahl, omitted consideration of certain parasitic groups and the marine tintinnids. Also, since 1935, the number of taxa of ciliates has nearly doubled at every level below the ordinal group: in families, genera, and species. In the meantime, furthermore, important revisions in the scheme of classification of these protozoa, essentially the first major changes since the time of Stein (1867), have been proposed. But these suggested revisions, and the hypotheses upon which they are based, have never been presented and discussed extensively in any single paper.

It is time to at least stop and take stock. New genera and families need to be fitted into the framework of the proposed classificational scheme endorsed in the present study. It is becoming increasingly difficult to undertake comparative taxonomic studies today until we have gained a broader background knowledge of the current over-all problems facing the ciliate systematist.

The present work represents an attempt to carry out three main objectives: to offer concise characterizations of the major taxa comprising the new scheme of classification; to present an up-to-date list of all the described genera of ciliates considered acceptable; and to include annotated reference to all significant, sizeable works, including the most recent, in the principal areas of research in ciliate protozoology. Major concepts are illustrated and "typical" or representative genera are figured. Particular attention is given to nomenclatural problems, since a number of these have gone unattended for many years.

It is earnestly hoped that specialists in all areas, perhaps in systematics above all, will attack with renewed vigor the many important problems remaining to be done. Certainly the present work has revealed more problems than it has solved.

I am indebted to many persons for concrete assistance during the preparation of this work. Specifically I must at least mention my deep gratitude to Professor E. Fauré-Fremiet, Paris, for his constantly stimulating help, advice, and encouragement first given me during my stay in his laboratories at the Collège de France and at Concarneau, 1951–1952, and continued ever since that most profitable year; to my research assistants and graduate students at the University of Illinois, in particular Miss Margaret Dysart, Miss Louise Weisberg, and Mr. Jacques Berger, for their unstinting aid, especially in checking the bibliographical material involved; to Mr. Lyle Bamber and the library staffs at the University of Illinois for their well-stocked stacks and their patient assistance in locating rare or obscure publications; to Miss Alice Boatright, for her painstaking and most sympathetic execution of all the drawings used here; to Mrs. Ruth Bruckner and Mrs. Suzanne Ford for such cheerful diligence in typing the manuscript; to my understanding wife, Dorothy, for her unselfish moral support in particular; and to Professor P. B. Medawar, University College London, for graciously providing accommodation in his Department of Zoology during completion of the book while I was on sabbatical leave from the University of Illinois, 1960–1961. Finally, I wish to acknowledge the indispensable aid of grants from the National Science Foundation, Washington, D.C.

JOHN O. CORLISS

Part I

CHARACTERIZATION OF THE PRINCIPAL GROUPS

CHAPTER 1

INTRODUCTORY CONSIDERATIONS

THERE is a definite need for revision of the systematics of the ciliates. Extant schemes of classification of this circumscribed assemblage of protozoa stem principally from the authoritative 19th century treatises of Stein, Bütschli, and Schewiakoff. Even the most modern comprehensive taxonomic monographs available, the prodigious works of Kahl, appeared over a quarter of a century ago. In the meantime innumerable descriptions of new ciliates have been published, improved techniques of study have been devised, new ideas of importance concerning phylogenetic inter-relationships have been promulgated. This great accumulation of pertinent data has yet to be digested and carefully incorporated into a revised classificational system of the entire subphylum Ciliophora.

In the present section of this book concise, up-to-date character-izations of the major ciliate groups, accompanied by illustrations of representative genera, are presented in the framework of such a new scheme of classification. Key references to the literature concerned with the biology and systematics of these groups are included, but generally limited to works published within the past twenty-five or thirty years; in fact, the emphasis is on the results of researches completed within the past decade. The invaluable older literature is not neglected in this book, but citation of such papers is reserved primarily for Part III.

The general classificational system followed in Chapters 1–9 is extended and applied to the lower taxonomic levels in Part II, where families and their included genera are considered and where pertinent nomenclatural details are supplied for all taxa.

The final chapter of the present section is devoted to brief treatment of the evolutionary and phylogenetic problems which have influenced the structure of the new classification.

What are the bases for suggesting *any* major changes over

1

conventional classificational schemes? And what is the nature of the specific revision endorsed in this book? These questions recently have been discussed elsewhere (Corliss, 1956a, 1959b, 1960c) and therefore need to be considered only briefly here. Appropriate examples illustrating the several main points made below are provided in the figures of Plates I–VIII.

BASES FOR REVISIONS

1. Emphasis on the infraciliature, as opposed to the externally visible ciliature, in comparative morphological and morphogenetic studies. The infraciliature, consisting essentially of the subpellicularly located basal granules or kinetosomes and associated fibrils of both the somatic and buccal ciliature, has been found to be a more conservative, universal property of ciliates. Thus it is considered a fundamental characteristic of greater reliability in

---

Explanation of Plate I opposite

Photomicrographs, entirely unretouched, of various ciliates impregnated with silver according to the Chatton–Lwoff technique [from Corliss (1959b)].

FIG. 1. A group of *Tetrahymena pyriformis*, showing a number of features of their silverline system: ciliary meridians (longitudinal rows of the argentophilic basal granules or kinetosomes), buccal infraciliature in the oral area of the body, pair of contractile vacuole pores, cytoproct, etc. FIG. 2. Ventral view of *T. setifera*, showing silverline structures at a higher magnification.

FIG. 3. Apico-ventral view of *T.* sp., revealing particularly the infraciliary bases of the AZM (adoral zone of membranelles) in the buccal cavity. FIG. 4. Subequatorial view of the ventral surface of *T. pyriformis* in an early stage of binary fission; note that stomatogenesis has nearly been completed in the posterior filial product, the opisthe. FIG. 5. Apical view of one of the products of division of *T. patula*, depicting clearly the tetrahymenal organization of the buccal apparatus.

FIG. 6. Ventral view of *Glaucoma scintillans*, at a deep focal level which shows the bases of the tripartite AZM with diagrammatic clarity. FIGS. 7 and 8. Ventral views of *Euplotes* spp., revealing the infraciliary bases of the somatic cirri and the buccal membranelles; the longitudinal rows of argentophilic granules seen here, bases of the so-called sensory bristles, are showing through from the dorsal surface of these dorso-ventrally flattened ciliates.

PLATE I

comparative taxonomic investigations than any other single anatomical feature. Even when external ciliature is absent in some stage of the life cycle, an infraciliature persists.

2. Renewed attention to full life cycles. The forms of ciliates most commonly found in nature generally represent " mature " stages in the life history. As has long been known, study of such forms alone may be quite misleading from the point of view of the organism's most appropriate taxonomic position. Discovery and proper recognition of " larval " or other developmental stages in ciliate ontogenies are highly desirable and are of particular value today with the availability of new techniques and hypotheses (see pp. 7–8). In modern approaches to comparative ciliate systematics less commonly known parts of life cycles have, in several outstanding instances, played a significant role in revision of conventional classificational schemes. In such cases the facts discovered have been coupled with the hypothesis that ontogenetic stages may hold clues of phylogenetic, and thus classificational, value.

3. Realization of the importance of morphogenetic phenomena in solution of systematic and phylogenetic problems. Morphogenesis, " the coming-into-being of characteristic and specific form in living organisms " (Needham), can be studied to advantage in protozoa as well as metazoa. This is particularly true in studies which I have called " experimental embryology at the protozoan level " (Corliss, 1953d). Morphogenetic events may be investigated from a comparative taxonomic point of view in natural life cycles as well as in experimentally planned laboratory problems involving regeneration, etc.

Explanation of Plate II opposite

A single specimen of *Tetrahymena setifera* impregnated with silver by the Chatton–Lwoff technique.

FIGS. 1–12. Unretouched photomicrographs taken under oil immersion at twelve different optical levels from the apical to the posterior pole. Note the continuity of the ciliary meridians or kineties down the entire length of the organism's body. The prominent dark spot marks the location of the oral apparatus; the centrally located dark area in FIGS. 9–11 represents the macronucleus.

[I am indebted to Mr. Luis de la Torre for preparation of this unusual set of photomicrographs.]

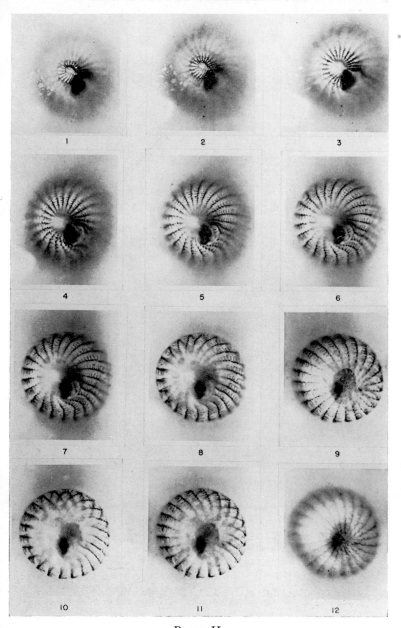

PLATE II

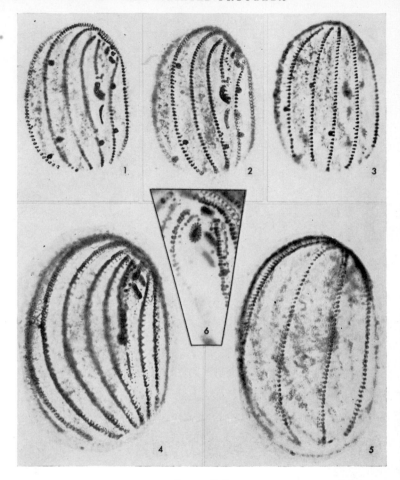

PLATE III

Unretouched photomicrographs of two species of *Pseudomicro-thorax* impregnated with silver by the Chatton–Lwoff technique [from Corliss (1958d)].

FIGS. 1–3. Three focal levels of a single specimen of *P. agilis*, from high ventral to dorsal surface. To be noted especially are these components of the silverline system: the kinetosomes comprising the ciliary meridians, the bases of the four parts of the buccal apparatus (upper right), the contractile vacuole pore and curved tubule (centrally located), and the slit-like cytoproct.

FIGS. 4–6. Ventral and dorsal surfaces of *P. dubius*, showing the

4. Recognition of homologous structures in ciliates assigned to different taxonomic groups. There has long been a natural tendency among specialists to develop a particular terminology for characteristics revealed in studies of a circumscribed group without an attempt to consider the possible homologies with features exhibited by organisms belonging to the other major taxa within the same subphylum. This has especially been true with regard to structures in the oral region, and an extensive " mouth-part terminology " has impeded our taxonomic progress because it has not allowed ready recognition of identical or homologous features possessed in common by diverse ciliates (Corliss, 1955b, 1959b; Fauré-Fremiet, 1961).

5. Application of new techniques of study. Foremost among these must be mentioned the discovery of methods of silver impregnation, since the ciliary basal granules were found to be argentophilic. Thus the infraciliature could be studied intensively during all stages in the life cycle, morphogenetic events could be examined in detail, mouth-part structures could be elucidated with precision. Leaders in development of these all-important silver techniques include Klein, who discovered the dry method in 1926 in Vienna; von Gelei, who used modifications of the technique in an impressive series of investigations carried out in Hungary; and Chatton and Lwoff, who produced the French refinement which has played the most significant part of all in comparative studies of ciliates since 1930. (See Part III for further discussion of specific contributions of these protozoologists.) Within the past decade electron microscopical investigations, now steadily on the increase, have begun to serve as an indication that ultrastructural studies will be of considerable value in systematic work of the future.

---

same anatomical features just noted. In the enlarged picture of the buccal area (FIG. 6) may be detected the proximal ends of the so-called trichites comprising the armature of the organism's cytostome-cytopharyngeal complex. It is the simultaneous possession of a hymenostome-like AZM and UM (adoral zone of membranelles and undulating membrane) plus the gymnostome-like cytopharyngeal trichites that places *Pseudomicrothorax* in the possible role of a taxonomic " missing link " (see text).

6. Promulgation of new hypotheses plus reinterpretation of older ones. Most important in this connection have been the heuristic ideas of Chatton and Fauré-Fremiet (see Corliss, 1956a, for specific consideration of these proposals; and see citations in Part III). Hypotheses of greatest significance in revision of conventional ciliate schemes of classification include: the autonomy and genetic continuity of the kinety (the infraciliary basal granules or kinetosomes plus associated fibrils or kinetodesmata); the rule of desmodexy (the kinetodesma lies to the right of its row of kinetosomes); the pluripotency of the kinetosome in morphogenetic phenomena (such as new mouth formation or stomatogenesis); the

---

Explanation of Plate IV opposite

Drawings of various features of taxonomic importance which comprise the silverline system of ciliates.

FIG. 1. Ventral view of a dividing *Tetrahymena pyriformis*, showing diagrammatically the primary meridians formed by the rows of argentophilic basal granules or kinetosomes and the essential infraciliary structures of the tetrahymenal buccal apparatus in both the proter and the opisthe [redrawn from Corliss (1952a)]. FIG. 2. Enlargement of the anterior end of the ventral surface of the same species; the lines coursing between the primary meridians represent the argentophilic but generally non-granular secondary meridians [redrawn from Corliss (1953a)].

FIG. 3. Posterior polar view of *T. pyriformis*, showing details of structures revealed by silver impregnation: note particularly the primary and secondary meridians, the two contractile vacuole pores, and the single cytoproct [from Holz and Corliss (1956), originally redrawn from Corliss (1952a)]. FIG. 4. Posterior polar view of *T. setifera*, showing the same details as mentioned for Fig. 3 plus the prominent polar basal granule-complex which represents the infraciliature of the long caudal cilium possessed by this species [redrawn from Holz and Corliss (1956)].

FIG. 5. Ventral view of *Euplotes eurystomus*, showing particularly the prominent infraciliary bases of the cirri, the bases of the individual parts of the AZM (adoral zone of membranelles), and the " chicken-wire " mesh-work of argentophilic fibres(?) all over the surface [redrawn from Chatton and Séguéla (1940)]. FIG. 6. Dorsal view of the same silver-impregnated specimen of *E. eurystomus*: note especially the rows of the bases of the so-called sensory bristles; the short black lines at the anterior end represent an extension of the AZM from the ventral surface [redrawn from Chatton and Séguéla (1940)].

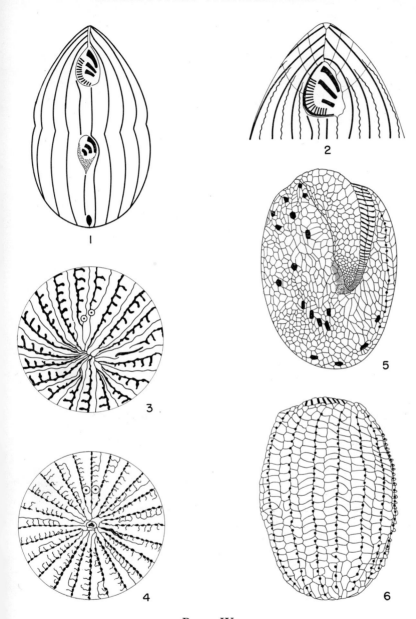

PLATE IV

Explanation of Plate V opposite

Illustration of certain concepts of value in ciliate systematics (see also Pls. VI–IX).

Figs. 1–3. The " Rule of Desmodexy," illustrating the independence and polarity of the kinety — the all-important infraciliary structure comprised of the allegedly autonomous, self-duplicating argentophilic basal granules or kinetosomes plus the argentophobic kinetodesma which always lies to the (organism's) right of the associated kinetosomes [modified from figures in Chatton and Lwoff (1935b)]. Fig. 1. View of the left side of a ciliate such as *Tetrahymena*, showing diagrammatically the path of a kinety on this side and also, depicted with a lighter line and circles instead of dots, the path of a kinety on the opposite (right) side of the organism, as it would be seen *through* the body. Two points, especially, should be noted: the position of the kinetodesma to the right of the line of kinetosomes, endowing the organism with polarity; the independence, at both poles of the body, of the two kineties shown. In reproduction of the ciliate the kineties are transected (" perkinetal fission "), replacing their missing halves with subsequent growth. Fig. 2. Apical polar view, illustrating how the rule of desmodexy shows the absolute impossibility of continuity " over the top " of the two kineties coursing poleward from left and right sides of the body: if the kinetodesmata were one (i.e., united), the kinetosomes would have to jump across the single kinetodesma at the pole, an inconceivable situation. Fig. 3. Posterior polar view, offering equally strong support for the independence of the longitudinal kineties. Modern electron microscopical studies have verified this important Chattonian concept.

Figs. 4 and 5. The contrast between homothetogenic and symmetrogenic types of fission [figures original but based on text and diagrams offered by Chatton and Villeneuve (1937)]. Fig. 4. View of the right side of a ciliate such as *Tetrahymena*, a stage late in fission. The condition of homothety is ideally illustrated in the shapes and locations of the two oral areas and of various silverline structures such as the ciliary meridians, the cytoproct, and the contractile vacuole pores. Fig. 5. View of fission in a generalized phytoflagellate. The symmetrogenic or mirror-image type of division is deliberately idealized here for sake of contrast. Even as many ciliates fail to demonstrate perfect homothetogenic fission, flagellates may not show completely mirror-image duplication of cytoplasmic organelles. Such modifications or exceptions, however, probably should not be considered to invalidate the basic Chattonian hypotheses involved.

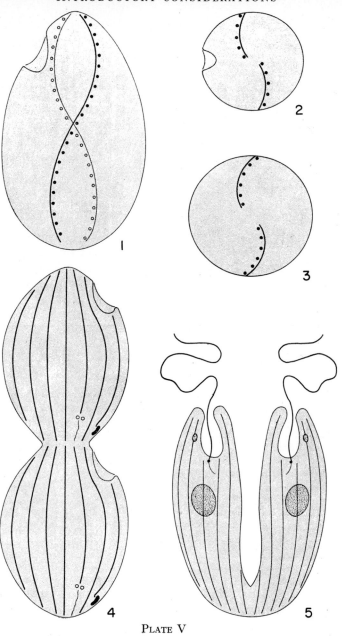

PLATE V

concept of homothetogenic fission for ciliates (as opposed to the symmetrogenic division of flagellates); recognition of the probable homology of buccal organelles comprising the oral apparatus of a great variety of ciliates; full realization of the taxonomic significance of larval or migratory stages in the life cycles of sedentary forms.

Major Differences in New Scheme

The classification of ciliates adopted in this book had its inception in the brief but stimulating paper published by Fauré-Fremiet (1950a) eleven years ago. There are four areas of major change in comparison with the systems contained in the current authoritative texts of Doflein and Reichenow (1949–1953), Dogiel (1951), Grell (1956), Hall (1953), Jírovec *et al.* (1953), and Kudo (1954). The ciliate classification in these widely followed text-books is fundamentally derived from Kahl's (1930–1935) refinement of Bütschli's (1887–1889) scheme, although a certain commendable amount of extension and modernization exists in several of the works cited.

Explanation of Plate VI opposite

Illustration of ideas concerning the ultrastructure of the infraciliature of ciliated protozoa.

Fig. 1. A drawing of pellicular and subpellicular elements of *Paramecium* offered by Grell, who bases his concept primarily on the electron microscopical observations of Metz *et al.* (1953): note particularly the cilia, the trichocysts, and the relationship between the basal granules of the cilia and the associated kinetodesmal fibrils [redrawn from Grell (1956)].

Fig. 2. A composite drawing of pellicular and subpellicular organelles of *Paramecium* (*P. bursaria*) representing the ideas of Ehret and Powers, who suggest several differences at both factual and interpretative levels: note the entwined, twisted nature of the kinetodesma compounded of the individual kinetodesmal fibrils; a newly discovered structure, the minute parasomal sac; and the relationship of the complex pellicular units to each other and to the cilia, which occur in pairs in this species [redrawn, with some modification, from Ehret and Powers (1959)]. The paper of Ehret and Powers should be consulted for a clear exposition of their findings and of preceding concepts of both current and historical significance.

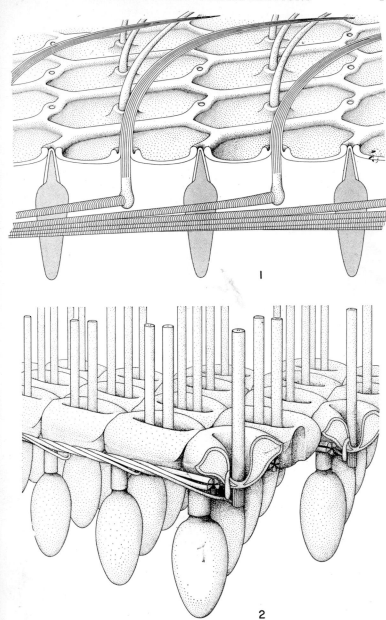

1

2

PLATE VI

Explanation of Plate VII opposite

Illustration of certain concepts of value in ciliate systematics.

FIGS. 1 and 2. Views of the infraciliature, somewhat schematized, of mature and dividing stages in the life cycle of the trichostome *Tillina*, illustrating a simplification of axial relationships in the divisional stage which may be considered to recapitulate ancestral conditions [from Corliss (1953d, 1956a), originally redrawn from Tuffrau (1952)]. FIG. 1. Mature, free-swimming stage: note the contorted arrangement of the ciliary meridians or kineties; the large depression represents the vestibulum (the cytostome is out of sight). FIG. 2. Stage of division, occurring within a cystic membrane which is not depicted: note the loss of a specialized oral area, the gain of a simple polarity, and the straight-forward perkinetal mode of fission. This stage is strikingly reminiscent of the division stage of a typical rhabdophorine gymnostome.

FIGS. 3 and 4. The infraciliature in pre-budding stages of the suctorian *Podophrya*, revealing both the existence of kinetosomes in the mature stages in the life cycle and the origin of the kineto-somes *and the cilia* in the free-swimming migratory (larval) stage of the cycle [from Corliss (1956a), originally redrawn from Chatton *et al.* (1929)]. FIG. 3. Erratic distribution of the argentophilic basal granules or kinetosomes of the cilia-less adult suctorian, with an area of multiplication of granules destined to be involved in the morphogenetics of the fission-by-budding process. FIG. 4. A slightly later stage; note that the granules in the specialized, formerly anarchic, field have now become aligned in rows to form an orderly pattern: these are the kinetosomes which, as part of the body of the bud, will produce the holotrichous ciliation of the larval suctorian. For a much later stage, showing the ciliated bud nearly separated from the parental form, see Fig. 2, Pl. XIII.

FIGS. 5 and 6. Ventral views of a bud of the chonotrich *Chilo-dochona* and of the mature stage of the cyrtophorine gymnostome *Chilodonella*, illustrating the striking similarities in their infraciliary patterns [Fig. 5 redrawn from Guilcher (1950); Fig. 6 from Corliss (1956a), originally redrawn from MacDougall (1936)]. FIG. 5. The transient, migratory stage in the life cycle of *Chilodochona*, revealing a morphology which is totally unlike the mature, sedentary stage (e.g., contrast it with the adult stage of the related genus *Spirochona* shown in Fig. 2, Pl. XII). In many details (see text), on the other hand, it resembles closely various members of the second suborder of the Gymnostomatida. FIG. 6. A representative cyrtophorine gymnostome, *Chilodonella*, showing characteristics which, from a postulated phylogenetic point of view, allow one to consider it much more closely related to the chonotrichs than ever suspected before the work of Guilcher (1950, 1951).

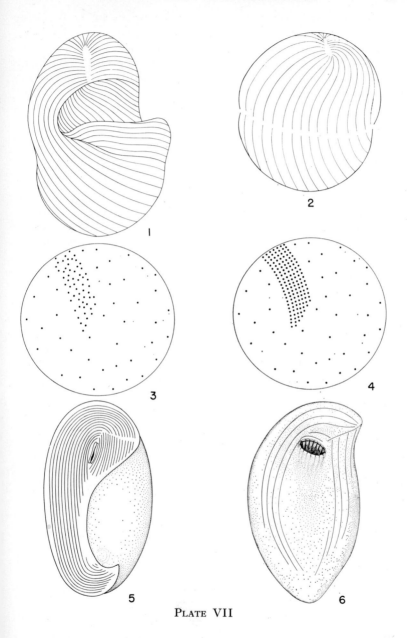

PLATE VII

The significant revisions are discussed briefly in the following paragraphs. Minor alterations at the lower taxonomic levels are explained and incorporated into the system in Part II.

1. The " protociliates " or opalinids (Metcalf, 1909, 1923, 1940) have been excluded *in toto* from the Ciliophora. Recent reviews of this still-controversial subject may be found in Grassé (1952) and Corliss (1955a, 1960c). Arguments for the zooflagellate

---

Explanation of Plate VIII opposite

The problem of " the most primitive ciliate." A common view is that the opalinids are truly " protociliates," with all " euciliates " derived therefrom. Other protozoologists hold that the mouthless astome ciliates must have been " first " among ciliated protozoa. The view which I endorse is that the rhabdophorine gymnostomes are today's representatives of the most primitive ciliates. Although everyone is in general agreement that ciliates probably had a zooflagellate ancestry, which — if any — present day group of flagellates is to be implicated is quite unanswerable. The figures show some of the characteristics of representatives of the kinds of protozoa involved in the controversy of ciliate prototypes. FIG. 1. A mouthless, hypermastigote zooflagellate, *Holomastigotoides*, showing extensive coverage of the body by spirally wound rows of flagella, organelles ultrastructurally identical with cilia; it is unlikely that such a specialized, highly evolved, symbiotic flagellate would be the progenitor of any ciliate group [redrawn from Cleveland (1949)]. FIG. 2. A mouthless, opalinid " paraflagellate," *Opalina*, with indication of the many diagonally oriented rows of short locomotor organelles and a large number of monomorphic nuclei (lightly dotted circles); for reasons explained in the text, I do not consider this protozoon directly ancestral to ciliates [from Corliss (1960c), originally redrawn from various sources]. FIG. 3. A mouthless, astome holotrich, *Anoplophrya*, showing a superficially simple body form and ciliation; but astomes, living entirely symbiotic lives, show a number of specializations (see text) and it is likely that their mouthlessness is a secondary acquisition related to their mode of life [from Corliss (1959b), originally redrawn from various sources]. FIG. 4. A primitive-appearing, rhabdophorine gymnostome holotrich, *Prorodon*, with apically located mouth unadorned with any vestibular or buccal ciliature and with a body exhibiting essentially radial symmetry; it is not difficult to imagine this type of protozoon as the prototype of the ciliate subphylum (see text) [from Corliss (1956a, 1959b), originally redrawn from Fauré-Fremiet (1924)].

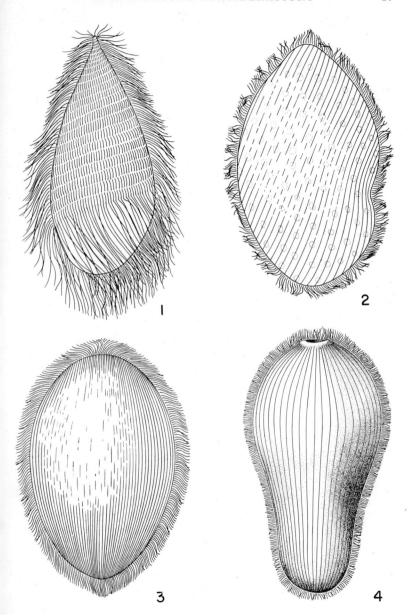

PLATE VIII

affinities of these taxonomically enigmatic protozoa include recognition of their nuclear monomorphism, their alleged symmetrogenic type of fission, their exhibition of syngamy. Their acentric mitoses, possession of " cilia " (very weak argument), and occasional demonstration of presumed homothetogenic division (Wessenberg, 1957) appear to ally them with ciliates. Other characteristics, such as large body size, mouthlessness, and various features of their host–parasite relationship, are of no taxonomic value at the higher levels.

If one admits that the opalinids surely have enjoyed a long evolutionary history of their own and that they are not closely allied to any present-day group of " higher " zooflagellates, then it would seem that their non-ciliate characteristics would similarly prevent their being considered a taxon within the subphylum Ciliophora. In endorsing this view, I am in agreement with the authoritative works of several European taxonomists who have recently treated the problem (Biocca, 1957, 1958; Fauré-Fremiet, 1950a; Grassé, 1952; Jírovec et al., 1953, Piekarski, 1954; Raabe, 1948; Ulrich, 1950).

In Plate VIII, *Opalina* may be compared pictorially with a hypermastigote flagellate, an astome ciliate, and a gymnostome ciliate, forms which all represent major groups involved in the controversial taxonomic disposition of Metcalf's ill-named " protociliates." Still further studies are needed on the problem, but it is doubtful if absolutely indisputable " proof " in support of either of the opposing views can ever be found.

2. The number of major groups comprising the subphylum Ciliophora has been reduced to two. These two taxa, the Holotricha and the Spirotricha, are recognized as subclasses within a single class, the Ciliata. This represents a major change in that the entire ciliate assemblage is now considered much more homogeneous and more closely knit than heretofore supposed. Even the level at which the two groups themselves are separated is low enough to indicate a closeness of relationship not recognized in current schemes of classification.

3. Several groups conventionally accorded high independent status are relegated to subordinate positions. Specifically, the chonotrich, peritrich, and suctorian groups are considered as orders within the subclass Holotricha. The change is greatest for

the suctorians but, nevertheless, major for the other groups as well, particularly in view of the additional changes noted below (point 4). The bases for these moves have been discussed previously (Corliss, 1956a, 1958e, 1960c) and the shifts are intimately involved in certain evolutionary considerations treated in Chapter 10. Thus only brief mention of the cases need be presented here.

The chonotrichs are taken into the holotrich fold on the evidences of their close relationship with cyrtophorine gymnostomes uncovered by Guilcher (1951). Use of the silver technique in study of the morphogenetic events associated with the production of larval forms in the life cycle of a variety of species led her to the irrefutable conclusion that close affinities must exist between these two groups, relationships never suspected before. Figures 5 and 6, Plate VII, illustrate one of the striking parallels discovered by Guilcher. Supporting evidences have been found in comparative studies of macronuclear structure and of the area of the body which produces an organelle of fixation in both gymnostomes and chonotrichs (Fauré-Fremiet, 1957b,c; Fauré-Fremiet and Guilcher, 1947; Fauré-Fremiet et al., 1956a; Tuffrau, 1953).

The peritrichs are considered holotrichs on comparative morphological evidence and on theoretical phylogenetic evidence (see esp. Corliss, 1956a, 1960c). Further discussion in the present work is reserved for Chapters 6 and 10, but it may be briefly emphasized here that the seemingly unique characteristics possessed by peritrichs are also found scattered among other orders of holotrichs. Although recognizing that these interesting ciliates have undergone considerable evolutionary development apart from even their closest relatives, I continue to believe that they are best considered as holotrichs, in spite of doubts expressed in the recent literature (Finley et al., 1959; Hyman, 1959).

The shift of the suctorians, probably considerably less like other ciliates than the two groups discussed above, into the subclass Holotricha apparently will meet, however, with little resistance (see Hyman, 1959; and the trend is even apparent in Doflein and Reichenow, 1949–1953). The principal work of significance is again that of Guilcher (1951), although her thorough investigations were preceded by important papers of Kahl (1931a) and Chatton et al. (1929). Figures 3 and 4 of Plate VII are based on the important discovery made by Chatton and colleagues, *viz.*, that there is a direct continuity between the infraciliature of the mature suctorian, devoid of external ciliature, and that of the cilia-bearing larval form. Kahl made much of the possession of tentacles by certain rhabdophorine gymnostomes (see Fig. 2, Pl. XI).

4. A number of erstwhile suborders have been raised to ordinal rank within the two subclasses Holotricha and Spirotricha. These taxonomic shifts have been proposed in recognition of a greater independence of certain of the groups, some of which have been set up relatively recently, than heretofore acknowledged. Also, in many cases, such revision was almost inevitable inasmuch as the holotrichs and spirotrichs are conventionally considered to represent ordinal groups only, themselves: thus former subordinal taxa would be raised automatically upon consideration of "Holotricha" and "Spirotricha" as subclasses. In a few instances this procedure has necessitated creation of new suborders within the groups now recognized as independent orders.

Uniform endings of ordinal and subordinal names are adopted in the present work: specifically, the suffixes "-ida" and "-ina." This is in accord with my own previous usage (e.g., Corliss, 1956a, 1957a, 1959b); also, see Part II of this book. Use of such terminations for these higher taxa does not alter the original authorship or date of the name, and a certain amount of uniformity seems desirable for obvious reasons.

Table I is offered as a convenient summary of the major changes in the scheme of ciliate classification followed here.

Selection of " Typical " Genera

In Chapters 2–9, " typical " or " representative " genera are proposed for each of the higher taxa. Some explanation of this action is in order.

The desirability of having actual *type* (not " typical ") genera for suprafamilial categories was considered in a favorable way at the Colloquium on Zoological Nomenclature which met in Copenhagen eight years ago (Hemming, 1953). The proposal that such type genera would aid in bringing about greater uniformity and stability in zoological taxonomy was subsequently

TABLE I

COMPARISON OF THE CONVENTIONAL SCHEME OF CILIATE
CLASSIFICATION WITH THE REVISED SCHEME ENDORSED IN
THE PRESENT WORK

Conventional Scheme	*Present Scheme*
Subphylum CILIOPHORA	Subphylum CILIOPHORA
Class I. Ciliata	Class Ciliata
Subclass 1. Protociliata	Subclass I. Holotricha
2. Euciliata	Order 1. Gymnostomatida
Order 1. Holotricha	Suborder (1) Rhabdophorina ✓
Suborder 1. Astomata	(2) Cyrtophorina ✓
2. Gymnostomata	2. Trichostomatida ✓
Tribe (1) Prostomata	3. Chonotrichida ✓
(2) Pleurostomata	4. Suctorida
(3) Hypostomata	5. Apostomatida
3. Trichostomata	6. Astomatida
4. Hymenostomata	7. Hymenostomatida
5. Thigmotricha	(1) Tetrahymenina
(1) Stomodea	(2) Peniculina
(2) Rhynchodea	(3) Pleuronematina
6. Apostomea	8. Thigmotrichida
2. Spirotricha	(1) Arhynchodina
1. Heterotricha	(2) Rhynchodina
2. Oligotricha	9. Peritrichida
3. Tintinnoinea	(1) Sessilina
4. Entodiniomorpha	(2) Mobilina
5. Ctenostomata	Subclass II. Spirotricha
6. Hypotricha	Order 1. Heterotrichida
3. Chonotricha	Suborder (1) Heterotrichina
4. Peritricha	(2) Licnophorina
1. Mobilia	2. Oligotrichida
2. Sessilia	3. Tintinnida
	4. Entodiniomorphida
Class II. Suctoria	5. Odontostomatida
	6. Hypotrichida

7 Stoymuyamashita

incorporated into Bradley's (1957) exhaustive draft of a revision of the International Rules of Zoological Nomenclature. But at the Colloquium convening with the XVth International Congress of Zoology in London in July, 1958, the Copenhagen decisions on this matter were completely reversed: it was decided that the revised *Code* (still awaited at the time of this writing) will make no attempt to control nomenclatural practices at the higher systematic levels.

In the interim between the two colloquia mentioned above, I made attempts to lay the groundwork for later formal designation of types for the orders and suborders of the ciliated protozoa (Corliss, 1958a–c). The difficulties in applying the type concept at such levels became apparent in this preliminary work. The genera which I once had in mind as " type genera " will now serve adequately as " typical genera," having been chosen as the most appropriate or most representative, taxonomically, morphologically, and, when possible, even nomenclaturally. I believe that there is some value in associating certain specified genera and their names with given high-level taxa, particularly if the genera are widely known, easily identified, of common occurrence, and quite typical in their exhibition of anatomical features important in characterization of these higher taxa. In some instances the genus may have been chosen from among the more primitive members of an order; in others, from quite highly evolved forms.

Thus, in the present work, "typical" (but without maintaining the quotation marks) genera are designated for each taxonomic category above the family-level. This is done with full awareness of the attendant difficulties and drawbacks. Other generic names of common forms also are frequently mentioned, but generally only species of the so-called typical genera are used as illustrations in the figures comprising Plates XI–XXI.

CHAPTER 2

THE SUBPHYLUM CILIOPHORA
AND ITS SUPRAORDINAL TAXA

THE ciliates, embracing nearly 6,000 species described to date, comprise a highly differentiated assemblage of forms which is generally agreed to represent the most homogeneous group in the entire phylum Protozoa. Ranging in size from ten to 3,000μ, most ciliates are free-living forms found abundantly in a variety of fresh-water and marine habitats. A few groups live wholly in symbiotic association with other organisms, generally as harmless ecto- or endocommensals. Many species are seemingly ubiquitous; others have very restricted or specialized habitats. In any situation ciliates generally are the most conspicuous of the protozoa present, even in such an environment as the soil.

Six major characteristics are useful in distinguishing members of the Ciliophora from protozoa belonging to the other commonly recognized subphyla:* the Sarcodina, Mastigophora, and Sporozoa. Although not entirely unique, these properties *in combination* are definitely distinctive of ciliates. They may be treated very briefly as follows:

(1) Possession of simple cilia or compound ciliary organelles, often in abundance, in at least one stage of the life cycle. Examples of externally visible ciliary structures, buccal and somatic, simple or complex, may be found in the illustrations of typical ciliates in Plates XI–XX.

(2) Presence, without exception, of some sort of *infra*ciliature located at a subpellicular level in the cortex. The infraciliature

---

*There is considerable interest today in revision of these non-ciliate groups. In one suggested scheme (Corliss, 1960c), three subphyla are recognized (under the names of Mastigamoebaea, Sporozoa, and Cnidosporidia); but their boundaries do not correspond with the three conventional groups listed above.

consists essentially of the basal granules or kinetosomes associated with cilia and ciliary organelles at their bases plus certain more or less interconnecting longitudinal fibrils, the kinetodesmata (Figs. 1, 2, Pl. VI). The universality, stability, and persistence of this complex throughout the entire life cycle of all ciliates (" once a ciliate, always an infraciliature:" Corliss, 1959a) strongly suggest that it is a conservative, fundamental property of these protozoa.

(3) Possession of two kinds of nuclei. Their manifestation of nuclear dimorphism has long set ciliates apart from other protozoa (Figs. 1–12, Pl. X). The smaller, frequently spherical micronucleus, of which there may be several in a single organism or occasionally none (in amicronucleate strains), contains recognizable chromosomes and appears to behave much as the unitary nucleus possessed by other protozoa and by cells of multicellular organisms in general. Centrioles are yet to be indisputably demonstrated in ciliates, however, so mitotic divisions are considered acentric. The macronucleus is typically larger, fewer in number, but more bizarre in form. At least one macronucleus is indispensable* for continued life of a ciliate; and, although chromosomes as such have not yet been identified here, this polyploid nucleus is considered to have genic control over the ciliate phenotype.

(4) Exhibition of a unique type of binary fission best described as homothetogenic†. Typically, division cuts across the kineties or ciliary meridians of the body; in such cases the convenient term " perkinetal fission " may be used (Fig. 4, Pl. V).

(5) Lack of the usual methods of sexual reproduction. Ciliates do not show syngamy, with fusion of free isogamous or anisogamous gametes. Important processes involving meiotic divisions, such as conjugation, autogamy, and cytogamy, may be considered

---

*And yet its own origin is micronuclear in nature during the occurrence of sexual, and occasionally asexual, phenomena. Some macronuclei, incidentally, appear to be able to undergo reorganizational processes independently of the micronucleus.

†Division of a single ciliate into its filial products, the anterior of which is known as the proter, the posterior as the opisthe, demonstrates homothety with respect to identical structures possessed by each resulting organism (see Fig. 4, Pl. V). The descriptive term " transverse," widely used in definition of ciliate fission, unfortunately is both too restrictive and less exact, although popularly employed.

examples of sexual phenomena but not, strictly speaking, sexual reproduction. " Gametic " and " zygotic " nuclei are involved, but not true gametes and zygotes in the conventional meaning of these terms. The reproduction in or following the ciliate sexual processes is by straightforward means of asexual binary fission. Recognition of parallels at the genetic level is not precluded by considering that these protozoa lack means of " true " sexual reproduction. The fundamental significance of the micronuclear events which take place during conjugation, autogamy, or cytogamy, is, of course, identical with that of the nuclear processes occurring in gamete formation in metazoa and other protozoa.

(6) Possession of a functional mouth, often associated with a well-defined buccal or peristomial cavity equipped with compound ciliary organelles of aid in feeding (Figs. 1–8, Pl. IX). Some ciliates, however, are completely astomatous; these forms live saprozoically, frequently as endocommensal symbionts of metazoan hosts. Certain other species possess sucking tentacles, functionally related to cytostomes but not necessarily structurally homologous.

Other quite notable features in ciliate life cycles, such as the widespread occurrence of encysted forms at certain stages, the ability to secrete stalks or build loricae, and the exhibition of a variety of nutritional proclivities, are not listed in the preceding characterization for two reasons: either they are not shown by or known for the majority of ciliates or they are displayed by some species belonging to non-ciliate taxa of the Protozoa.

It is, of course, impossible to select a single genus to represent adequately all the diverse groups within the extensive subphylum Ciliophora. For any large group of plants or animals there always will be difficulty in designating any one form as " representative " or " typical." Nevertheless, if a single genus is to be chosen, I should favor *Paramecium* (Fig. 3, Pl. XIV), whose long-studied species represent well-known, easily recognized holotrichous ciliates which share many characteristics with members of all major groups within the subphylum. I cannot endorse Copeland's (1956) choice of the peritrich *Vorticella*, a much less typical ciliophoran (see Fig. 1, Pl. XVI). His reason for selecting this Linnean genus was based solely on the antiquity of its name.

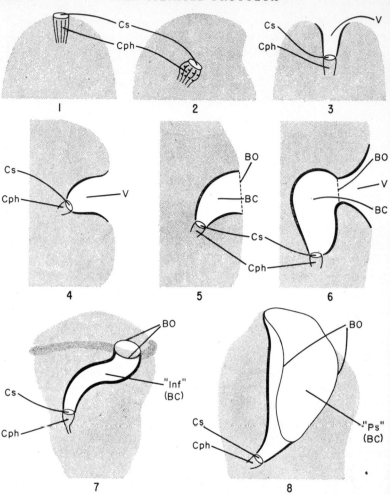

PLATE IX

Diagrammatic representations of non-ciliary structures or cavities in the oral area of the body of various ciliates. An outline of adjacent parts of the body is shown by the stippling [from Corliss (1959b)]. Legend and abbreviated definitions: BC — buccal cavity, containing the bases of buccal membranes and membranelles (not shown); BO — buccal overture; Cph — cytopharynx (re-enforced with " trichites " in organisms of Figs. 1 and 2); Cs — cytostome or true " cell mouth "; " inf " — infundibulum (a specialized kind

Class CILIATA

Single class. The characteristics are thus those of the sub-phylum, as enumerated on preceding pages. I strongly favor retention of this single class instead of elevating the two sub-classes which comprise it to independent class status, a move which, admittedly, would allow us to dispense with the category " Class Ciliata " entirely. The latter action may seem attractive to some protozoologists. My own reason for preservation of the Ciliata is simply this: keeping the Holotricha and Spirotricha at the lower (subclass) level emphasizes the unity of the entire membership of the subphylum Ciliophora. Even its most diverse forms are thus not considered distinctive enough to require separation at the high level of class. A closely-knit assemblage, the ciliates therefore differ markedly from their counterparts among the other three protozoan subphyla, as conventionally comprised*, where separation even into classes may not reflect their degrees of dissimilarity sufficiently.

*See footnote on page 23.

---

of buccal cavity); " Ps " — peristome (a time-honored term for the buccal cavity of many spirotrich ciliates); V — vestibulum, a depressed part of the body containing more or less modified somatic ciliature. Note the similar locations of homologous structures in the several diverse kinds of ciliated protozoa illustrated here. All figures schematically depict " mouth-parts " of selected ciliates belonging to the ordinal, or subordinal, groups named.

Fig. 1. A rhabdophorine gymnostome. Fig. 2. A cyrtophorine gymnostome. Fig. 3. A simple trichostome or chonotrich: first appearance of a vestibulum.

Fig. 4. A more complex trichostome. Fig. 5. A tetrahymenine hymenostome: first appearance of a buccal cavity. Fig. 6. A peni-culine hymenostome: buccal cavity plus a reappearing vestibulum.

Fig. 7. A sessiline (similar in mobiline) peritrich: buccal ciliary organelles (not shown) conspicuously extended outside the buccal overture to encircle the oral pole of the organism. Fig. 8. A hypotrich (sole member of subclass Spirotricha depicted in this series): buccal cavity has broadened and flattened: an extensive adoral zone of membranelles may extend out of this " peristomial " area anteriorly; but note that the cytostome–cytopharyngeal complex remains essentially identical with that seen in all the other " lower " orders of ciliates.

Subclass I. **HOLOTRICHA**

Presumably containing the more primitive orders of ciliates, from an evolutionary point of view (see Chapter 10), this first great subclass, twice the size of the second subclass, embraces species typified by possession of uniform somatic ciliature and generally inconspicuous buccal ciliature, if the latter is present at all. The cilia are usually arranged in orderly longitudinal rows over the body, although important exceptions, probably secondarily derived, are known in scattered groups among the nine included orders. Striking examples of compound ciliature on the body, such as cirri, are totally absent. Trichocysts of various kinds occur widely throughout the subclass. A true cystostome is absent in some groups. In the three orders in which a true buccal cavity has evolved — the Hymenostomatida, Thigmotrichida, and Peritrichida — the ciliary organelles associated with it are, in general, conspicuously developed only in the last-mentioned group.

The prototype of the holotrichs presumably was such a form as seen today in certain of the genera belonging to the rhabdophorine

---

Explanation of Plate X opposite

Variations in size, number, shape, and distribution of the two kinds of nuclei characteristic of ciliates, the micronuclei and the macronuclei. The ciliates used in the figures have purposely been chosen from a variety of orders and suborders, in illustration of the fact that sizes, shapes, and numbers of nuclei are of very little differential value in higher level systematics within the subphylum Ciliophora. In fact, considerable differences exist even among members of the same family. The drawings are schematic, based on various figures available in the literature, but they all have been carefully adjusted to the same scale of magnification except Fig. 12, which arbitrarily has been reduced by one-half to permit its inclusion in this plate. Only the outline of the ciliate's body is depicted. The micronuclei are shown in solid black; the macronuclei are stippled.

FIG. 1. *Vorticella* sp., a peritrich. FIG. 2. *Uroleptus* sp., a hypotrich. FIG. 3. *Dileptus* sp., a gymnostome. FIG. 4. *Paramecium* sp., a hymenostome. FIG. 5. *Cyclidium* sp., a hymenostome. FIG. 6. *Anoplophrya* sp., an astome. FIG. 7. *Didinium* sp., a gymnostome. FIG. 8. *Tintinnopsis* sp., a tintinnid. FIG. 9. *Ephelota* sp., a suctorian. FIG. 10. *Euplotes* sp., a hypotrich. FIG. 11. *Deltopylum* sp., a hymenostome. FIG. 12. *Stentor* sp., a heterotrich.

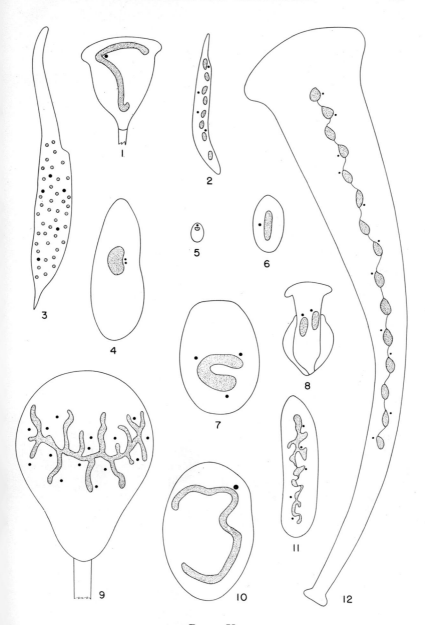

PLATE X

suborder of the gymnostomes (e.g., see Fig. 4, Pl. VIII; Fig. 1, Pl. XI). The typical genus of the entire subclass may be considered to be the same as that suggested for the subphylum, viz., *Paramecium* (Fig. 3, Pl. XIV).

In the scheme of classification adopted here, nine orders and nine suborders are included in this subclass. A list of these taxa, with subordinal names appearing in parentheses after their orders, may be given as follows: Gymnostomatida (Rhabdophorina, Cyrtophorina); Trichostomatida; Chonotrichida; Suctorida; Apostomatida; Astomatida; Hymenostomatida (Tetrahymenina, Peniculina, Pleuronematina); Thigmotrichida (Arhynchodina, Rhynchodina); and Peritrichida (Sessilina, Mobilina). General characterizations appear in Chapters 3–6. Nomenclatural details, distribution of families and their included genera, with abbreviated descriptions, and estimation of numbers of species are offered in Part II of this book.

Subclass II. **SPIROTRICHA**

The second subclass of ciliates, whose six orders represent a more compact group of forms with considerably less diversification in fundamental features than that manifest among the holotrichs, is typified by its display of conspicuously developed compound ciliary structures. The morphology of spirotrich species is dominated by the buccal ciliature, especially the extensively developed AZM (adoral zone of membranelles) arising on the left side of the oral area. Somatic ciliature of a simple nature is practically non-existent above the level of the first order, the Heterotrichida. The complex somatic ciliature typical of most orders may be quite sparse or, again, it may rival the buccal ciliature in prominence. The cirri, so characteristic of the Hypotrichida, are excellent examples of this (see Figs. 1, 2, Pl. XX).

The largest ciliates are commonly found among the spirotrichs, with some scattered exceptions from such holotrich groups as the Gymnostomatida. Considerable variation exists in body form, although, as seen also among most holotrichs, the body is frequently oval to round in cross-section. In one order, however, there is a very pronounced flattening dorso-ventrally (the Hypotrichida); and in another, laterally (the Odontostomatida).

Euplotes, whose widely distributed species are well known to many workers (systematists, morphologists, and experimentalists alike), may be named as a typical genus of spirotrichs. Its members illustrate clearly the subclass feature of the domination of compound ciliary structures over all other anatomical characteristics (see Figs. 1, 2, Pl. XX).

Six orders and two suborders are included in this ciliate subclass, according to the scheme of classification followed here. These taxa, with subordinal names appearing in parentheses after the sole order containing such subdivisions, are as follows: Heterotrichida (Heterotrichina, Licnophorina); Oligotrichida; Tintinnida; Entodiniomorphida; Odontostomatida; and Hypotrichida. General characterizations appear in Chapters 7–9. Nomenclatural details, the distribution and description of families and genera, and estimation of numbers of species are offered in Part II of this book.

CHAPTER 3

THE LOWER HOLOTRICHS: ORDERS GYMNOSTOMATIDA, TRICHOSTOMATIDA, CHONOTRICHIDA

THE gymnostomes, trichostomes, and chonotrichs are united by their common lack of compound ciliature in the oral area of the body. They seem to be very closely related groups, with the trichostomes apparently having arisen directly from the more primitive rhabdophorine gymnostomes and the chonotrichs from the more specialized cyrtophorines. Subsequent modifications of various kinds, related particularly to adaptations made to a diversity of environments, have given us today a great variety of shapes and sizes among the many species belonging to these orders.

Modern systematic and biological monographs are sorely needed on these groups. Since Kahl's (1930–1935) rapidly ageing work, only the Chonotrichida have been treated in a comprehensive way (Guilcher, 1951). Dragesco (1958) has included many gymnostomes in his monograph on the sand-dwelling ciliates of intertidal zones, but a detailed systematic treatment of all gymnostome groups has not been possible there. A number of workers in recent years have made valuable contributions to our understanding of trichostome interrelationships (e.g., Fauré-Fremiet, 1950d, 1955; von Gelei, 1952; Tuffrau, 1952), but a thorough treatment of the many difficult problems involved remains an unanswered challenge.

Order GYMNOSTOMATIDA

A large, widely distributed group of forms which I consider to be little-modified descendants of the most primitive of ciliated protozoa. Typically (although there are important exceptions in the second suborder) its numerous species possess a simple axis of symmetry, uniform body ciliation, straightforward modes of fission (perkinetal) and of stomatogenesis, and oral areas unadorned by any truly compound ciliature. Buccal organelles are absent, but the cytopharynx is always re-enforced by some system of organized fibrils commonly called trichites, but better "nematodesmata" (after Fauré-Fremiet). Body size is usually large.

Habitats include a wide range of environments, and gymno-stomes have been favorites in modern ecological studies in which natural protozoan populations have been considered. Along with other ciliate groups (particularly the Trichostomatida, Hymeno-stomatida, and Hypotrichida), they have been found in abundance in a variety of both common and uncommon environments.

The following types of habitats will serve as examples, with citations limited primarily to recent works of importance: in the sands of intertidal zones and in intertidal pools (Bock, 1952a, b, 1953; Fauré-Fremiet, 1949c, 1950b,e, 1951b,c; Fjeld, 1955; Kahl, 1933b; Dragesco, 1958, 1959, and earlier short papers not cited here); in soils of all kinds (see Grandori and Grandori, 1934; Singh, 1955; and the comprehensive review by Sandon, 1927); in moss and humus (Fantham and Porter, 1945; Gellért, 1955, 1956, 1957; Wenzel, 1953); in a quaking bog (de Graaf, 1957); in peat bogs (Mermod, 1914); in the fluid held by the leaves of pitcher plants (Hegner, 1926b); in the water of caves (Griepenburg, 1933); in a temporary meadow pool (von Gelei, 1954); in a small artificial pond (Wang, 1928), with interesting re-examination of the same pond thirty years later by Bamforth (1958); in a chalk stream (Gray, 1952); in salt marches (Fauré-Fremiet, 1912; Kirby, 1934); in brackish waters (Webb, 1956); and in harbors and gulfs as causative agents of "red water" (Bary, 1953; Bary and Stuckey, 1950; Powers, 1932).

Other papers* dealing with specific ecological aspects of proto-zoology, involving a variety of environments in which gymnostomes particularly abound, include: Ax and Ax (1960), Bary (1950a, b),

---

*More or less local protozoan "checklists," often papers of only a few pages in length, generally are seldom cited in this book, although their ecological value is recognized. Two quite inclusive recent reports are those by Bovee (1960) and West (1953).

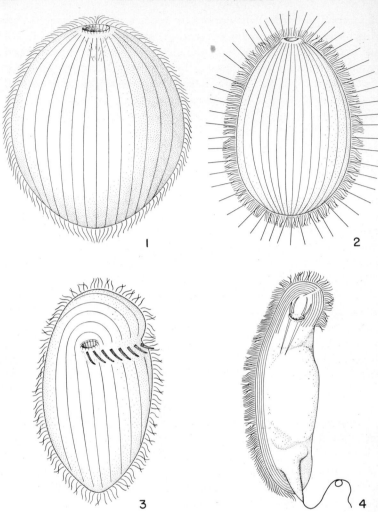

PLATE XI
Representative holotrichs: order GYMNOSTOMATIDA.
Fig. 1. *Holophrya*, suborder Rhabdophorina. *H. simplex*,
redrawn from various sources. Fig. 2. *Actinobolina*, suborder
Rhabdophorina. *A. vorax*, redrawn from Wenrich (1929a), a
curious gymnostome with retractable tentacles. Fig. 3. *Nassula*,
suborder Cyrtophorina. *N. aurea*, redrawn from various sources.
Fig. 4. *Trochilioides*, suborder Cyrtophorina. *T. filans*, redrawn

Bick (1958, 1960), Brook (1952), Canella (1954), De Morgan (1925, 1926), Fauré-Fremiet (1924, 1945a), Gajewskaja (1933), Gellért and Tamás (1958, 1959), Hegner (1926a), Horváth (1951, 1956), Kahl (1926, 1928), Kurihara (1958), Lackey (1925, 1936, 1938), Lepşi (1926b, 1957a,b, 1959), Noland (1925a), Penard (1922), Picken (1937), Shawhan *et al.* (1947), Stout (1956a, 1958), Šrámek-Hušek (1957), Stephanides (1948), Tamás and Gellért (1959), Verschaffelt (1930), Vörösváry (1950), Wang and Nie (1932), Wenzel (1955), Wetzel (1928). A number of additional works are cited in Kahl's (1930–1935) monograph and in Kitching's (1957a) recent review of protozoan ecology. The three most outstanding authorities of the 20th century in ecological studies on free-living fresh-water and marine ciliates have been Fauré-Fremiet, von Gelei, and Kahl. See lists of their works in Part III.

Members of only two families of gymnostomes are endosymbionts, the Buetschliidae and the Pycnotrichidae, groups little studied in recent years. Their species live as commensals in the digestive tract of certain mammals (Buisson, 1923; Chatton and Pérard, 1921; da Cunha and Muniz, 1925, 1927a; Gassovsky, 1919; Hsiung, 1930; Kopperi, 1937; Strelkow, 1939). A number of the cyrtophorine gymnostomes, notably of the family Chlamydodontidae, may act as ectocommensals (see such studies as those by Kidder and Summers, 1935; Krascheninnikow, 1953).

The carnivorous rhabdophorine gymnostomes have been favorite objects of study from the point of view of mechanics of ingestion, physiology of digestion, etc. The *Didinium–Paramecium* relationship, in particular, has been the subject of a number of papers since the classical one by Mast (1909). Complex predator–prey and other competition problems have been investigated in a series of well-known experiments by Gause summarized in his book (Gause, 1934). Very recently Evans (1958), employing species of the same two genera, has attacked one aspect of the problem anew; and Burbanck and Eisen (1960), another.

Gymnostomes are thought to be the " first ciliates," at least the

---

from Fauré-Fremiet and Guilcher (1947), a highly evolved cyrtophorine with a posteriorly located secretory organelle producing a filament used in attachment to the substrate.   [*N.B.* The pre-oral suture of *Nassula* is inadvertently omitted in Fig. 3.]

most primitive-appearing ciliates still represented among the protozoan fauna of today. Yet their origin (from zooflagellates?) still remains too much of a mystery even for speculation! Most representative of the less highly evolved gymnostomes are species belonging to such genera as *Enchelys*, *Holophrya*, and *Prorodon*. Thus the genus *Holophrya* Ehrenberg, 1831, is arbitrarily selected as a genus typical of the order (Fig. 1, Pl. XI).

Suborder (1) **Rhabdophorina**

The larger, more generalized group of gymnostomes, principally carnivorous forms, with uniform somatic ciliature and relatively simple morphogenetics of both fission and stomatogenesis. The cytostome is apically or laterally (really ventrally?) located. The difference in its position has served as the basis for recognition of two tribes (the Prostomata and the Pleurostomata) since the work of Schewiakoff (1896), but I believe that the taxonomic importance of this difference has been over-emphasized. The birefringent, skeletogeneous, fibrillar structures in the cytopharyngeal wall generally occur as " rods " (giving the suborder its name) loosely enough arranged to allow dilation during ingestion of prey. The cytostome always opens directly onto the body surface, a fundamental characteristic of all gymnostomes, and no buccal ciliature is ever present. Explosive and toxic trichocysts have been described from a number of species (Canella, 1951a,b; Dragesco, 1952; Jones, 1956; Jones and Beers, 1953; Krüger, 1936; Penard, 1922; and many others). Macronuclei are very small and numerous in some of the gymnostomes included here, and a true kind of " endomixis " has been described with precision from several genera (Fauré-Fremiet, 1954a; Raikov, 1958, 1959a,b). Certain rhabdophorine gymnostomes have lent themselves to fairly intensive investigations of the phenomena of en– and excystment (e.g., see Beers, 1945, 1946b, 1947, and many earlier important papers of his not cited here; and Jones, 1951). Curious intracytoplasmic bodies or " vesicles " have been described from various rhabdophorine gymnostomes as well as from other ciliate groups: see Fauré-Fremiet and Gauchery (1957) for new data and a review of the pertinent literature, which includes the well-known report by Dogiel (1929). The ectoplasmic spines and platelettes of *Coleps* have been the subject of considerable research (Geiman, 1931; Noland, 1925b, 1937; and more recently, Fauré-Fremiet and Hamard, 1944; Fauré-Fremiet *et al.*, 1948).

Holophrya, considered representative of the whole order, is also chosen as the typical member of this widely distributed suborder (Fig. 1, Pl. XI). Other well-known, common genera include *Amphileptus, Buetschlia, Coleps, Didinium* (Fig. 7, Pl. X), *Dileptus* (Fig. 3, Pl. X), *Enchelys, Litonotus* (usually written, in error, as *Lionotus*), *Loxodes, Loxophyllum, Prorodon* (Fig. 4, Pl. VIII), *Spathidium*, and *Trachelius*. All of these, as well as more than a hundred others (see Part II), can be recognized quite readily by a trained ciliate taxonomist; but the characteristics used for making such separations are too minute or too specialized to be treated in the present work. Members of several curious genera, the best known of which are *Actinobolina* (Fig. 2, Pl. XI) and *Legendrea*, possess retractable tentacles (von Gelei, 1954; Kahl, 1930; Moody, 1912; Penard, 1914a, 1922; Tuffrau, 1956; Wenrich, 1929a). This fact is considered by some protozoologists to be of great significance in relating suctorians to prostomatous gymnostomes (e.g., see Kahl, 1931a).

Suborder (2) **Cyrtophorina**

The smaller, more specialized group of gymnostomes, all herbivorous in their nutritional habits. The cyrtophorines, essentially comprising the tribe Hypostomata of the literature, possess a ventrally located cytostome (as the older name implies) generally about one-third the body length from the anterior end. Their fused cytopharyngeal armature, popularly known as the " pharyngeal basket " and serving as the basis for the subordinal name, is more complex and typically less expansible than its counterpart among the rhabdophorines. In spite of the more highly organized nature of this skeletogeneous structure in the cyrtophorine group, its fibrillar ultrastructure, studied by electron microscopy (Rouiller *et al.*, 1957), is identical with that of the non-fused trichite-rods of the first suborder. The macronuclei of some genera appear to be more highly differentiated than commonly known for members of most other orders of holotrichs (Fauré-Fremiet, 1957b; Seshachar, 1950).

The somatic ciliature is often drastically reduced in species belonging to this suborder; furthermore, the body may show a pronounced flattening dorso-ventrally, reminiscent of the form seen again among some of the most highly evolved spirotrich ciliates. Fission is quite straightforward, but stomatogenesis may involve rather complex morphogenetic movements (Fauré-Fremiet, 1950c; Kaneda, 1959, 1960a, b; Krascheninnikow, 1953; MacDougall, 1936). Complications are caused by the non-apical location of the cytostome and the occurrence of short, specialized ciliary rows (forerunners of the hymenostome-type buccal membranelle?) in the oral area, some of which are sometimes localized in a little depression which has been designated the oral atrium (Corliss, 1959b).

Nassula Ehrenberg, 1833, may be considered as a typical cyrtophorine genus (Fig. 3, Pl. XI). Although it shows many of the specialized features characteristic of the suborder, it is probably at the base of the phylogenetic tree *within* the group as it is known from present-day forms.

Very recently a brief, but up-to-date, review of the family Nassulidae has appeared (Fauré-Fremiet, 1959b). Among genera showing a striking loss of somatic ciliature and the development of only a few rows of ciliature near the oral area, which are active in stomatogenesis, is the well-known genus *Chilodonella* (Fig. 6, Pl. VII). Species assigned to the family Dysteriidae represent the most bizarre forms of all (e.g., see Fig. 4, Pl. XI), possessing, among other specialized features, a posteriorly located secretory apparatus which produces an organelle of fixation (Fauré-Fremiet, 1957c; Fauré-Fremiet and Guilcher, 1947).

Order **TRICHOSTOMATIDA**

A rather heterogeneous group of families, as currently composed (see Part II), many of whose species have been inadequately described. It is not within the province of the present work to attempt a full-scale revision of this order. A fundamental characteristic of the trichostomes *sensu stricto*, in my opinion, should be the possession of a clearly delimited vestibulum, a vestibulum being defined as an indentation of the body pellicle leading to the true cytostome and bearing ciliature of a fairly simple nature. Thus vestibular ciliature is somatic in origin, seldom modified from the type occurring elsewhere on the body. There is no true buccal cavity, and therefore, no compound buccal ciliature in members of this order, according to my present concept of its limits. The somatic ciliature ranges from entire coverage of the body in regular, longitudinally oriented rows to restricted coverage or to rows patterned to fit contorted, highly asymmetrical body forms. The secondarily imposed torsion typical of some genera inevitably complicates the morphogenetics of fission of their included species.

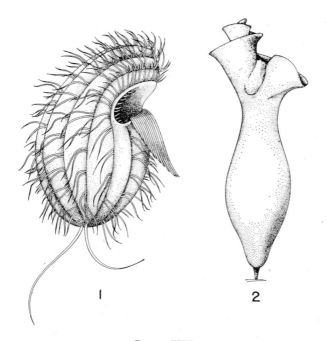

PLATE XII

Typical holotrichs: orders TRICHOSTOMATIDA and CHONOTRICHIDA.
Fig. 1. *Colpoda*, a highly evolved trichostome, inter-divisional stage. *C. steinii*, from Corliss (1956a, 1959b), originally redrawn from Taylor and Furgason (1938). Fig. 2. *Spirochona*, a fresh-water chonotrich, mature stage. *S. gemmipara*, from Corliss (1956a, 1959b), originally redrawn from various sources.

The cytostome and cytopharynx, located at the base of the ever-present vestibulum (see Figs. 3,4, Pl. IX), may be found in different places on the body in different species: at the apical pole, on the ventral (or a lateral) surface, at the posterior pole.

Certain trichostomes are quite common; but the size and distribution of the entire group as conventionally composed will be drastically reduced when the order eventually is restricted, as it should be, to a collection of forms of monophyletic origin. As currently treated in modern textbooks, the Trichostomatida includes genera which are really hymenostomes (*Paramecium* being the outstanding example of this) or, in some other cases, probably members of such holotrich groups as the thigmotrichs or such spirotrich groups as the oligotrichs. At the same time, certain genera appear to have been derived from rhabdophorine gymnostome-like progenitors, while others show affinities with the more specialized cyrtophorine gymnostomes. I favor retention as true trichostomes only those species with an apparent ancestry from rhabdophorine gymnostome stock (see Pl. XXI), but much work remains to be done to clarify the over-all picture. Preliminary steps in revision of the order have been taken by Fauré-Fremiet (1950a,d) and von Gelei (1952).

Colpoda O. F. Müller, 1773, is depicted as a representative genus (Fig. 1, Pl. XII). Although quite highly evolved, as seen, for example, in its specialized vestibular ciliature known as " the beard," it also shows simple gymnostome affinities, particularly in its direct, perkinetal mode of fission (Burt, 1940, 1945; Kidder and Diller, 1934; Taylor and Furgason, 1938; Tuffrau, 1952; and see important earlier works cited in these papers). Species of this genus have been widely used in both descriptive and experimental researches. The phenomena of encystment and excystment* are perhaps more precisely understood for members of the genus *Colpoda* than for any other ciliate (Biczók, 1957; Brown, 1939; Brown and Taylor, 1938; Burt *et al.*, 1941; Garnjobst, 1947; Kidder and Claff, 1938; Kidder and Stuart, 1939a,b; Padnos *et al.*, 1954; Pigoń, 1959; Stout, 1955; Strickland

---

*Long ago Goodey (1915) demonstrated that members of two species of *Colpoda* which had survived as cysts for some 38 years in dried, bottled soil excysted readily in a hay-infusion medium.

and Haagen-Smit, 1948; Stuart *et al.*, 1939; Taylor and Garnjobst, 1939; Taylor and Strickland, 1938, 1939; and consult the brief but comprehensive review by van Wagtendonk, 1955). *Colpoda* also is known as a facultative parasite (e.g., see Reynolds, 1936; Windsor, 1959).

Tillina is another common genus (Beers, 1946a,c; Bridgman, 1948, 1957; Bridgman and Kimball, 1954; Tuffrau, 1952; Turner, 1937, 1940). It abandons its highly asymmetrical form during stages in its ontogeny preceding fission, thus appearing to recapitulate a rhabdophorine gymnostome ancestry (see Figs. 1, 2, Pl. VII).

Bresslaua, *Plagiopyla*, *Sonderia*, and *Woodruffia* also may be mentioned as probably " good " genera of trichostomes. *Coelosomides*, superficially identical with common prostomatous (rhabdophorine) gymnostomes (and often so classified), possesses a true vestibulum. It may be considered a representative of the more primitive trichostomes. Recent studies of importance on the biology of the last-mentioned five genera include the works by Beers (1954), Claff *et al.* (1941), Evans (1944), Fauré-Fremiet (1950b,d), Fauré-Fremiet and Tuffrau (1955), von Gelei (1954), Gellért (1955), Johnson and Evans (1940, 1941), Johnson and Larson (1938), Kahl (1928, 1931b), Stout (1960), Tuffrau (1952). Among the most curious of trichostomes are the little-known members of the family Marynidae, forms dwelling in branched gelatinous loricae. The only major research on these ciliates in recent years is that of von Gelei (1950c).

Balantidium, one species of which represents the sole ciliate parasitic in man, with others occurring in a wide range of vertebrate and invertebrate hosts (Kudo and Meglitsch, 1938), generally is classified as a heterotrich, in the subclass Spirotricha. But it is better considered as a trichostome (Fauré-Fremiet, 1955; Krascheninnikow and Wenrich, 1958; and see Part II of the present work). The species of *Balantidium* from man, incidentally, is, according to some workers, identical with a species originally described from the pig (a view which I favor myself); other investigators disagree. Pertinent data appear in Auerbach (1953), Cheissin and Pick-Levontin (1946), Hegner (1934), Hsiung (1938), Lamy and Roux (1950), Levine (1940), McDonald (1922), Pick-Levontin and Cheissin (1940), Pritze (1928), Scott (1927),

Svensson (1955), Young (1950). Certain coprophilic "balantidia" are considered to be members of the hymenostome genus *Balantiophorus* by Watson (1945a).

Pseudomicrothorax, conventionally considered to be a trichostome, is assigned more reasonably to the Hymenostomatida, as is also true for the genus *Paramecium* (Corliss, 1958d,e; Yusa, 1957).

Species of *Isotricha* and *Paraisotricha*, genera which I tentatively leave in the order, live symbiotically in the digestive tracts of cattle and sheep, and of the horse, respectively (e.g., see Hsiung, 1930). The genera *Cyathodinium*, from colon and caecum of the guinea pig (da Cunha and de Freitas, 1941; Lucas, 1932a,b; Nie, 1950), and *Conidiophrys*, episymbiotic on amphipods and isopods (Chatton and Lwoff, 1936a; Kirby, 1941a; Mohr and LeVeque, 1948), represent interesting groups whose true taxonomic affinities remain to be elucidated.

A number of other alleged trichostomes are perhaps equally in need of restudy, preferably with the use of such techniques as silver impregnation. Among these are several genera whose species are quite commonly found in echinoderms; for example, *Entorhipidium*, *Lechriopyla*, *Plagiopyla*. Certain other genera likewise represented in the commensal fauna of echinoids are considered as trichostomes by some workers but are classified as hymenostomes in the present work (see Part II); e.g., *Anophrys*, *Biggaria*, *Cryptochilum*, *Entodiscus*. Papers of particular significance with regard to the biology of ciliate members of the unique microcommunity in the digestive tract of certain echinoderms include the following: Beers (1948b, 1954), Berger (1960, 1961a–c), Dain (1930), Jacobs (1914), Kahl (1934a), Kirby (1941a), Lucas (1940), Lynch (1929, 1930), Madsen (1931), Poljansky (1951a,b), Poljansky and Golikowa (1957, 1959), Powers (1933a,b, 1936), Russo (1930), Strelkow (1959a,b), Uyemura (1934), Yagiu (1933, 1940).

Order CHONOTRICHIDA

Typically vase-shaped, sedentary organisms occurring as ectocommensals on marine (one genus on fresh-water) crustaceans. The true ventral surface secondarily has been pulled out apically to give the characteristic funnel-like appearance of the mature forms (see Fig. 2, Pl. XII). The "funnel" is commonly lined with what I consider to be vestibular ciliature. There is no buccal ciliature, and somatic ciliature in general also is conspicuously absent. A localized somatic infraciliature persists throughout the life cycle, however.

The migratory larval form of these gemmiparous ciliates shows a remarkable resemblance to certain cyrtophorine gymnostomes, particularly in its infraciliature (Guilcher, 1950, 1951). As transformation to the adult form takes place, the production of a non-contractile stalk corresponds exactly to the mode shown by the gymnostome *Dysteria* (Fauré-Fremiet *et al.*, 1956a). There is no involvement of a scopula as there is in suctorians, thigmotrichs, peritrichs, and others. Furthermore, the unusual structure of the chonotrich macronucleus is strongly reminiscent of that of many cyrtophorine gymnostomes (Fauré-Fremiet, 1957b; Tuffrau, 1953). Thus the seeming distinctiveness of the Chonotrichida is not borne out by modern researches; consideration of the group as holotrichs derived from a cyrtophorine gymnostome ancestry is amply justified.

Spirochona Stein, 1851, has been chosen as a typical genus because the features of its mature stage illustrate so well the characteristics long believed to be unique (Fig. 2, Pl. XII). Had it not been for study of their infraciliature and the morphogenetic movements involved in their ontogenies, the chonotrichs still would be occupying a most enigmatic systematic position within the Ciliophora.

Species of *Spirochona* occur widely as ectocommensals on freshwater gammarids. All other chonotrichs are restricted to marine habitats; common genera among these include *Chilodochona* (Fig. 5, Pl. VII), *Stylochona*, and *Trichochona*. Mohr (1948, 1959) has provided important data related to chonotrich distribution, host relationships, and evolution within the order. Earlier studies of significance include those of Swarczewsky (1928a,f), while classical works of lasting importance date back to the papers by Balbiani (1895), Hertwig (1877), Plate (1886), Stein (1851), and Wallengren (1895).

CHAPTER 4

HOLOTRICHS OF UNCERTAIN AFFINITIES: ORDERS SUCTORIDA, APOSTOMATIDA, ASTOMATIDA

PROBABLY the most enigmatic of all ciliophoran groups, at least with regard to their origins and present-day affinities, are the suctorians, the apostomes, and the astomes. In fact, even treatment of the Suctorida as an order of holotrichs represents a major departure from conventional schemes of ciliate classification. Their mode of feeding, lack of ciliature in the mature stage, and curious life histories combine to justify consideration of suctorians as specialized forms with a long evolutionary history of their own.

The apostomes and astomes exhibit in common the symbiotic way of life; but there most similarities stop. Possibly both groups arose from some sort of hymenostome ancestry. The Apostomatida represents a much more closely-knit group within its own boundaries. The true extent of the astomes remains one of the most important problems to be solved, although de Puytorac (1954a, 1959a), especially, has made very significant contributions in this field.

These three orders were not considered in the major monograph by Kahl (1930–1935). Since the time of his separate, condensed compilation (Kahl, 1934b), the suctorians have been treated comprehensively only by Guilcher (1951); a thorough systematic monograph of the kind produced by Collin (1912) is greatly needed. The Apostomatida have not been considered in detail since the culminating work of Chatton and Lwoff (1935a). Fortunately, de Puytorac and several other workers are currently attacking major portions of the taxonomically uncertain " order " Astomatida.

Order **SUCTORIDA**

An order long considered quite separate from " true " ciliates because of the exhibition of a number of specialized features by the species included in it. Yet perhaps not a single one of them represents a unique characteristic: species scattered among the other orders of holotrichs possess one or another of all of these unusual features. The persistence of an infraciliature, showing a holotrichous pattern, throughout the entire life cycle of a suctorian, on the other hand, may be considered one of the strongest arguments for inclusion of the group within the first great subclass of the Ciliophora. The morphogenetics of suctorian ontogenies has been traced with precision by Guilcher (1948, 1950, 1951). More recently an important series of papers on the significance of the budding process and other features of suctorian life cycles has been published by Kormos and Kormos (1957a,b, 1958a,b, 1960a,b; and earlier papers not cited).

The mature forms of suctorians are the most bizarre: typically they are stalked (with non-contractile peduncles) and completely devoid of external ciliature, but equipped with several to many tentacles of a suctorial or, much less commonly, prehensile type. No cytostome exists; holozoic nutrition is carried out by means of the suctorial tentacles, which actively suck out the cytoplasm of the prey (other ciliates) by a mechanism still not fully understood although under investigation in several laboratories (Dragesco and Guilcher, 1950; Dragesco *et al.*, 1955; Hull, 1954, 1961a,b; Kitching, 1954; Okajima, 1957; Rudzinska and Porter, 1954a,b; and see references in Canella, 1957). These specialized sedentary creatures, often occurring as episymbionts on a variety of aquatic animals (both invertebrate and vertebrate, and fresh-water or marine), reproduce by means of budding processes which are classified as either endogenous or exogenous. The buds or larval forms are mouthless, cilia-bearing organisms of obvious importance in distribution of the species. An area known as the scopula produces a stalk for the larva as it commences transformation into the mature sedentary form. At the same time, tentacles grow out, replacing the external ciliature, which is simultaneously resorbed.

In species in which the sexual phenomenon of conjugation is known its nature is quite atypical of ciliates in general, as it often involves disparity in the size of the conjugants and/or a permanent fusion of members of the pair. Studies of the macronuclear anlagen in certain suctorians, incidentally, have cast important light on the mode of origin of the alleged polyploid state of the genic material in ciliate macronuclei in general (Fauré-Fremiet, 1953b; Grell, 1949, 1953a,b, 1956; Kormos and Kormos, 1960a,b; Piekarski, 1941).

The suctorians as a unified group have been known under more than a dozen different taxonomic names (see Part II). In spite of the confused nomenclatural history, there is considerable support today for conservation of the ordinal designation Suctoria or Suctorida (Corliss, 1957a). The most recent compilation which reviews many aspects of suctorian bionomics is the 457-page treatise by Canella (1957). But the work which remains the classic in the field was produced half a century ago by Collin (1911, 1912).

Several groups of investigators of suctorian morphology and physiology recently have been engaged in electron microscopic studies of great interest. For example, see works by Pottage (1958), Rouiller *et al.* (1956b), Rudzinska (1956, 1958, and earlier papers), and several of the papers cited under studies on tentacles (p. 45).

The systematics of the Suctorida, as a group, is in need of thorough restudy and revision, at all taxonomic levels. Since Swarczewsky's (1928b–e) work on several families and Kahl's (1934b) compilation, little has been published, with the notable exception of Guilcher's (1951) monograph, which treats over-all problems in any detail. A large number of species and several new genera have been added in the past twenty-five years, principally by a rather small group of investigators. Some of these papers, including only the most recent ones if they are parts of a series by the same author, may be mentioned: Davis (1942), Fauré-Fremiet (1943b), Gajewskaja (1933), Gönnert (1935), Goodrich and Jahn (1943), Hadži (1940a), Kormos (1935a,b), Kormos and Kormos (1958a), Kunz (1936), Matthes (1954, 1956), Nie and Lu (1945), Nozawa (1938, 1939), Rieder (1936a,b), Schultz (1938), Sewell (1951), Stammer (1935), Wailes (1943), Willis (1945).

Acineta Ehrenberg, 1833, may be considered a typical genus of this aberrant assemblage of holotrich ciliates (see Fig. 1, Pl. XIII). The principal characteristics of the mature form of suctorians in general are illustrated in the drawing: sessile body, attached to the substrate by a stalk; occurrence of tentacles; absence of cilia and cytostome.

Other common genera include *Dendrocometes, Discophrya, Ephelota* (Fig. 9, Pl. X), *Ophryodendron, Podophrya* (Figs. 3, 4, Pl. VII; Fig. 2, Pl. XIII), *Solenophrya,* and *Tokophrya.* Members of the genus *Endosphaera* possess no tentacles, living most of their interesting life as symbionts inside the peritrich *Telotrochidium* (Lynch and Noble, 1931). Members of the curious genus *Pottsiocles* parasitize folliculinid heterotrichs and several kinds of peritrichs, many of the hosts being loricate forms (Chatton and Lwoff, 1927; Nozawa, 1939). An excellent, though brief, review of the older literature on the symbiotic relationship between certain suctorians and other ciliates is included in the comprehensive work by Kirby (1941b).

Order **APOSTOMATIDA**

A small group of little-studied forms, typically associated with marine crustaceans but in a more intimate way than that shown by the chonotrichs. Characteristically present is the rosette, a unique structure located in the vicinity of the cytostome (see Fig. 3, Pl. XIII). Also characteristic of the order is the presence of fewer than twenty-two rows of somatic ciliature arranged in dextral spirals in organisms in mature stages of their life cycles.

The cytostome is small and mid-ventrally located. Stomatogenesis is a complex process intimately associated with the morphogenetics of body fission. Life histories of most species are strikingly polymorphic. The terminology for various stages, e.g., trophont, tomont, tomite, and phoront, now available for use in describing life cycles of ciliates in general, originated in the classical apostome studies of Chatton and Lwoff, culminating in their monograph of 1935. Two hosts are often involved in the life cycle. What is particularly significant in the ontogeny of these curious ciliates is the reversion to a simple axis of symmetry and to longitudinally oriented bipolar meridians, quite unlike the arrangement characteristic of the mature trophonts.

The exact systematic position of this group poses an enigmatic problem; possibly its species represent degenerate hymenostomes

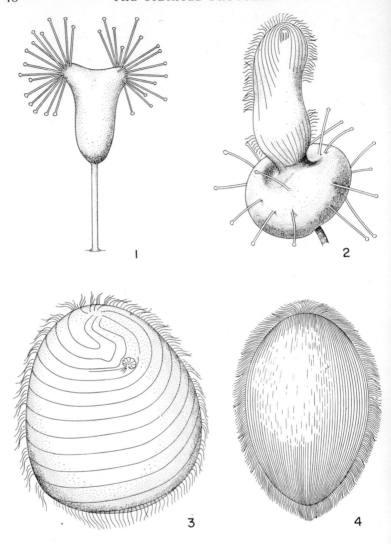

PLATE XIII

Representative holotrichs: orders SUCTORIDA, APOSTO-MATIDA, ASTOMATIDA.

Fig. 1. *Acineta*, a suctorian, mature state. *A. tuberosa*, from Corliss (1959b), originally redrawn from Calkins (1902a). Fig. 2. *Podophrya*, a suctorian, showing production of ciliated bud from

or thigmotrichs (Corliss, 1956a) or, with a structural homology between the cytopharyngeal basket and the rosette, an offshoot from cyrtophorine gymnostomes (Corliss, 1958e).

Foettingeria Caullery and Mesnil, 1903, has been depicted as a typical genus (Fig. 3, Pl. XIII). Other common ones include *Gymnodinioides, Ophiuraespira, Polyspira*, and *Spirophrya*, genera containing species made well known by the detailed studies of French protozoologists in particular (see especially Chatton and Lwoff, 1935a; and Lwoff, 1950). In their morphogenetic studies these workers included valuable information on conjugation and trichocyst formation as well as on fission and stomatogenesis. And in their investigation of the details of host-symbiont relationships they discovered a curious fact, worthy of further study, that the molting cycle of the crustacean host has a direct effect on the succession of stages in the life history of the symbiont (see also Debaisieux, 1957, 1960; Trager, 1957). The ciliates belonging to one genus, *Cyrtocaryum*, occur in association with a marine annelid, are mouthless, and, curiously enough, do not even show the rosette, a structure so typical of nearly all the other genera (Fauré-Fremiet and Mugard, 1949a). *Pericaryon*, also without a rosette, occurs in the gastrovascular cavity of a ctenophore. The genus *Hyalospira* (=*Gymnodinioides?*) has been described as a parasite of a fresh-water crustacean (Miyashita, 1933).

Order **ASTOMATIDA**

A large group of species united by the strictly negative characteristic of being mouthless. The astomatous forms customarily placed here are those commonly found as symbionts in the gut or coelom of oligochaete annelids; but also included are forms from amphipod crustaceans and molluscs and certain ciliates from the digestive tracts of turbellarian worms and tailed amphibians. A number of workers have insisted or implied that this

---

sedentary non-ciliated mature form. *P. collini* (syn. *Discophrya piriformis*), from Corliss (1956a, 1959b), originally redrawn from Guilcher (1951). FIG. 3. *Foettingeria*, an apostome, trophont stage. *F. actinarium*, from Corliss (1959b), originally redrawn from Chatton and Lwoff (1935a). FIG. 4. *Anoplophrya*, an astome. *A. lumbrici*, from Corliss (1959b), originally from various sources.

heterogeneous assemblage of mouthless holotrichs represents the most primitive order of holotrichs. It is far more likely, however, that they are secondarily degenerate forms showing certain specializations which may be associated with their entirely symbiotic mode of life (Corliss, 1956a).

De Puytorac (1954a, 1955, 1957a,b, 1959a,b, 1960; and other papers cited in these), who has carried out and is continuing to perform some of the most authoritative and most comprehensive researches on the " astomes " in modern times (since the works of Cépède, 1910; Cheissin, 1930; Georgévitch, 1941a,b, 1950; Heidenreich, 1935a–c; Rossolimo, 1926a,b; and Rossolimo and Pertzewa, 1929), is convinced that the majority of them are, in fact, thigmotrichs. Others, according to the French worker, are degenerate apostomes or (a few) hymenostomes. De Puytorac (1959a) thus favors incorporation of the Astomatida *sensu stricto* as a suborder of the Thigmotrichida. There is a great deal of merit in this very recent suggestion, although it is not fully endorsed here where, unfortunately, the matter can receive only brief attention (also see Chapter 10). One factor in particular, it seems to me, must be further investigated: whether or not such a taxonomic shift would render the thigmotrichs a polyphyletic group from a phylogenetic point of view. The present thigmotrichs are presumed to have arisen in a single line from pleuronematine-like hymenostomes; can the ancestry of the astomes be traced back exactly along the same (monophyletic) line?

The body ciliation of astomes is typically very uniform. The body size is often large, and certain species are noted for their ability to form catenoid colonies. Fission is uncomplicated; life cycles are not complex; stomatogenesis is, of course, non-existent. Many species, however, possess scleroproteinaceous endoskeletons and elaborately developed holdfast organelles. Appearance of the latter uniquely specialized structures, used in attachment to host epithelial tissues, suggests a long evolutionary history as symbiotic organisms.

Anoplophrya Stein, 1860, has been depicted as a typical genus of astomes (Fig. 3, Pl. VIII; Fig. 6, Pl. X; Fig. 4, Pl. XIII). *Hoplitophrya*, *Intoshellina*, *Metaradiophrya*, and *Radiophrya*, represent other well-known genera. In an important series of recent papers Lom (1956, 1957, 1959a,d, 1960) has described several new genera. Species of *Haptophrya*, frequently of very large size, occur in certain amphibians and possess a prominent antero-ventral sucker and a unique contractile vacuolar canal (see the well-known papers by Bush, 1934, and MacLennan, 1944). De Puytorac's continuing series of works should be consulted for references to the many known species of astomes. Considerable revision is still needed at all taxonomic levels within the " order " (see Part II of the present book).

CHAPTER 5

THE PIVOTAL GROUP OF HOLOTRICHS: ORDER HYMENOSTOMATIDA

As discussed in Chapter 10 (also see Corliss, 1956a, 1958e), the hymenostome holotrichs appear to occupy a central position in the first subclass of the Ciliophora. Their possession of buccal ciliature recognizably compound in nature sets them above the more primitive groups, yet their retention of simple body form and uniform somatic ciliature, coupled with their exhibition of considerable variation in such morphogenetic phenomena as stomatogenesis, suggests that they represent a non-specialized assemblage of forms capable of having given rise to several more restricted and complex groups. It has even been postulated that the subclass Spirotricha may have had its origin within this order (Corliss, 1956a; Fauré-Fremiet, 1950a; Furgason, 1940).

Over-all treatments of the biology and systematics of the Hymenostomatida have not appeared since the important, but outdated, section in the great ciliate monograph by Kahl (1930–1935). Modern investigations of significance have been published (e.g., by Dragesco, 1958, and Mugard, 1949), but most of these papers have been brief or rather limited in scope.

The order may be characterized as a group containing many species, often of small size, typically possessing uniform somatic ciliature and definite, although inconspicuous, buccal ciliature. I consider the hymenostomes to be the first, phylogenetically, to exhibit a true buccal cavity equipped with organized compound ciliature: an undulating membrane (UM) on the right side of the cavity and a primitive adoral zone of membranelles (AZM), three in number, on the left. This tetrahymenal complex is presumed to represent the forerunner of the buccal organization characteristic of the remaining orders of holotrichs and of the orders of spiro-trichs as well (see citations on preceding page). Earlier phylogenetic studies still of considerable importance include those of von Gelei (1934), P. Horváth (1935), and Párducz (1936, 1939).

The majority of hymenostome species are free-living, fresh-water forms, although many marine species, in particular, probably remain to be described. A few are truly parasitic; some are com-mensals. Species capable of facultative parasitism also are known. Many are bacteria-feeders, others are carnivorous, some are obligate tissue-feeders. Classical studies of the explosive, ecto-plasmic type of trichocyst and of the sexual phenomenon of conjugation* have been carried out extensively, as is well known, on members of the hymenostome genus *Paramecium* (see the general, well-documented review of such subjects in Wichterman, 1953; for additional recent investigations, see citations under suborder Peniculina, p. 59 ff). One of the most precise modern ecological studies of a microbiocenosis, carried out by Fauré-Fremiet (1951), involves several hymenostome species. Other ecological studies of importance involving a number of members of this order have been listed in Chapter 3, under the order Gymnostomatida. Intensive studies of contractile vacuolar systems in protozoa frequently have included one or more genera of hymenostome ciliates (King, 1935; J. von Gelei, 1935a, 1938b; G. von Gelei, 1939; Schneider, 1960; and see the recent general review by Kitching, 1956a). Amicronucleate races of ciliates (Woodruff, 1921a; Beers, 1946a) have included hymenostomes, particularly members of the important genus *Tetrahymena* (Corliss, 1953a). Bullington (1930, 1939) has carried out some rather unique studies on spiraling in *Paramecium* and *Frontonia*.

---

*Sonneborn's (1937, 1939) invaluable recognition of the occurrence and significance of *mating types* within " varieties " (now known as " syngens ") of the taxonomic species *Paramecium aurelia* marked the beginning of an era of refined genetic researches on all kinds of ciliated protozoa. Other pioneering studies on types of sexuality in *Paramecium* include the extensive investigations of Jennings on *P. bursaria* (to cite a few: Jennings, 1939, 1944, 1945; Jennings and Opitz, 1944); the discovery of autogamy by Diller (1936), sounding the death knell of " endomixis " (Woodruff and Erdmann, 1914) in *Paramecium*; the discovery of cytogamy, in *P. caudatum*, by Wichterman (1940).

It is *Paramecium* O. F. Müller, 1773, long considered a genus of trichostome ciliates, which is selected as a typical hymenostome in the present paper (Fig. 3, Pl. XIV; see also Figs. 1, 2, Pl. VI; Fig. 4, Pl. X). This choice is influenced by the fact that *Paramecium* already has been designated as representative of the entire subphylum Ciliophora, class Ciliata, and subclass Holotricha (see Chapter 2), and of one of the hymenostome suborders (see p. 60). It follows, then, that it also should represent its order. Although quite specialized, species of *Paramecium* typify characteristics of the order in the simple holotrichous arrangement of their somatic ciliature and in their possession of compound yet inconspicuous buccal ciliature. An additional feature seen in this genus, and in a number of others, is the vestibulum, a structure of the oral area already noted for trichostomes and chonotrichs (Chapter 3). When present in hymenostomes, this depressed area of the body pellicle is always external to the buccal cavity and is not to be confused with it (see Fig. 6, Pl. IX). I consider it to be a secondary acquisition of limited phylogenetic significance within the order.

Suborder (1) **Tetrahymenina**

The least highly differentiated species of hymenostomes, generally small in size, with buccal cavity ordinarily not preceded by a vestibulum. In the past the origin of this suborder has been sought in a trichostome-like ancestry. Very recently the argument has been made for its close affinity with certain present-day cyrtophorine gymnostomes, with *Pseudomicrothorax* (Fig. 1, Pl. XIV; see also Figs. 1–6, Pl. III) playing the role of a " missing link " genus (Corliss, 1958d,e). Whether *Pseudomicrothorax* Mermod, 1914, itself belongs in this suborder, or should be assigned to a separate more primitive hymenostome group especially created for it, poses a question unanswerable with the limited pertinent data available at the present time. The exciting features of this genus are its simultaneous possession of a cyrtophorine-like cytopharyngeal armature and a UM–AZM complex of buccal ciliature.

The mode of stomatogenesis varies from group to group within the Tetrahymenina. From one, or none, to many stomatogenous meridians may be involved in the morphogenetics of the process, depending on the genus (Corliss, 1956a, 1958e; Mugard, 1949). This plasticity within the suborder is considered as one line of evidence supporting the hypothesis that the tetrahymenine ciliates represent a major pivotal group in the evolution of the Ciliophora in general, since various higher groups often show one or the other of the modes of stomatogenesis first seen here. (See Chapt. 10 for further discussion of this point.)

Tetrahymena Furgason, 1940, may be considered typical of the suborder (Fig. 2, Pl. XIV; see also Figs. 1–5, Pl. I; Figs. 1–12, Pl. II; Figs. 1–4, Pl. IV). In this genus the bases of the membranelles comprising the AZM are definitely located on the left side of the midline of the buccal cavity; in others, such as *Anophrys*, *Colpidium*, *Glaucoma** (Fig. 6, Pl. I), *Paralembus*, and *Philaster*, the membranelles in part or altogether have been shifted secondarily toward the right. In extreme cases the AZM is thrown entirely up against the UM on the right side (Mugard, 1949).

Other important genera may be mentioned briefly. *Ichthyophthirius*, a destructive fish parasite often erroneously classified as a gymnostome, has been studied extensively by Haas (1933), MacLennan (1935b, 1943; and intermediate papers not cited), and Mugard (1948, 1949). The relatively new genus *Deltopylum* (Fig. 11, Pl. X) has been the subject of recent investigations by Bacq *et al.* (1952), Fauré-Fremiet and Mugard (1946), Mugard (1949), and Mugard and Lorsignol (1957). *Porpostoma* possesses membranelles which have undergone a kind of segmentation suggestive of the possible mode of origin of the multipartite AZM characteristic of the orders of spirotrich ciliates (Corliss, 1956a; Mugard, 1949). *Ophryoglena*, with its enigmatic watchglass organelle, large body, histophagous feeding habit, and reproductive cystic stage, represents an important genus little studied in modern

---

*The most recent paper, with figures, on " mouth parts " of a *Glaucoma* (*G. frontata*) is that by Corliss (1954b). The species investigated, potentially of considerable value as an experimental organism in sexuality studies (e.g., see Wenrich, 1954), is still commonly, although mistakenly, called *Dallasia frontata*, the name used in the interesting papers of Calkins and Bowling (1928, 1929). A new species of *Glaucoma* being used in modern researches, including electron microscopy, is *G. chattoni* (see Corliss, 1959d; Pitelka, 1959b; and, added in proof, the two very recent papers of importance by Frankel, 1960a,b).

times, aside from the monographic work of Mugard (1949) and one study by von Gelei (1950b). Species of *Colpidium* have been studied by scores of protozoologists over the period of the past 125 years; members of this genus were involved in the recent significant discoveries concerning chromosomes and chromosome-aggregates in ciliates (Devidé, 1951; Devidé and Geitler, 1947).

Although the generic name *Tetrahymena* dates only from 1940, the genus is clearly the best known of all those assigned to the hymenostome suborder under present discussion. The reasons for this are several, but the principal one has been the great success in cultivating its species in axenic (bacteria-free) media, thereby allowing completion of a tremendous amount of refined researches on their biochemistry and physiology (see Corliss, 1954a, 1957d; Elliott, 1959a,b; Hutner, 1961; Kidder, 1951; Kidder and Dewey, 1951; Seaman, 1955; Zeuthen, 1958). To André Lwoff belongs the credit for initiating the bulk of these works through his own pioneering investigations (Lwoff, 1923, 1932, 1943).

A number of selected specific citations to recent papers on *Tetrahymena* are made here, not only for their own value but also because they represent areas of modern biological research in which the problems attacked often are of great interest to a large group of workers who are not professional protozoologists. In all of the fields mentioned, research is actively continuing. Citations given include papers which mark modern discoveries of major importance, discoveries which have served as a basis for continuation and expansion of research efforts by an increasing number of investigators. Most references are purposely limited to results published within the past six years. Space does not permit

---

Explanation of Plate XIV opposite

Representative holotrichs: order HYMENOSTOMATIDA.
Fig. 1. *Pseudomicrothorax*, suborder Tetrahymenina (or more primitive? See text). *P. agilis*, from Corliss (1959b), originally redrawn from Corliss (1958d). Fig. 2. *Tetrahymena*, suborder Tetrahymenina. *T. pyriformis*, from Corliss (1959b), based on a figure of a related species in Corliss (1956a) which was originally redrawn from Kozloff (1946a). Fig. 3. *Paramecium*, suborder Peniculina. *P. aurelia*, from Corliss (1959b), originally redrawn from various sources. Fig. 4. *Pleuronema*, suborder Pleuronematina. *P. coronatum*, from Corliss (1956a, 1959b), originally redrawn from Noland (1937).

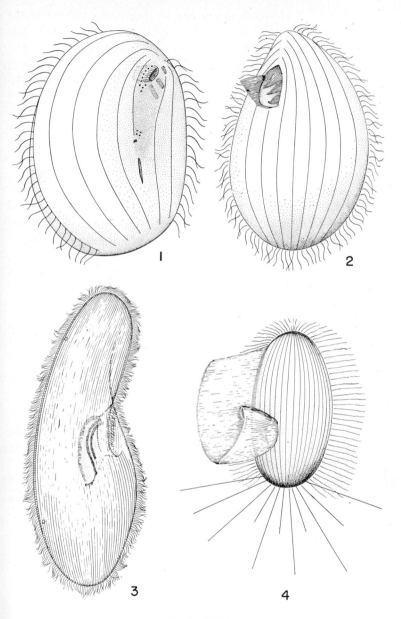

PLATE XIV

discussion of the topics; inspection of the titles included in the reference section of this book will reveal the general nature of the works. Through the year 1960, over 1,000 papers have been published on species of *Tetrahymena*, the bulk since 1950!

(1) In biochemistry and growth studies (only a few cited here), serology, and morphogenesis, including induction of synchronous division in controlled populations: Albach and Corliss (1959), Corbett (1958), Corliss (1953c), Dewey and Kidder (1958, 1960a,b), Dewey *et al.* (1957), Ducoff (1956), Fauré-Fremiet (1948c, 1949a), Hall (1950, 1954; and many earlier papers of importance in the field of growth; see also 1953), Holz (1960), Holz *et al.* (1957), Hull and Morrissey (1960), Inoki and Matsushiro (1958), Jírovec (1950), Kamiya (1959, 1960), Kidder and Dewey (1945, 1957; and many papers of intermediate date, part of a long series of nutritional and biochemical investigations), Kidder *et al.* (1940), Kidder *et al.* (1945), Loefer (1959), Loefer *et al.* (1958), Margolin *et al.* (1959), Markees *et al.* (1960), Miyake (1959, 1960), Mučibabić (1957a,b), Nanney (1953), Phelps (1959), Prescott (1957, 1959), Robertson (1939a,b), Scherbaum (1957a, 1960), Scherbaum and Rasch (1957), Scherbaum and Williams (1957), Scherbaum and Zeuthen (1954, 1955), Seaman (1952, 1955, 1959, 1960; and many not cited), Slater (1952), Sullivan (1959), Tanzer (1941), Thormar (1959), Williams (1959, 1960a), Williams and Scherbaum (1959), Zeuthen (1958), Zeuthen and Scherbaum (1954); and see reviews in Hutner (1961) and Hutner and Lwoff (1955).

(2) In genetics, cytogenetics, and cytology, including investigations of senescence, search for heritable biochemical markers, electron microscopical research, chromosome studies, and quantitative work on the protein and nucleic acid content of the nuclei: Alfert and Balamuth (1957), Alfert and Goldstein (1955), Allen and Nanney (1958), Child (1959), Christensen and Giese (1956), Corliss (1952b, 1956b, 1960a), Corliss and Dysart (1959, 1960), Dysart (1959, 1960), Dysart and Corliss (1960), Elliott *et al.* (1960), Elliott and Clark (1957, 1958a,b), Elliott and Gruchy (1952), Elliott and Hayes (1953), Elliott and Nanney (1952), Gruchy (1955), Holz *et al.* (1959), Iverson and Giese (1957), McDonald (1958), Metz and Westfall (1954), Nanney (1956, 1957, 1958, 1959a,b, 1960), Nanney and Allen (1959), Nanney and Caughey (1953, 1955), Nanny *et al.* (1955), Nanney and Rudzinska (1960), Orias

(1958, 1959, 1960), Pitelka (1959a,b), Ray (1956a), Ray and Elliott (1954), Scherbaum (1957b; *et al.*, 1958, 1959), Walker and Mitchinson (1957), Wells (1959, 1960a,b), Zebrun (1957).

(3) In comparative morphology and systematics, including recent descriptions of new species and strain differences: Buhse (1960), Corliss (1952a,c,d, 1953a, 1954a, 1957b, 1959c, 1960a), Furgason (1940), Holz and Corliss (1956), Kazubski (1958b), Kozloff (1946a, 1956b, 1957), Loefer (1952), McArdle (1960a,b), Mugard (1949), Thompson (1955), Williams (1960b), Windsor (1960).

(4) In the field of facultative parasitism (the discovery of the natural or experimental adaptability of certain tetrahymenid species to existence as symbionts in many different hosts): Barthelmes (1960), Corliss (1953a, 1960a, 1961a), Dobrzańska (1959), Epstein (1926), Janda andJírovec(1937),Kazubski(1958b), Keilin (1921), Knight and McDougle (1944), Kozloff (1946a, 1956a,b, 1957), Lwoff (1924), McLaughlin (1959), Shumway (1940), Stolk (1959a,b, 1960a,b), Stout (1954), Thompson (1958a), Thompson and Speidel (1955), Windsor (1959); and see reviews in Corliss (1954a, 1960a).

(5) Finally, the growing use of species of *Tetrahymena*, especially *T. pyriformis*, as the food organism in refined monoxenic cultures with pure strains of carnivorous amoebae, suctorians, and hypotrichs should be mentioned. The physiological and biochemical investigations made possible by such employment of *Tetrahymena* have been initiated in the laboratories of Guilcher, Lilly, Mazia, and Rudzinska and the techniques involved have now become quite widespread. Selected references include: Cohen (1957), Goldstein (1958), Guilcher (1951), Hull (1961a,b), Iverson (1958), Lilly (1942, 1953), Lilly and Cevallos (1956), Lilly and Henry (1956), Palincsar (1959), Prescott and James (1955), Rudzinska (1951), Rudzinska and Porter (1954), Sterbenz and Lilly (1956); also see comments in Corliss (1954a, 1957d), Hutner (1961), Hutner and Lwoff (1955), and Lwoff (1951).

Suborder (2) **Peniculina**

More complex, larger species of hymenostomes, characterized by possession of the so-called peniculi, compound buccal organelles supposedly homologous with the standard membranellar equipment (AZM) of members of the preceding suborder. The hymenostomes assigned here include specialized forms which are considered to represent a " dead-end " group from an evolutionary point of view. A well-defined vestibulum is present in some genera. Stomatogenesis appears to be of an autonomous type in the better-known forms.

Paramecium is considered typical of this suborder (Fig. 4, Pl. X; Fig. 3, Pl. XIV). In species of this much-studied genus the homology of the buccal ciliature with that known for *Tetrahymena* is as follows: the endoral membrane of the literature (see von Gelei, 1934a) equals the UM (undulating or paroral membrane) of *Tetrahymena*-like hymenostomes; the ventral and dorsal peniculi, probably plus the enigmatic quadrulus, represent the tripartite AZM of the less specialized groups. Much light has been thrown on these relationships by a careful study of the morphogenetics of fission and stomatogenesis in *Paramecium* carried out quite recently by Yusa (1957).

This well-known genus has long been the object of intensive researches from many approaches: cytological, genetic, physiological, biochemical, serological, ecological, etc. The best single source of information on the biology of *Paramecium* is the thorough compendium published by Wichterman (1953), but many new papers of note have appeared since then. Other valuable reviews, especially of the genetics and refined physiology of *Paramecium* species, are included in the works of Beale (1954), Hutner (1961), Hutner and Lwoff (1955), Johnson (1956), Preer (1957), Sonneborn (1947, 1949, 1950, 1954a,b, 1957, 1959), and Wenrich (1954). Special mention should be made of Jensen's (1959) very recently published experimental behavioral study in which he included a comprehensive review of this controversial subject.

The findings of most lasting importance with regard to ultrastructure of ciliated protozoa are perhaps yet to be published, but electron microscopical investigations carried out to date on species of *Paramecium* certainly have laid a solid foundation of knowledge in this field of research.* Thorough works which have appeared

---

*The pioneering research in the area was carried out at the Massachusetts Institute of Technology by Jakus and colleagues (Jakus, 1945; Jakus and Hall, 1946; Jakus *et al.*, 1942).

principally within the past five or six years deserve special mention, but it is beyond the scope of this chapter to attempt a list that is complete: Beyersdorfer and Dragesco (1952b), Blanckart (1957), Bretschneider (1950), Dippell (1958), Dragesco (1952), Ehret and Powers (1957, 1959), Metz *et al.* (1953), Nemetschek *et al.* (1953), Pease (1947), Potts (1955), Potts and Tomlin (1955), Powers *et al.* (1955), Powers *et al.* (1956), Schneider (1959, 1960), Sedar and Porter (1955), Sedar and Rudzinska (1956), Tsujita *et al.* (1957), Wohlfarth-Bottermann (1956, 1957, 1958a,b; and earlier works not cited*).

Other lines of mostly very recently completed or continuing research, involving *Paramecium* to a large extent, which should be mentioned specifically here but which must be limited to citation of titles in the reference section of this book include: Beale (1957), Bradfield (1955), Butzel *et al.* (1960), Chen (1951, 1956, and other papers not cited), Courtey and Mugard (1958), Danielová (1959), Diller (1954, 1958), Dippell (1954), Djordjevic (1958), Egelhaaf (1955), Ehret (1953, 1958, 1959a,b, 1960), Ehret and Powers (1955), Evans (1953), Evans and Pendleton (1952), Giese (1957), Gilman (1941, 1958, 1959), Hairston (1958), Hanson (1955, 1957), Hiwatashi (1958, 1959; and earlier papers), Jennings (1942), Johnson and Miller (1956), Kaudewitz (1958), Kimball (1953), Kimball and Barka (1959), Kimball *et al.* (1959), King (1935, 1954), Kitching (1956a,b, 1957b), Margolin (1954), Mast (1947), Metz (1954), Miller and Johnson (1957), Miller and van Wagtendonk (1956), Miyake (1956, 1958), Moses (1950), Mugard and Renaud (1960), Párducz (1954, 1957, 1958a,b, 1959; and others not cited here), Pigoń (1950), Poljansky (1959), Porter (1960), Powers (1955), Preer (1959), Preer and Preer (1959), Roque (1956a,b), Sato and Sato (1956), Schwartz (1946, 1947, 1956, 1957, 1958), Siegel (1958, 1960), Siegel and Larison (1960), Siegel and Preer (1957), Sonneborn (1958, 1960; and many earlier papers), Sonneborn and Sonneborn (1958), Sonneborn *et al.* (1959), Tarantola and van Wagtendonk (1959), Tartar (1939, 1954a), Tchang-Tso-Run and

---

*The ultrastructural investigations of Wohlfarth-Bottermann and colleagues which often involve protozoological material (but not restricted to *Paramecium*) are mainly contained in two continuing series of studies started in 1953–1954 (Wohlfarth-Bottermann, 1954; Wohlfarth-Bottermann and Pfefferkorn, 1953).

Tang (1957), van Wagtendonk *et al.* (1952), Viaud and Bonaventure (1956), Vivier (1955, 1960), Watanabe (1957a,b, 1959), Wichterman (1948, 1951, 1952, 1955, 1959), Wittner (1957a,b), Wohlfarth-Bottermann (1950), Yusa (1957, 1960a,b). [Added in proof: Beale and Jurand (1960); Sonneborn and Dippell (1960).]

The taxonomic-nomenclatural observations of Wenrich (1928b) and Woodruff (1945), the precise and detailed cytological observations of von Gelei (e.g., 1925, 1934a,c, 1935a, 1938a, 1939), and the review of the fibrillar system by Taylor (1941) also should be cited. New varieties and even new species of *Paramecium* continue to be described: see reports, since review in Wichterman (1953), by Beale (1954), Diller and Earl (1958), Rafalko and Sonneborn (1959), Sonneborn (1957, 1958), and Šrámek-Hušek (1954).

Other genera assignable to the Peniculina include *Disematosoma, Espejoia, Frontonia, Stokesia,* and *Urocentrum.* Studies on these forms which have provided much information of significant *systematic* value have been limited, in recent years, almost entirely to works by members of the Fauré-Fremiet school, except for von Gelei's (1954) paper. See Fauré-Fremiet (1949b, 1950a, 1954b, 1961), Fauré-Fremiet and Mugard (1949b), Roque (1957a,b, 1961), Rouiller and Fauré-Fremiet (1957a), Tuffrau and Savoie (1961). In general studies, however, *Frontonia* in particular has always been quite popular as a source of cytologically and experimentally interesting species. Important investigations carried out on *Frontonia* since the turn of the century include: Beyersdorfer and Dragesco (1952a), Brodsky (1908, 1924), Bullington (1939), Dragesco (1954, 1958), Goldsmith (1922), Kahl (1928), Krüger (1931, 1936), Müller (1936), Oberthür (1937), Okada (1956), Pai (1948), Penard (1922), Popoff (1908, 1909b), Rouiller and Fauré-Fremiet (1957a), Rouiller *et al.* (1957), Small and Profant (1960a,b), Stout (1956b), Thompson (1959), Tonniges (1914), Wetzel (1927).

Suborder (3) **Pleuronematina**

A small group of hymenostomes characterized by the extensive development of the undulating membrane, the subequatorial location of the cytostome, and the possession (typically) of a more or less pronounced area of thigmotactic ciliature located dorsally. The species generally are quite small and sparsely ciliated, with a prominent caudal cilium (" bristle "). The adoral zone of membranelles may be inconspicuous and thrown over to the right side of the broad but shallow buccal cavity.

These hymenostomes, occurring in both fresh-water and marine habitats and as coprozoic organisms as well (Hoare, 1927b; Watson, 1946b), are obviously closely related to the Tetrahymenina; the exact degree of this relationship remains an intriguing problem to be investigated. Their systematic significance lies principally in the groups that seem to have been derived from them rather than in their own exact origin (see remarks in Chapt. 6, under the order Thigmotrichida). Dragesco (1958) has added new information to our knowledge of the group in his very recent study of *Pleuronema* species collected from intertidal zones.

Pleuronema Dujardin, 1841, may be chosen as a genus typical of this suborder (Fig. 4, Pl. XIV). It illustrates nicely the structural advances or specializations over the tetrahymenine hymenostomes. Lack of proper comparative studies makes it difficult, at the present time, to list other genera definitely belonging to the group; surely a number of the genera conventionally comprising the family Pleuronematidae will be found to belong quite properly in the suborder Pleuronematina. A fresh attack on various aspects of the over-all problem has been initiated very recently by workers studying species of *Cyclidium* (Fig. 5, Pl. X): Berger (1959), Berger and Thompson (1960), Ruiz (1959), Thompson (1958b). Earlier papers of particular significance include those by G. von Gelei (1940), Hoare (1927b), Kahl (1926, 1928), Mugard (1949), Noland (1937), Párducz (1940), Penard (1922), Powers (1935), Watson (1940, 1944, 1946a), Yagiu (1933).

CHAPTER 6

SPECIALIZED HOLOTRICHS:
ORDERS THIGMOTRICHIDA
AND PERITRICHIDA

SPECIES belonging to both the smaller, rather restricted order of thigmotrichs and the large, well-known assemblage of peritrichs seem to show little affinity with other groups assigned to the subclass Holotricha, if only their more striking, and often superficial, characteristics are studied. Careful attention to the infraciliature, however, particularly in the buccal area, suggests a close relationship with certain of the hymenostome ciliates (see Chapts. 1 and 10). That they represent groups more highly evolved than the other holotrich orders is a conclusion generally conceded by all ciliate protozoologists.

As is true for practically all major protozoan taxa, monographic treatment by specialists competent for the task is greatly needed for these two ciliophoran orders. Chatton and Lwoff's (1949, 1950) culminating treatises on the thigmotrichs are invaluable, but even during the past decade a large amount of new data has been accumulating which is in need of comprehensive consideration. Kahl's (1934a) and Kirby's (1941a) reviews are very helpful, but still more out-dated. Fortunately, we may expect that Raabe's excellent series (most recent: Raabe, 1959a) will result in a single summarizing monograph in due time. An over-all treatment of the biology and systematics of the Peritrichida has not appeared since Kahl (1930–1935), although scores of new species have been described, in rather scattered publications, and our knowledge of the ecology of the group has been extended considerably.

Order **THIGMOTRICHIDA**

A restricted group of forms, generally found in association with marine or fresh-water bivalve molluscs, characterized by possession of an antero-dorsal field of thigmotactic ciliature, giving the order its name. By means of such an area of specialized cilia, whose infraciliary counterpart may be considered the forerunner of the scopula of stalked peritrich ciliates, attachment is made to body parts of the invertebrate hosts. Generally, a great loss of (other) somatic ciliature has occurred. Cytostome and buccal organelles, when present at all, are subequatorially located; in fact, the oral area is directly at the posterior pole in some forms (see Fig. 1, Pl. XV). An anteriorly located sucker, functional as an ingestatory organelle, is characteristic of one mouthless group of genuine thigmotrichs. The possibility that the entire " order " Astomatida should be included as a subordinal group in the order under present discussion is mentioned in a preceding chapter (see order Astomatida, Chapt. 4).

Binary fission involves complicated morphogenetic movements in the species in which it has been studied adequately (see Chatton and Lwoff's culminating monographs, 1949, 1950). Results of the cytological work of Chatton and Lwoff on the mouth parts may be reinterpreted to support full homologies with the patterns, both anatomical and morphogenetic, established in the hymenostomes. In this regard the Pleuronematina are of particular value, if one considers them as direct ancestors of the Thigmotrichida (see Chapt. 10). Stomatogenesis is of an autonomous type.

The relationship of thigmotrichs to their hosts has been discussed in a number of important but scattered, and often very short, papers in the literature (most recent: Beers, 1959). Kirby (1941a) and Raabe (1947a) have offered concise summaries of much of this information. The reader is also referred to Chatton and Lwoff (1949) and Kahl (1934a) for citation of many earlier investigations.

The outstanding thigmotrich studies of the past twenty-five years, aside from those carried out by Chatton and Lwoff, are to be found in the numerous publications of Kidder (1933a–e; 1934a,b) and Kozloff (1945, 1946b–e, 1960) in America, and Z. Raabe (1933, 1936, 1938, 1947b, 1949a,b, 1950a) and Jarocki

(1934, 1935; Jarocki and Raabe, 1932) in Poland. The most recent comprehensive works on systematics of thigmotrichs are those of Kazubski (1958a), Kozloff (1955), and Raabe (1956, 1959a).

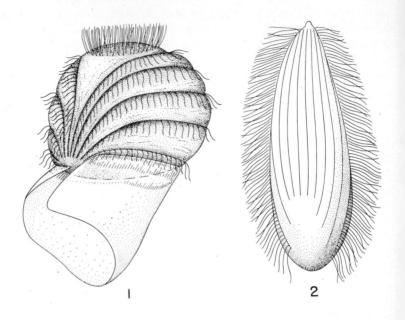

1   2

PLATE XV

Representative holotrichs: order THIGMOTRICHIDA.
FIG. 1. *Hemispeira*, suborder Arhynchodina. *H. asteriasi*, from Corliss (1959b), originally redrawn from Fauré-Fremiet (1905). FIG. 2. *Ancistrocoma*, suborder Rhynchodina. *A. pelseneeri*, from Corliss (1959b), originally redrawn from Kozloff (1946b). [*N.B.* Chatton and Lwoff (1950) consider that Kozloff's figure represents the species *A. myae.*]

Representing the order as a typical genus is *Hemispeira* Fabre-Domergue, 1888 (Fig. 1, Pl. XV). Its prominent undulating membrane is strikingly reminiscent of that possessed by many pleuronematine hymenostomes (see Fig. 1, Pl. XV and Fig. 4, Pl. XIV).

Suborder (1) **Arhynchodina**

The mouthed thigmotrichs, including the majority of the genera in the order as it is now composed. The buccal apparatus may be homologized completely with the tetrahymenal organization known for typical hymenostomes; its posterior poleward migration was foreshadowed by conditions seen in the Pleuronematina. The bases of the tripartite AZM are always aligned in a curve alongside the base of the right-hand UM. Fission and stomatogenesis, as mentioned above, are complex processes involving considerable morphogenetic movements, primarily because of the posterior location of the parental mouth parts.

Hemispeira, cited as representative of the entire order (p. 66), also is considered as a typical genus of this suborder of commensal or parasitic holotrichs (Fig. 1, Pl. XV). Other representative genera include *Ancistrum*, *Proboveria*, and *Thigmophrya*. *Boveria* has been made popular through the important works, now considered classical, carried out some years ago by two American women (Stevens, 1901, 1903; Pickard, 1927). The exact taxonomic status of *Conchophthirus*, whose species are perhaps the best-known of all thigmotrichs to American protozoologists (principally through the papers by Kidder cited on page 65), must be considered unsettled (see Part II).

Suborder (2) **Rhynchodina**

Thigmotrichs characterized by the functional replacement of the cytostome by an anteriorly located sucker. In some species this organelle appears on the end of a distinct tentacle. Important details concerning the morphology, physiology, and genesis of these curious suckers appear in the works of Chatton and Lwoff (e.g., 1939, 1949). The somatic ciliature is quite sparse in certain genera; in fact, in at least one group the mature form is completely devoid of external cilia, although it is important to note that there is ontogenetic continuity of the infraciliature. A vestige of buccal ciliature occurs in some rhynchodine thigmotrichs.

The mode of fission is complex. A budding process is the rule in certain species, such as members of the aberrant family Sphenophryidae, in which cilia are absent in the mature stage (most recent papers: Kozloff, 1955; Raabe, 1949a).

F

Ancistrocoma Chatton and Lwoff, 1926, is chosen as a typical genus (Fig. 2, Pl. XV). *Hypocoma* and *Hypocomella* also are quite representative of this highly specialized group of thigmotrichs.

Order **PERITRICHIDA**

A very large group of distinctive-appearing ciliates known to microscopists since the time of van Leeuwenhoek, nearly 300 years ago (see account in Dobell, 1932). Many of the stalked, sessile species exhibit an arboroid colonial organization, thus forming masses easily visible to the naked eye; others are solitary. The body of the mature sedentary form, shaped like a solid inverted bell and generally devoid of any but peristomial (buccal) ciliature, stands in marked contrast to the free-swimming stage in the life cycle, known as the telotroch or swarmer. This typically transient motile stage, indispensable for distribution of the species, is mouthless and equipped with a single girdle of posteriorly located locomotor ciliature.

Peritrichs occur in both fresh-water and marine habitats. The attached forms are frequently ectocommensals living on parts of the body of a wide variety of aquatic plants and animals. Sexuality is represented by a specialized type of conjugation in which highly differentiated micro- and macroconjugants pair up for exchange of nuclear material, with total subsequent loss of the body of the microconjugant (see Finley, 1943; Müggc, 1957; and reviews by Dass, 1953b; Finley, 1952; Wenrich, 1954). Recently Finley and his students have been attempting chemical analysis of differences between the conjugants (e.g., see Finley and Williams, 1955).

Stomatogenesis is of an evolved autonomous nature, and binary fission itself, although presumably homothetogenic, is not of a kind typical of most ciliates.

Certain prominent features in the anatomy of peritrichs (mature stages) have long been considered of great systematic importance and have resulted in separation of these forms from other holotrich ciliates. Restudy and reinterpretation of these characteristics have convinced some protozoologists in very recent years (see Corliss, 1956a, 1960c) that they are not separately unique and that even in combination they do not require setting the peritrichs apart at a taxonomic level above the ordinal rank. The following statements are offered in brief review of the subject. There is evidence that the conspicuous oral ciliature is homologous with the UM–AZM complex of hymenostomes and thigmotrichs; its counterclockwise winding, although possibly of some value as a " key " character, is of secondary importance phylogenetically among the holotrichs as a group. The stalk and its associated scopula, of ciliary origin, are not unique among peritrichs, since suctorians, apostomes, hymenostomes, thigmotrichs, and others (although not chonotrichs) show homologous structures. The telotroch larval stage is similarly not an exclusive feature. And the modes of binary fission and conjugation are likewise found more or less duplicated among species of several other holotrich orders.

The difficult problems of polarity and exact axial homologies remain unsolved. Chatton (1936, 1938) and Fauré-Fremiet (1950a), for example, have disagreed completely concerning interpretations in this area (see Corliss, 1956a). The vorticellid silverline system (early seen by Klein, 1927) seems to confuse rather than help resolve the issues involved. But the proposed phylogenetic sequence of hymenostomes→thigmotrichs→peritrichs, first tentatively explored over fifty years ago by Fauré-Fremiet (1905; see also 1910a, 1924) and strengthened greatly either directly or indirectly by more recent hypotheses (Corliss, 1956a; Fauré-Fremiet, 1950a; Mugard, 1949) seems a sound one which is not contradicted by any significant data published to date.

Vorticella Linnaeus, 1766, is the obvious choice as typical genus of the order (Fig. 1, Pl. XVI). One of the most important and most thorough studies of a comparative morphological nature on vorticellid species was that carried out thirty years ago by Noland and Finley (1931). In recent years the leading students of ecology and systematics of vorticellids and their relatives have been members of the Stammer school at Erlangen, in particular Nenninger, Matthes, Lust, and Biegel (e.g., see Biegel, 1954; Lust, 1950; Matthes, 1950, 1958; Nenninger, 1948; and Stammer, 1948, 1955). But also see the comprehensive works by such investigators as Precht (1935), Sommer (1951), and Stiller (1939–1941, 1946a,b, 1953, 1960; and others not cited).

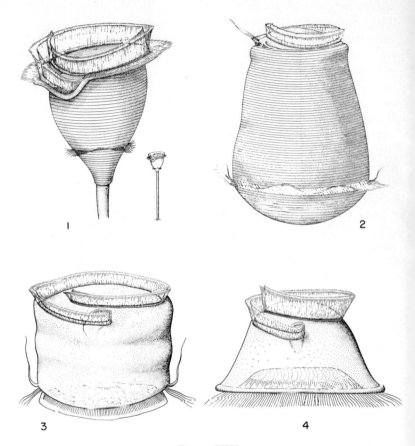

PLATE XVI

Representative holotrichs: order PERITRICHIDA.
FIG. 1. *Vorticella*, suborder Sessilina. *V. convallaria*, from Corliss (1956a, 1959b), originally redrawn from Noland and Finley (1931). FIG. 2. *Telotrochidium*, a stalkless representative of the suborder Sessilina. *T. henneguyi*, from Corliss (1956a, 1959b), originally redrawn from Fauré-Fremiet (1924) and Lynch and Noble (1931). FIG. 3. *Urceolaria*, suborder Mobilina. *U. korschelti*, redrawn from Zick (1928). FIG. 4. *Trichodina*, a more widely distributed genus of the suborder Mobilina. *T. urinicola*, from Corliss (1959b), originally redrawn from Lom (1958).

Suborder (1) **Sessilina**

Primarily composed of forms attached to some substrate by a peduncle; often colonial; some loricate. Hundreds of species are included in this first great suborder, some taxonomically distinguishable only to the expert students of the group. Somatic ciliature is limited to the ciliary girdle characteristic of the migratory telotroch. The buccal ciliature forms a prominent circular wreath at the oral pole of the organism.

The contractility characteristic of most peritrich stalks has aroused intensive study and speculation since Leeuwenhoek's discovery of it. Taylor (1941) presents a comprehensive review of this topic, a subject of considerable importance to physiologists as well as morphologists. In the past few years most exciting have been the investigations of myoneme ultrastructure, carried out by such precise workers as Fauré-Fremiet and Randall on several ciliates including, especially, peritrichs and heterotrichs. The most recent papers published on various aspects of peritrich fine structure: Fauré-Fremiet (1957a, 1958b, 1959a), Fauré-Fremiet and Rouiller (1959), Fauré-Fremiet et al. (1956c), Randall (1959a–d), Rouiller and Fauré-Fremiet (1957b, 1958), Rouiller et al. (1956b). Until utilization of electron microscopy, one of the most comprehensive and enduring analyses of the vorticellid fibrillar system has been the classical study by G. Entz, Sr. (1893).

Another area of importance recently coming under investigation with the aid of modern cytochemical techniques is refined study of the peritrich nuclear apparatus. For example, see papers by Dass (1953a, 1954a,b) and Seshachar and Dass (1953, 1954; and earlier works not cited). Finley and colleagues have been making refined studies on nutritional problems of vorticellids (most recent paper: Finley et al., 1959), following earlier work of a more general physiological nature by various investigators (e.g., see Mast and Bowen, 1944).

Vorticella, the non-colonial genus chosen to represent the order, also is typical of this first and larger suborder (Fig. 1, Pl. X; Fig. 1, Pl. XVI). The majority of the hundreds of peritrich species belong to either this contractile-stalked genus or these few colony-forming genera: *Epistylis* and *Opercularia*, with non-contractile stalks; *Carchesium*, with each zooid independently contractile; and

Zoothamnium, with myonemes continuous throughout the colony. Morphogenetic aspects of growth among colonial members of the Sessilina have long interested biologists (see Fauré-Fremiet, 1922, 1925, 1930, 1948d; and the review by Summers, 1941).

Cothurnia, Lagenophrys, and *Vaginicola* are well-known solitary loricate forms (Awerinzew, 1936; Debaisieux, 1959; Hadži, 1940b; Hamilton, 1952a; Kahl, 1930–1935; Penard, 1914b, 1922; Shomay, 1953, 1954a,b; Stammer, 1935; Swarczewsky, 1930; von Ubish, 1913; Willis, 1942, 1948). To this group Matthew (1958) recently has added a new genus, *Cyclodonta*.

Astylozoon represents a curious family in which the stalk has been replaced by one or two short spines. *Hastatella*, with fantastic conical ectoplasmic processes protruding conspicuously from the body, is another stalkless member of the same family. In *Scyphidia* the scopula functions as a holdfast organelle. Selected references to work on members of the family Scyphidiidae, many of the species of which have been described only recently, should include the interesting accounts of Chatton and Lwoff (1929), Kahl (1930–1935), Kufferath (1953), Laird (1953, 1959), Noirot and Noirot-Timothée (1959), Raabe (1952), Rudzinska (1952).

In *Telotrochidium* (Fig. 2, Pl. XVI), to mention another fascinating genus, no stalked stage is known. The seemingly mature form, free-swimming by means of its oral ciliature and locomotor fringe, may be considered to represent a permanent telotroch stage in the abbreviated life cycle of this " sessiline " peritrich. Its general biology and life history have been capably investigated by Fauré-Fremiet (1924, 1950f), Kofoid and Rosenberg (1940), Lynch and Noble (1931), and Rosenberg (1938, 1940), usually under the name *Opisthonecta*, a junior synonym.

Suborder (2) **Mobilina**

Forms without stalks, characteristically with shortened " oral-aboral " axis and generally equipped with a basal or adhesive disc of considerable structural complexity. This organelle of attachment may include myonemes, a circlet of specialized ciliature, and a skeletal or denticulate ring composed of precisely fashioned and elaborately arranged articulated " teeth."

Although only a few genera are allocated to this suborder, one or two of them are of some economic importance to man because of their destructive actions as parasitic symbionts of certain fishes, both marine and fresh-water. Somatic ciliature, as such, is essentially absent in this as well as the first suborder of peritrichs except for the locomotor ciliary girdle. The buccal ciliature is basically like that known for the sessiline species. Although no stalked stages are known among the mobiline forms, some species do show separate telotroch stages in their full life cycles.

Urceolaria Lamarck, 1801, is chosen to represent the group primarily because it is type of the only family included in the suborder (Fig. 3, Pl. XVI). A number of recent papers of importance on the cytology, ecology, and sexuality of species belonging to this genus should be mentioned: Brouardel (1951), Colwin (1944), Fauré-Fremiet *et al.* (1956c), Hirshfield (1949), Reynoldson (1955).

Trichodina (Fig. 4, Pl. XVI) is also figured because it is a more commonly encountered genus. It contains some fifty species whose modes of life range from harmless ectocommensalism, in association with such animals as the coelenterate *Hydra*, to true parasitism, in such vertebrates as salamanders and fishes. *Trichodina,* primarily on the basis of the presence of certain projections (rays and blades) on the denticles of its adhesive disc, is considered to be more highly evolved than *Urceolaria*. Uzmann and Stickney (1954) and Lom (1958) have offered modern characterizations and up-to-date host check-lists of the trichodinids. Other quite recent papers of significance include the cytological study by Davis (1947), the biometric and cytochemical investigations by Fauré-Fremiet (1943a) and Fauré-Fremiet and Thaureaux (1944), the comparative morphological study by Hirshfield (1949), the systematic investigation by Lom (1959c), and the ecological and taxonomic works by Raabe (1950b, 1959b,c), Raabe and Raabe (1959), Šrámek-Hušek (1953), Tripathi (1956), and Vojtek (1957).

Z. Raabe (1947) included a consideration of the mobiline peritrichs in his thorough discussion of morphological adaptations of ciliates to symbiotic modes of life. He also has described an interesting species of his new genus *Ambiphrya* which he believes is a form truly intermediate between the two peritrich suborders (Raabe, 1952).

CHAPTER 7

STEM GROUP OF THE SPIROTRICHS: ORDER HETEROTRICHIDA

Last monographed by Kahl (1930–1935) and Villeneuve-Brachon (1940), the heterotrichs comprise a diversified collection of forms which include a number of large, well-known ciliates. The morphology of members of this extensive order of the subclass Spirotricha is dominated by the generally conspicuous buccal ciliature; the somatic ciliature is actually holotrichous in nature in many species. The diversity in body form, the lack of such highly specialized structures as cirri, and the variation in modes of stomatogenesis within the order, as well as the common uniformity in body ciliature, lend a lability and plasticity to the group as a whole which suggest two things: that the heterotrichs arose from some similarly generalized holotrichous group, such as the Hymenostomatida; and that the heterotrichs represent the stem or ancestral group of the other more specialized spirotrich orders.

Binary fission sometimes is complicated in this group by secondary factors such as highly asymmetrical body form. Also somatic ciliation is drastically reduced in certain genera. Modes of stomatogenesis range from involvement of one to several ciliary meridians to highly evolved autonomous types (Villeneuve-Brachon, 1940). It may be recalled that a similar series is manifest in the hymenostome holotrichs (Mugard, 1949).

Heterotrichs have become adapted to a wide variety of habitats, including the digestive tracts of a number of invertebrate and a few vertebrate hosts. No species is found in man: *Balantidium*, causative agent of human balantidiosis, is conventionally classified in this order, but actually it is a trichostome holotrich (see Chapter 3). Cyst formation is common, even among the largest species (e.g., see the works on *Bursaria* by Beers, 1948a, 1952;

and Miyake, 1957). A physiological–ecological study on *Bursaria* and *Blepharisma* has been carried out very recently by Beadle and Nilsson (1959). Dragesco (1958) has studied sand-dwelling forms.

Although myonemes, the miniature " muscles " of protozoa, have been noted elsewhere (such as in the stalks of contractile peritrichs), they are particularly obvious and are lending themselves to most convenient modern study in certain heterotrichs, such as *Stentor* and *Spirostomum*. Work with electron microscopy, still in its infancy at the present time, should prove most fruitful for study of the ultrastructure of these complex contractile fibrillar systems (Fauré-Fremiet, 1957a, 1958b, 1959a; Fauré-Fremiet and Rouiller, 1958a,b; Finley, 1955; Randall, 1956, 1957, 1959a,b; Randall and Jackson, 1958).

Some heterotrich species contain pigment granules, typically aligned in rows patterned after the arrangement of the ciliary meridians and the myonemes, rendering the ciliates blue, pinkish rose, blue-green, yellowish, or brown, depending on the type of pigment(s) present. Recent papers on this subject include Barbier *et al.* (1956), Giese (1953), Inaba *et al.* (1958), Møller (1958), Weisz (1950a). Others are colorless but contain symbiotic zoo-chlorellae; the most recent paper on this subject is that by Schulze (1951), concerned with *Stentor*. Some heterotrichs are parasitized by other protozoa; for example, suctorians in the loricae of folliculinids (Chatton and Lwoff, 1927), and flagellates in a species of *Stentor* (Shönfeld, 1959).

Because of their large size, common occurrence, ease in culturing, and amazing regenerative powers, a number of species (especially those in the genus *Stentor*) have been long and widely employed in experimental researches paralleling the studies on metazoan organisms in the important fields of morphogenesis and differentiation. Attention is directed to the reviews and hypotheses of Balamuth (1940), Dierks (1926), Fauré-Fremiet (1945b, 1948a), Kimball (1958), Sokoloff (1924), Schwartz (1935), Tartar (1941, 1956, 1961), Uhlig (1960), Weisz (1951a, 1954). Tartar's (1961) very recent book, incidentally, provides a most helpful and comprehensive review of all aspects in the biology of *Stentor*.

Condylostoma Bory, 1824, is chosen as a typical genus (Fig. 1, Pl. XVII). Other representative genera are mentioned under the two suborders treated on the following pages.

Suborder (1) **Heterotrichina**

The heterotrichs *sensu stricto* of the literature. All genera of the order but one are assigned here. Essentially all the information given under the ordinal characterization (pp. 74–75) is thus applicable and does not need to be repeated.

The typical genus, appropriately, is that of the entire order: *Condylostoma* (Fig. 1, Pl. XVII). Most recent studies of interest on members of this genus include the work by Fauré-Fremiet (1958a), Yagiu (1956a,b), and Yagiu and Nakata (1956). Genera large in body size, their species often measuring greater than one millimeter in length, and containing colored forms include *Blepharisma, Folliculina,* and *Stentor* (Fig. 12, Pl. X). Other well-known species of large dimensions are members of the genera *Bursaria, Climacostomum* (Fig. 2, Pl. XVII), *Fabrea, Nyctotherus,* and *Spirostomum.*

For obvious reasons many species belonging to the genera just mentioned have long been known and studied, often with great precision even in work published a century ago. Quite recently there seems to have been a revival of interest in cytological investigation of some of these species. For example, *Bursaria* and its close relatives have been the subject of research by Balech (1941), Bary (1950a), and Beers (1952). *Metopus* and *Caenomorpha* contain smaller, not as well-known species (Kahl, 1926, 1927a), but they may be genera of importance in the supposed evolution of other spirotrich ordinal groups from the Heterotrichida. Lucas (1934) has reported *Metopus* from sea urchins, where mostly only trichostomes and hymenostomes occur (see Chapter 3). Schulze (1958)

Explanation of Plate XVII opposite

Representative spirotrichs: order HETEROTRICHIDA.
Fig. 1. *Condylostoma,* suborder Heterotrichina. *C. patens,* redrawn from Stein (1867). Fig. 2. *Climacostomum,* another representative of the suborder Heterotrichina. *C. salinarum,* from Corliss (1956a, 1959b), originally redrawn from Fauré-Fremiet (1948a). Fig. 3. *Metopus,* a curious member of the large suborder Heterotrichina. *M. intercedens,* redrawn from Kahl (1927a). Fig. 4. *Licnophora,* suborder Licnophorina. *L. macfarlandi,* from Corliss (1959b), originally redrawn from Balamuth (1941).

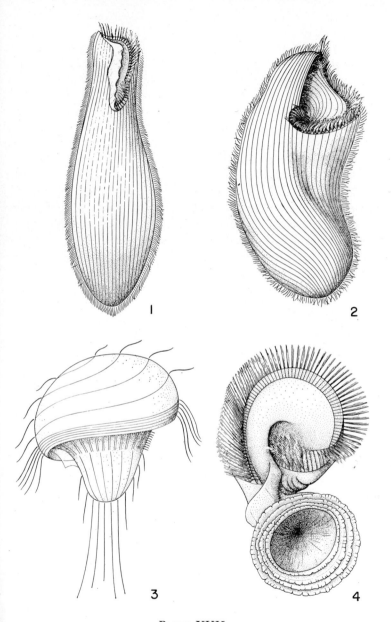

PLATE XVII

has recently completed an extensive investigation of the cytology and ecology of two sapropelic species of the same genus.

Free-living heterotrichs occur in a great variety of habitats: fresh-water, brackish, salt-water, and even highly concentrated salt marshes. A species of *Fabrea* from the last-mentioned type of ecological niche has been studied in some detail (Ellis, 1937; Kirby, 1934; Villeneuve-Brachon, 1940). *Folliculina*, a fascinating loricate genus with curiously drawn out " peristomial wings " and a life cycle which includes a vermiform migratory swarmer, generally has been considered as marine only. Recently, however, fresh-water forms have been reported (Hamilton, 1952b). Interesting, also, is the discovery of fossilized folliculinid loricae (Deflandre and Deunff, 1957). *Folliculina* and closely related genera, incidentally, have long been subjects of taxonomic, cytological, and ecological studies (see such works, including the most recent, since the turn of the century as: Andrews, 1914, 1923, 1953, 1955, and many others not cited; Das, 1953; Dons, 1913–1914, 1928, 1948; Fauré-Fremiet, 1932, 1936; Ringuelet, 1955; Silén, 1947; Villeneuve-Brachon, 1940), and they have recently been capably monographed by Hadži (1951).

Nyctotherus, a genus of many species (e.g., see lists in de Puytorac, 1954b, and Wichterman, 1937), some of which are surely of doubtful distinctiveness, may be found in hosts ranging from reptiles to cockroaches. I consider reports of its occurrence in man as unfounded. The fibrillar system of *Nyctotherus* has been studied by Pai and Wang (1948), Rosenberg (1937), and Villeneuve-Brachon (1940); its nuclear apparatus, by Kudo (1936) and a number of earlier workers. Very distinctive heterotrichine ciliates were described as generically new, independently, by two different workers (Kidder, 1937, 1938; Yamasaki, 1939) from the intestinal tract of an Indonesian wood-feeding roach.

Sexuality is as common among members of this suborder as in other ciliate groups of comparable size, although precise breeding systems are yet to be recognized. Many papers of a purely descriptive nature have been published on conjugation (see citations in Wenrich, 1954). One of the most extensive studies, carried out some years ago, is that of Poljansky (1934) on *Bursaria*. Weisz (1950b) recently has observed an interesting occurrence of " multi-conjugation " in *Blepharisma*. Members of this last-mentioned genus show a curious variation in their number of macronuclear nodes, even within a single species (most recent literature: Bhandary, 1959, 1960; Helson *et al.*, 1959; McLoughlin, 1957; Padmavathi, 1959; Suzuki, 1954; Yagiu and Shigenaka, 1956). Possibly this is of evolutionary significance; it is definitely a source of taxonomic confusion at the species-level. An important announcement is that of the very recent discovery of a kind of sexuality in *Spirostomum* yielding viable lines of progeny (Seshachar and Padmavathi, 1959a).

Although regenerative and other morphogenetic work continues to be carried out with various heterotrichs as the experimental animal [for example, by Clark (1946) and Seshachar and Padmavathi (1959b), on *Spirostomum;* by Giese and Lusignan (1960), Suzuki (1959), Weisz (1949, 1950c), on *Blepharisma;* by Yagiu (1956a,b), on *Condylostoma*], the most intensively and extensively studied genus of the group is *Stentor*. The most significant series of such investigations in modern times are those by Tartar and Weisz. Some of the major works of these men, other than those papers already specifically cited (p. 75), should be mentioned here: Tartar (1953, 1954b, 1957a,b, 1958a, 1959); Weisz (1948, 1951b, 1955, 1956). Johnson's (1893) masterpiece remains the classic among early papers published in this fascinating field of research. [Physiologically-oriented investigations which have been reported while the present work was in press are the experimental studies of considerable interest by De Terra (1960a,b) and Whiteley (1960).]

A few other recent studies on *Stentor*, more or less isolated from the usual fields of investigation covered in earlier paragraphs, may be cited. For example, Andrews' (1945, 1946) work on ingestion and on anchoring devices; the investigation of *micronuclei* and mitotic events by Guttes and Guttes (1959, 1960); Sleigh's (1956, 1957, 1960) precise study of ciliary coordination; the ecological work by Sprugel (1951); and Tuffrau's (1957) research on phototropism in *S. niger*. Five new species of *Stentor* have been described since Kahl's (1930–1935) monographic review of the genus, two by Bary (1950c) and one each by Silén (1948), Tartar (1958b), and Villeneuve-Brachon (1940).

Suborder (2) **Licnophorina**

Containing species of a single genus, *Licnophora*, long considered an aberrant or highly specialized member of the heterotrichs but not formally separated at the subordinal level until recently (Corliss, 1957a). These ciliates are marine ectocommensals (e.g., associated with echinoderms, certain molluscs and annelids, and even algae) with a very prominent oral disc bearing a conspicuous AZM, followed by a constricted region of the body devoid of cilia and, at the posterior end, a complex basal disc serving as an organelle of attachment. Binary fission is an involved morpho-genetic process, and stomatogenesis is of an autonomous type unique among the Heterotrichida. A very complex internal fibrillar system has been described.

Licnophora Claparède, 1867, automatically is the typical genus, being the only one included in the suborder at the present time (Fig. 4, Pl. XVII). The most authoritative recent researches on the general biology, cytology, comparative morphology, and morphogenesis of these specialized forms are those of Balamuth (1941, 1942) and Villeneuve-Brachon (1940). These works are rich in bibliographic references to the earlier literature on species of *Licnophora*; very little has been published on them in the past 18–20 years.

CHAPTER 8

OLIGOTRICHOUS SPIROTRICHS: ORDERS OLIGOTRICHIDA, TINTINNIDA, ENTODINIOMORPHIDA, ODONTOSTOMATIDA

IN CONTRAST with the condition seen among many members of the large and plastic order of heterotrichs, a simple somatic ciliature in most other spirotrich species is conspicuous by its absence. Included in the non-heterotrich group are the " Oligotrichida " *sensu lato* [orders Oligotrichida (*sensu stricto*), Tintinnida, and Entodiniomorphida], the curious Odontostomatida (formerly known as the ctenostomes), and the highly specialized Hypotrichida (treated separately in the following chapter). All of these forms share in common an extensively developed buccal ciliature. Except for the tintinnids, only a rather small number of species are known for the groups under consideration in the present chapter.

Little attention has been paid to the systematics and over-all biology of the Oligotrichida and Odontostomatida since the monographic compilation of Kahl (1930–1935). The Tintinnida, primarily marine, pelagic forms, were left to one side by Kahl but were treated taxonomically in a condensed fashion by his contemporary Jörgensen (1927). We are fortunate to have the outstanding monographs on the tintinnids painstakingly produced by Kofoid and Campbell (1929, 1939) and quite recently brought up to date by Campbell (1954). The entodiniomorphids, more commonly known as the ophryoscolecids from the name of the larger of the two included families, are most in need of comprehensive taxonomic attention. The classical work on this group is Dogiel's (1927) great monograph; in recent years Lubinsky has published a series of significant but considerably shorter papers (Lubinsky, 1957a–c, 1958a,b).

Order OLIGOTRICHIDA

Spirotrichs in which somatic ciliation is either markedly reduced or has disappeared altogether, whereas membranelles of the AZM have been developed prominently and may function in locomotion as well as feeding. Unlike many species of the subclass, all oligotrichs exhibit a body form which is round in cross-section. Fission is of a unique kind, characterized as " enantiotropic " by Fauré-Fremiet (1953c) but still basically homothetogenic as well. Stomatogenesis is of a specialized autonomous type.

The order, as constituted in the present scheme of classification, is a small one. Species occur in both marine and fresh-water habitats; none lives in symbiotic relationship with other animals.

Halteria Dujardin, 1840, a very common fresh-water form, is designated as a typical genus (Fig. 1, Pl. XVIII). The rapid " springing " movements of the well-known species *H. grandinella* represent its characteristic mode of locomotion (Szabó, 1934, 1935). *Strombidium* (Fig. 2, Pl. XVIII) contains larger, marine forms (Busch, 1930; Dragesco, 1958; Fauré-Fremiet, 1924; Leegaard, 1915). One intertidal pool species appears to possess a remarkable sense of " tidal rhythm " (Fauré-Fremiet, 1948b). *Tontonia* is a curiously " tailed " marine form. *Strobilidium* shows one of the most exaggerated cases of extension of the original AZM into a spiral crown encircling the entire apical pole of the body.

In several extant schemes of ciliate classification the following two orders are considered as parts of the present one. I follow Hall (1953), however, in believing that these three " oligotrichous " groups of spirotrichs have undergone sufficient evolutionary differentiation to permit their separation at equivalent (ordinal) taxonomic levels.

Order TINTINNIDA

Conical or trumpet-shaped pelagic forms possessing loricae the composition and dimensions of which serve as the principal means of taxonomic differentiation within the order. Tintinnids are numerous both in species and individuals, being especially abundant in the great oceans and in various seas (e.g., see such works as Balech, 1959; Bernstein, 1931; Busch, 1948; Campbell,

1942, 1954; Hada, 1932a,b; Jörgensen, 1924, 1927; Jörgensen and Kahl, 1933; Kofoid and Campbell, 1929, 1939; Marshall, 1934; Nie and Ch'eng, 1947; Strelkow, 1953). A few forms have been described from non-marine sources; the species *Codonella cratera* is especially abundant in the plankton of large bodies of fresh water. The anterior part of the body, bearing a prominent AZM with unique organelles known as tentaculoids interspersed among the membranelles, may be extruded from the lorica. In locomotion, curiously enough, the oral end is directed backward. Somatic ciliature is often greatly reduced or even absent. The organism is attached to the inside of its test by its posterior end, which is equipped with an adhesive tip. Fission is quite complex, and stomatogenesis appears to be an involved autonomous process not unlike that known for the oligotrich ciliates (see discussion in Corliss, 1956a). A large ciliary (undulating?) membrane aids in molding the new lorica needed for one of the filial organisms following division (Campbell, 1926, 1927; Hofker, 1932).

Tintinnid loricae have been found by several workers in recent years as fossils (Campbell, 1954; Colom, 1948). Such reports stand to date as the only example of known fossil records for ciliated protozoa, except for the isolated discovery of a fossil folliculinid (cited in the section on the order Heterotrichida, Chapter 7) and the possible existence of a " fossilized " paramecium (Holotricha, Hymenostomatida) in amber (noted in Wichterman, 1953, p. 94). Unfortunately none of these findings is of any aid in ascertaining degrees of affinity among the various orders of ciliates.

Tintinnus Schrank, 1803, by name as well as structure, may be considered a logical choice as a typical tintinnid (Fig. 3, Pl. XVIII). Species in a number of other genera, however, including *Tintinnopsis* (Fig. 8, Pl. X) and *Codonella*, show much more picturesque loricae (cf. Figs. 3 and 4, Pl. XVIII). Factors pertaining to the *intra*-ordinal evolution of tintinnids have been discussed by Kofoid (1930). Differences in loricae serve as the most important feature in such considerations; unfortunately, as mentioned above with regard to the discovery of tintinnid fossils, such data are of no value in postulating *inter*-ordinal evolutionary relationships.

G

Order ENTODINIOMORPHIDA

Another spirotrich group with somatic ciliature greatly reduced, usually totally absent. The prominent ciliature at the oral end is buccal in origin; but it often occurs in separate clumps, known as the adoral zone and the dorsal zone(s) of membranelles (AZM and DZM). Kofoid (1935) has described two of the most bizarre forms. The pellicle is thick and firm, although pierced by the contractile vacuole pores and their permanent canals, and may be drawn out into a variety of spines posteriorly.

Internally the entodiniomorphids show great complexity, as recognized long ago. Indeed, the concept of a ciliate " neuro-motor apparatus " arose from study of ophryoscolecids, the forms comprising the bulk of the order (Sharp, 1914). In recent years renewed intensive studies of their fibrillar systems have been made, using both light and electron microscopy (e.g., by Bretschneider, 1959; Fernández-Galiano, 1949, 1955, 1958; and Noirot-Timothée, 1956a,b, 1957, 1958a,b, 1959, 1960).

The morphogenetics of fission is somewhat complex. Stomato-genesis appears to follow the general oligotrich (orders Oligo-trichida, Tintinnida, Entodiniomorphida) pattern. The presence of a subpellicularly located infraciliature, never bearing cilia, is possibly of considerable phylogenetic significance (Kantor, 1956). The long, separate evolutionary history which these ciliates must have undergone surely supports their exclusion from other orders of spirotrichs and justifies their assignment to an independent order of their own. Lubinsky (1957a–c) recently has made a thorough

---

Explanation of Plate XVIII opposite

Representative spirotrichs: orders OLIGOTRICHIDA and TINTINNIDA.

FIG. 1. *Halteria*, a common fresh-water oligotrich. *H. grandinella*, from Corliss (1959b), originally redrawn from various sources. Fig. 2 *Strombidium*, a common marine oligotrich. *S. lagenula*, from Corliss (1956a), originally redrawn from Fauré-Fremiet (1924). Fig. 3. *Tintinnus*, a common tintinnid with cylindrical, hyaline lorica. *T. fraknoii*, redrawn from Fauré-Fremiet (1924). Fig. 4. *Tintinnopsis*, a common tintinnid with a distinctively shaped, arenaceous lorica. *T. ventricosa*, from Corliss (1956a, 1959b), originally redrawn from Fauré-Fremiet (1924).

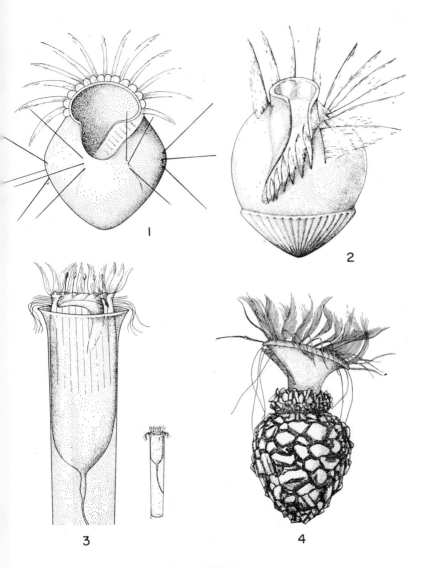

1

2

3

4

PLATE XVIII

study of evolution within the group, the first major investigation of this kind since Dogiel (1927, 1946).

All species of entodiniomorphids live as endocommensals in the digestive tracts of herbivorous mammals.* Most of them (the family of ophryoscolecids) are found in great abundance in the rumen or reticulum of ruminants, such as cattle and sheep, where a number of holotrichs, principally trichostomes, dwell as well. Outstanding papers on the distribution and general biology of such ciliates should include the following works, most of which were completed some years ago: Becker and Talbot (1927), Bush and Kofoid (1948), da Cunha (1914a), Dogiel (1927, 1932, 1934), Dogiel and Fedorowa (1929), Ferber and Winogradowa-Fedorowa (1929), Kofoid and Christenson (1934), Kofoid and MacLennan (1930, 1932, 1933), Krascheninnikow (1955), MacLennan (1935a), Sládeček (1946), Watson (1945b); also see papers by Lubinsky, cited on page 81 and in the preceding paragraph, and the very recent work by Latteur (1958).

Cycloposthiids, representing the only other family included in the order, commonly occur in horses (see monographic works by Bundle, 1895; Gassovsky, 1919; Hsiung, 1930; Strelkow, 1929, 1931, 1939; and shorter papers by such investigators as da Cunha and Muniz, 1927b,c; Adam, 1951, 1953). A few species are

---

*These forms probably are the best known of ciliated protozoa to many workers in fields of medical and, especially, veterinary protozoology. For some general references to sources of literature in these areas see Part III of this book.

Explanation of Plate XIX opposite

Representative spirotrichs: orders ENTODINIOMORPHIDA and ODONTOSTOMATIDA.

Fig. 1. *Entodinium*, an allegedly primitive ophryoscolecid (entodiniomorphid). *E. caudatum*, redrawn from Schuberg (1888). Fig. 2. *Epidinium*, a more highly evolved ophryoscolecid (entodiniomorphid). *E. parvicaudatum*, from Corliss (1956a, 1959b), originally redrawn from Kofoid and Christenson (1934). Fig. 3. *Saprodinium*, an odontostome (formerly known as ctenostomes). *S. dentatum*, from Corliss (1959b), originally redrawn from Kahl (1926, 1930–1935). Fig. 4. *Epalxella* (replacement for preoccupied name *Epalxis*), another common odontostome. *E. mirabilis*, from Corliss (1956a), originally redrawn from Kahl (1926).

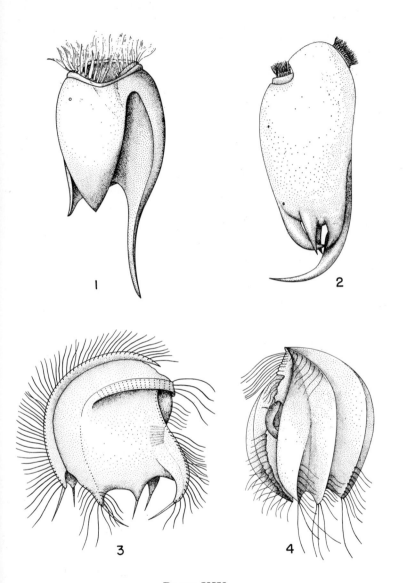

PLATE XIX

known from other mammals, including the rhinoceros and certain anthropoid apes (Hoare, 1937; Reichenow, 1920; Swezey, 1934). The literature is really scanty concerning members of this family.

Entodinium Stein, 1859, is a logical choice for a typical genus, although it is considered one of the more primitive genera (Fig. 1, Pl. XIX). Other well-known groups include *Epidinium* (Fig. 2, Pl. XIX), *Diplodinium, Ophryoscolex, Polyplastron:* all members of the major family, the Ophryoscolecidae, the entodiniomorphids classically monographed by Dogiel, Strelkow and associates (see Dogiel, 1925, 1927; Poljansky and Strelkow, 1938; and several of the citations given in a preceding paragraph). Important reviews concerned with the physiology of these rumen ciliates have been published recently (Hungate, 1955; Oxford, 1955). Significant papers since the reviews include, among others, those by Appelby *et al.* (1956), Coleman (1960), Gutierrez (1958), and Gutierrez and Davis (1959).

Cycloposthium, Tripalmaria, and *Troglodytella* may be mentioned as representative of the smaller but more highly evolved second family, the Cycloposthiidae.

Order **ODONTOSTOMATIDA**

Laterally compressed, wedge-shaped, carapaced ciliates with very sparse somatic ciliature and with reduction of buccal ciliature to an AZM of only eight or nine inconspicuous membranelles. The odontostomes are generally known in the literature as ctenostomes, although a serious case of preoccupation makes advisable the replacement of " Ctenostomatida " by the more recent name " Odontostomatida " (Corliss, 1957a; Sawaya, 1940). Typically these spirotrichs, quite possibly of heterotrich origin (through the genera *Metopus* and *Caenomorpha?*), are small, polysaprobic, fresh-water forms, preferring habitats rich in organic material but very low in oxygen.

Fewer than three dozen species of odontosomes have been described to date, and the whole order has been little studied since the systematic and ecological investigations of Penard (1922) and Wetzel (1928) and the several authoritative works and reviews by Kahl (1926, 1932, 1930–1935). In fact, the early intensive study by Lauterborn (1908) established the group essentially as it is still recognized today. Practically the only American proto-zoologist to publish on any of these interesting forms has been Lackey (1925, 1938). A number of French, German, and Swiss investigators, in addition to those cited on the preceding page, have included mention of the odontostomes (as " ctenostomes ") in works primarily devoted to studies of other groups. A very recent example of this may be found in Dragesco's (1958) compre-hensive ecological monograph on sand-dwelling ciliates.

Saprodinium Lauterborn, 1908, is a typical genus (Fig. 3, Pl. XIX). The genera *Discomorphella* and *Epalxella* (Fig. 4, Pl. XIX), formerly known as *Discomorpha* and *Epalxis* (see Corliss, 1960b), also contain important species.

CHAPTER 9

MOST HIGHLY EVOLVED OF THE SPIROTRICHS: ORDER HYPOTRICHIDA

HERE we have, once again, an example of a major ciliate group the comparative biology and over-all systematics of which stand in sore need of thorough and up-to-date treatment. The most recent comprehensive monographic consideration of these protozoa, a number of which are becoming of increasing importance in several areas of modern experimental biology, dates back to the work of Kahl (1930–1935), as might be expected.

From the point of view of the commonly assumed sequence of phylogeny within the subphylum Ciliophora, the Hypotrichida are quite universally considered to represent the peak of development in the evolution of ciliates. In fact, it is generally implied— and I can think of no sound basis for refutation of the notion—that the hypotrichs are the most highly evolved members of the entire phylum Protozoa. If modification of form and complexity of structure are valid criteria, there are surely grounds for the assumption.

Critical restudy of the individual genera and families of this last, large order of the subclass Spirotricha is needed, as well as a detailed treatment of the group as a whole. Modern models for such work may be found in the beautiful productions of Chatton (1942), Chatton and Séguéla (1940), and, more recently, Tuffrau (1960). These contributions, although limited in taxonomic scope, rightly emphasize the importance of the infraciliature, the significance of morphogenetic data, and the necessity for a comparative approach if the results obtained in such investigations are to be of lasting value.

The order Hypotrichida may be characterized by the dorso-ventrally flattened form of its species, their frequently rigid pellicle, and their exhibition of prominently displayed compound buccal and somatic ciliature. The adoral zone of membranelles is the most conspicuous part of the oral ciliature; sets of cirri confined to the ventral surface represent a kind of somatic ciliature practically unique among ciliates (see Figs. 1, 2, Pl. XX). So-called sensory bristles, through electron microscopical study now known structurally to be nothing more than modified individual cilia (e.g., see Roth, 1957), often occur in rows on the otherwise unadorned, slightly convex dorsal surface (von Gelei, 1938b, 1939b).

The cirri of hypotrichs allow these ciliates great mobility of action: swimming, crawling, jumping, darting forward or backward, even aiding in methods of food capture by coordination with movements of the peristomial (buccal) membranelles. The number, kind, and distribution of the groups of these all-purpose organelles are of great taxonomic value at the lowel levels within the order. Fission involves specialized morphogenetic movements associated with production of new cirri and with stomatogenesis. Origin of new mouth parts is a highly evolved autonomous process (Chatton and Séguéla, 1940).

Hypotrichs occur ubiquitously and abundantly as free-living forms in habitats of all kinds. Rich numbers may be found not only in the usual environments of fresh- and salt-water but also in moss, humus, and soils of various kinds (see reference to recent ecological papers under the section on the order Gymnostomatida, Chapter 3). A few species live as symbionts of other organisms. Encystment is common and a number of important studies have been made of the phenomenon. The more recent or more extensive ones include those by von Brand (1923), Fauré-Fremiet *et al.* (1954), Garnjobst (1928, 1937), Ilowaisky (1926), Ivanić (1931), Jeffries (1956), Kay (1945b), Penn (1935), Sokoloff (1945), Weyer (1930). Consult also the references in van Wagtendonk (1955).

Euplotes Ehrenberg, 1831, may be considered a typical genus (Fig. 1, Pl. XX; see also Figs. 7, 8, Pl. I; Figs. 5, 6, Pl. IV; Fig. 10, Pl. X). It already has been chosen as representative of the entire sub-class Spirotricha (see Chapter 2). A beautiful comparative study of the infraciliature and silverline system of the several species belonging to the genus has been completed very recently by Tuffrau (1954, 1960). *Euplotes* has been a favorite organism in important experimental and cytological researches. Outstanding papers published within the past twenty-five years in the fields of morphogenesis, regeneration, comparative taxonomy, genetics and cytogenetics, and ultrastructure, exclusive of references cited in the preceding paragraph, should be mentioned: Beers (1954), Bovee (1957), Chatton (1942), Chatton and Séguéla (1940), Fauré-Fremiet (1952a, 1956), Fauré-Fremiet *et al.* (1957b), Gall (1959), Gause (1941), Hammond (1937), Hammond and Kofoid (1937), Ivanić (1929a,b), Katashima (1952, 1953, 1959a,b),

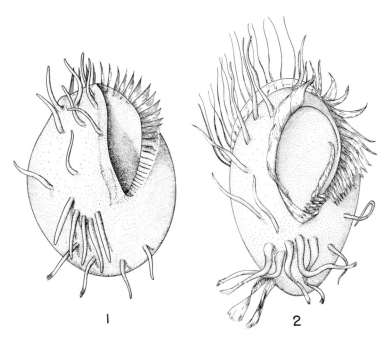

PLATE XX

Representative spirotrichs: order HYPOTRICHIDA.

FIG. 1. *Euplotes*, advanced hypotrich which clearly illustrates the domination of body morphology by the conspicuous cirri and the well-developed adoral zone of buccal membranelles. *E. patella*, from Corliss (1959b), originally redrawn from Pierson (1943). Fig. 2. *Diophrys*, an even more highly evolved hypotrich whose morphology would appear to support the contention that this spirotrich order represents the pinnacle of pellicular differentiation in the evolution of ciliates. *D. scutum*, from Corliss (1956a), originally redrawn from Fauré-Fremiet (1948a).

Kimball (1941, 1942), Pierson (1943), Powers (1943), Roth (1957, 1958), Tuffrau (1960), Yow (1958). Important investigations published during the period 1910–1935 may be found among the references in Chapter 13 (Part III of this book). Special mention, however, should be made of Taylor's (1920) significant micrugical work on the fibrillar system of *Euplotes eurystomus*. Probably the classical paper on the morphogenetics of fission in *Euplotes* is Wallengren's (1901) pioneering contribution.

Other well-known genera include *Aspidisca, Diophrys, Onychodromus, Oxytricha, Pleurotricha, Stylonychia, Uroleptus* (Fig. 2, Pl. X), *Uronychia*, and *Urostyla. Euplotaspis* and *Paraeuplotes* represent very unusual forms (Chatton and Séguéla, 1936; Wichterman, 1942).

Because of their large size, easy availability and culturability, and striking features (pellicular; cytoplasmic; and nuclear: e.g., the curious " reorganization bands " of the C-shaped *Euplotes* macronucleus), hypotrichs have always been favorite objects of microscopical or physiological research. Investigations of their genetics have been restricted to date primarily to the genus *Euplotes* (see above references, and reviews in Sonneborn, 1947, 1957), although work of great interest is in progress with species of *Stylonychia* (Downs, 1952, 1956, 1959; Rao, 1958) and *Oxytricha* (Kay, 1945a, 1946; Siegel, 1956). Conjugation *per se* has long been recognized, of course, in many hypotrichs. Descriptions of their nuclear apparatus, including the determination of numbers of chromosomes, have been quite numerous (Calkins, 1919; Dawson, 1919, 1920; Kay, 1946; Lichtenberg, 1955a,b; Manwell, 1928; Ördögh, 1959; H. Raabe, 1946, 1947; Summers, 1935; Turner, 1930, 1941). Nutritional studies of considerable interest have been undertaken by Lilly and colleagues (Lilly, 1942, 1953; Lilly and Cevallos, 1956; Lilly and Henry, 1956).

Noteworthy cytological and taxonomic investigations, especially of members of the Oxytrichidae, an unwieldy family containing more genera than any other family in the entire ciliate subphylum, have been carried out in relatively recent years by Bary (1950c), Bishop (1943), Bullington (1940), Chatton and Séguéla (1940), Dembowska (1938), Froud (1949), Gajewskaja (1933), von Gelei (1929, 1944, 1954), von Gelei and Szabados (1950), Gellért (1956), Horváth (1933, 1936a), Jeffries (1956), Kahl (1926, 1927a, 1928),

Kiesselbach (1936), Lund (1935), Nozawa (1941), Roth (1960), Rühmekorf (1935), Šrámek-Hušek (1952), Summers (1935), Wenzel (1953).

Note added in press: Dragesco's (1958) comprehensive monograph on marine sand-dwelling (principally gymnostome) ciliates, just now available in printed form (see Dragesco, 1960), includes study of the systematics and comparative morphology, as well as ecology, of over 30 species of hypotrichs. The species, nearly half of which are described as new, belong to some 17 genera (several named by Dragesco) assignable to the three major families of the order (see Part II of the present book).

CHAPTER 10

CILIATE EVOLUTION
AND PHYLOGENY

CLASSIFICATIONAL schemes supposedly reflect phylogenetic inter-relationships of the groups of organisms involved, but it is particularly difficult to trace evolutionary affinities within any major protozoan taxon (Corliss, 1959a, 1960c). The formidable obstacles which the ciliates, in contrast to most metazoan material, present to the systematist interested in their origins may be mentioned briefly: (1) Their widespread lack of fossils; (2) their microscopic size; (3) their subcellular type of organization*; (4) their ubiquity; (5) their frequent lack of recognized sexuality†.

If one important assumption is allowed, however, considerable progress can be made in postulating probable protozoan phylo-genies. This necessary assumption is that present ciliate groups have survived unchanged for many aeons and that they thus resemble ancestral groups which may be supposed to have arisen at distinctly different times in the ancient past history of the entire subphylum. Therefore careful comparative study of extant forms can overcome the major obstacle of lack of fossils, and the important dimension of time is not entirely neglected. Modern comparative studies, however, must be concerned with truly

*Whether protozoa be considered unicellular or acellular (Baker, 1948; Corliss, 1957c), an absorbing topic beyond the scope of the present work.

†A particularly vexatious hindrance to refined study of ciliate evolution at the level of species or subspecies, an important area of theoretical and experimental research discussion of which is beyond the scope of the present chapter. The reader interested in this field of investigation is referred especially to the stimulating works of Sonneborn and his students on *Paramecium*, whose species lend themselves so ideally to such study. For example, see Kimball (1943), Levine (1953), Siegel (1958), Sonneborn (1949, 1957), and additional references cited in those papers.

fundamental features if the data obtained are to be considered of phylogenetic value. As pointed out in Chapters 1 and 2, the *infraciliature* appears to be just such a fundamental characteristic, and it lends itself to thorough investigation from both static and dynamic approaches.

Interpretation of all pertinent data available, and a great accumulation of such information does exist, allows construction of a ciliate genealogical tree, admittedly a highly speculative venture but one not without some value. The obvious difficulties in producing a simplified, two-dimensional tree which will truly reflect the phylogenetic history of the major groups involved need not be mentioned. Historically, Schewiakoff (1896) seems to have been the first protozoologist bold enough to attempt the task for the ciliates. Lepşi (1926a) tried it a quarter of a century later, in the very year that Klein (1926a) discovered the technique— silver impregnation—which was destined to make these early trees quite obsolete. The modern scheme offered by Fauré-Fremiet (1950a) incorporated most of the important information made available between 1925 and 1950. His tree was refined and brought up nearer to date in work published by the writer (Corliss, 1956a, 1960c).

Comments should be made concerning major features of the illustrated genealogical tree of mine depicted in Plate XXI. Certain background details covered in earlier papers (Corliss, 1956a, 1958e) need not be repeated here. It should be emphasized that our ideas concerning interrelationships among the higher ciliate taxa are bound to change still further as additional studies are carried out: a perfectly healthy outlook!

Zooflagellate ancestry of the Ciliophora cannot be proven, but it is universally assumed and is, indeed, a reasonable hypothesis. The most primitive ciliates existing today appear to be the rhabdophorine gymnostomes, not the specialized astomes which have probably become astomatous secondarily. Such a genus as *Holophrya* (Fig. 1, Pl. XI) seems a perfect ciliate " prototype ": its simplicity in somatic and oral structures, its straightforward mode of perkinetal fission, its simple axis of symmetry, its generally unspecialized mode of life support the allegation.

Whether or not the Suctorida arose from rhabdophorine gymnostome stock is a debatable, and probably unresolvable, point. The problem has been discussed at some length in several works (Corliss, 1956a, 1960c; Guilcher, 1951; Kahl, 1931a.) The origin of trichostomes from these gymnostomes, however, seems certain. Lower trichostomes (such as *Coelosomides*) need only to have lost the cytopharyngeal trichites, as such, and acquired a simple vestibulum (Fauré-Fremiet, 1950d). Even in some of the most highly evolved forms, such as *Tillina*, we can observe a beautiful example of ontogenetical recapitulation of phylogeny at the time of fission: *Tillina* loses its contorted form, assumes a simple axis of symmetry, and divides exactly as a rhabdophorine gymnostome (see Figs. 1 and 2, Pl. VII). Subsequent morphogenetic movements (in a demonstration of allometric growth) re-establish the highly asymmetrical interdivisional form in the life cycle (Tuffrau, 1952). The origin of cyrtophorine gymnostomes from the obviously related rhabdophorines also seems unquestionable. All specializations exhibited by the cyrtophorines can be considered as secondary acquisitions appearing during their own long evolutionary history.

As already discussed in Chapter 1, the recognition of a close relationship between the cyrtophorine gymnostomes and the chonotrichs represents a modern discovery of significance. Application of the indispensable silver impregnation method in a brilliant study of the morphogenetics of chonotrich ontogenies allowed Guilcher (1951) to see the remarkable structural parallels between these formerly enigmatic ciliates and certain highly evolved gymnostomes (e.g., see Figs. 5 and 6, Pl. VII). Thus the affinities of these two groups seem firmly established.

The cyrtophorine gymnostomes also appear to be the forerunners of the important order of hymenostomes, a group which occupies a pivotal position of importance in our suggested tree. Many details remain to be worked out, but the very recent rediscovery and careful restudy of species belonging to the curious genus *Pseudomicrothorax* seem to offer excellent support for this contention (Thompson and Corliss, 1958; Corliss, 1958d,e). *Pseudomicrothorax*, traditionally considered a trichostome, possesses both the specialized cytopharyngeal armature of cyrtophorine gymnostomes and the compound ciliary buccal organelles of tetrahymenine hymenostomes (see esp. Fig. 3, Pl. XI and Figs. 1 and 2, Pl. XIV). It would appear to link members of the Clathro-

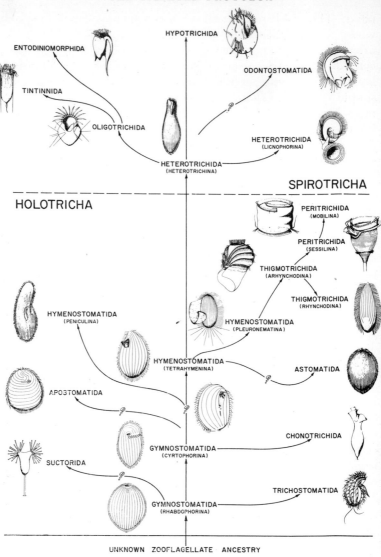

UNKNOWN ZOOFLAGELLATE ANCESTRY

PLATE XXI

A phylogenetic tree of the subphylum CILIOPHORA [from Corliss (1960c)].

An illustrated revision of the genealogical scheme published by

stomatidae, which I consider a gymnostome family, with members of certain families belonging to both the tetrahymenine and peniculine groups of the Hymenostomatida. Possibly a new hymenostome suborder should be established for *Pseudomicrothorax* (Corliss, 1958e), but I prefer awaiting results of additional investigations of a number of possibly related little-known forms still conventionally considered trichostomes.

The hymenostome assemblage has been declared the most plastic group of all the ciliates (Corliss, 1956a), and this assumption is perhaps well justified. The hymenostomes appear to be the first holotrichs to possess well-defined buccal organelles: membranelles and a true undulating membrane. The diversity in these oral structures throughout the order, the variation in modes of stomatogenesis, and the differences in location of the mouth and in disposition of the somatic ciliature bespeak a lability of great potential significance from a phylogenetic point of view. It is even reasonable to suppose that the hymenostome group provided the ancestors of the present-day Spirotricha.

The apostomes may have branched off some hymenostome line a long time ago. For the present, such a statement must be considered purely conjectural (Corliss, 1958e).

Perhaps the most significant evolutionary line represented in the drawing of the phylogenetic tree (Pl. XXI) is the hymenostome–thigmotrich–peritrich sequence. Recognition of these possible interrelationships has been most influential in allocating the long-separated Peritrichida to an ordinal position within the subclass Holotricha (see Chapter 1). Acknowledgment of buccal (or peristomial) homologies is of key importance here. A sequence of genera can then be established which effectively demolishes the " uniqueness " of such peritrich characteristics as the counter-clockwise winding of the oral ciliature, the scopula and stalk, the

---

Corliss (1956a) which, in turn, was based principally on the hypotheses presented by Fauré-Fremiet (1950a). The major changes included here involve the position, and thus the implied interrelationship, of certain of the orders of " lower " holotrichs (see text for discussion). Ordinal names are given in large capital letters; subordinal, in small caps and in parentheses. The inset figures of " typical " genera are reduced copies of drawings which have already appeared in various preceding plates.

nearly naked sedentary mature form, the mode of reproduction (Corliss, 1956a). One practical trouble in the past has been our ignorance of the existence of " intermediate " forms between the well-known hymenostomes and the well-known peritrichs: the pleuronematine hymenostomes and the arhynchodine thigmotrichs now provide abundant examples of well-studied connecting forms (e.g., see Berger and Thompson, 1960; Chatton and Lwoff, 1936b, 1949, 1950; Dragesco, 1958; Fauré-Fremiet, 1910a; Hoare, 1927b; Noland, 1937; Párducz, 1936, 1940).

The astomes represent a special problem of their own. There is growing evidence (de Puytorac, 1954a, 1959a) that the order as conventionally accepted includes groups of forms of diverse ancestry, united only by their common lack of a mouth and symbiotic mode of life. De Puytorac considers the majority of them to be thigmotrichs. At the present time it seems advisable to proceed cautiously in the matter of eliminating the entire " order " of astomes until probable affinities of more of them can be investigated. The order Thigmotrichida should have a mono-phyletic origin: I have proposed that it is to be found among the pleuronematine hymenostomes. If some of the " astome–thigmotrichs " are, for example, found to show very close trichostome affinities (see de Puytorac, 1959c), then the problem is made quite complex. For the moment, I suggest considering that the main group of present-day astomes has arisen from some sort of hymenostome ancestry, with the seemingly close relation-ship to thigmotrichs possibly a matter of parallel or convergent evolution.

The subclass Spirotricha appears to present fewer knotty prob-lems, primarily because it is smaller and its members have shown less structural diversification. The large order of heterotrichs is the most plastic, and it seems a likely source of the other more specialized groups. The odontostomes (formerly ctenostomes) are characterized by their bizarre forms, including lateral flattening of the body, plus a great reduction from the number of buccal membranelles usually found in spirotrichs. The oligotrichs *sensu lato* are distinguished by their loss of somatic ciliature and the prominence of their buccal membranelles. Adaptation to special habitats has certainly played a major role in the further evolution of such orders as the Tintinnida and Entodiniomorphida.

Although specialists of various other ordinal groups may object to a greater or lesser extent, protozoologists in general are in agreement that the hypotrichs represent the pinnacle of evolutionary development among all the ciliate groups. The basis for this assumption is related entirely to the type of ciliature possessed by members of the Hypotrichida. Here may be seen the unique compound ciliary structures known as cirri; these are located in specific patterns on the ventral surface of the dorso-ventrally flattened body. In the buccal area the adoral zone of membranelles is large and conspicuously developed.

Although direct evidences for the actual pathways of ciliate evolution are non-existent, the phylogenetic interrelationships discussed in this chapter have been based on carefully weighed interpretations of data of comparative value available to us at the present time. If certain key assumptions are considered reasonable, then the evolutionary hypotheses which I have endorsed here may at least serve tentatively as a foundation for further critical research into the many problems bearing on the subject.

PART II

THE PROPOSED SCHEME OF CLASSIFICATION

CHAPTER 11

INTRODUCTION AND
HISTORICAL CONSIDERATIONS

THERE is a real need for an up-to-date listing and brief characterization of ciliophoran taxa above the level of species. Families and genera have been neglected in recent revisions of the highest categories. Nomenclatural aspects of ciliate systematics, below the ordinal level, have received no special attention for nearly half a century. Except in textbooks, where limitation on space understandably precludes extensive treatment, all forms—parasitic, free-living, and pelagic—are seldom considered within the confines of a single work.

The scheme of classification offered in the section of this book following Chapter 12 is intended to be more than just a compilation of all described families and genera of ciliates. Of necessity, however, critical revision is restricted primarily to endorsement of recent conclusions reached by recognized specialists of the various groups concerned. Taxonomic innovations of my own, limited because of lack of time to gain first-hand familiarity with the numerous and detailed problems associated with each of the many separate ciliate groups, are discussed in a section of the following chapter (see pp. 115–117).

For reasons of convenience, utility, and readability, the format chosen for presentation of the classificational scheme is one which allows appearance of only the bare essentials, both nomenclatural and taxonomic. Historical consideration of each family and each genus, for example, would be entirely out of place in the present condensed treatment of ciliate systematics. Brief characterizations of the suprafamilial groups already treated in more detail in Part I are included for the sake of independent completeness of the present section of this book. But direct references to the literature are purposely held to a minimum here. I am responsible for the

105

brevity of the familial characterizations, but not for their actual substance. I would agree with any reader who feels that many ciliate families are in need of re-appraisal and re-definition. Such a thorough overhauling by competent specialists probably would result in a reduction in the total number of families, but such a task would require years of dedicated investigation.

A few facts of historical interest will serve to show the tremendous growth of the subphylum Ciliophora within the past 150 years. In the early decades of the 19th century only a dozen families of ciliates, allocated to a single " class," were recognized, according to lists in such works as Ehrenberg (1838). Genera numbered half a hundred with fewer than 200 included species. By the middle of that century there were 19 families, containing a total of 65 genera (Perty, 1852). Kent's (1880–1882) and Bütschli's (1887–1889) authoritative monographs listed some eight orders and suborders, with about 45 included families and subfamilies, and a total of some 150 genera and about 500 bona fide species. Shortly after the turn of the 20th century the number of higher taxa (orders and suborders) had increased only to ten, with some 60 families and 280 genera, according to the compilation by Poche (1913). With regard to species, Calkins (1919, p. 336) was able to conclude, " There are approximately 1800 species of ciliated protozoa known to science."

By the time of Kahl's great monographs (years 1926 through 1935) the numbers of genera and species, in particular, had increased significantly, in spite of Kahl's rather conservative treatment of " new " discoveries by other workers. His several works, considered together, recognized some 17 orders and suborders, 87 families and subfamilies, 430 genera and subgenera, and approximately 2,500 species, exclusive of the pelagic tintinnids. At about the same time Kofoid and Campbell (1929) listed 12 families, 51 genera, and some 700 species in this last-mentioned specialized group of ciliates left to one side by Kahl. Every year since then, and still today, genera and species of all kinds of protozoa are being described as new in considerable numbers (some 500 species annually since 1930!), although some textbooks of biology continue to cite 50-year-old figures in their sections concerned with the phylum Protozoa.

In the scheme of classification presented here I have included

26 orders and suborders, 129 families*, and 841 genera. These numbers are exclusive, of course, of the names of several hundred junior synonyms and homonyms, many of which are included in their proper place in my lists. Generic names unacceptable because of *wholly* inadequate descriptions of the organisms involved are excluded from this book: such cases are very rare.

A reasonable estimate of the total number of described species (exclusive of subspecies), through the year 1960, which may be considered truly distinguishable from one another would approach the figure of 6,000. This number is greater than that of all the animals together listed in Linnaeus (1758)! Thus the total of the kinds of ciliates known to man already compares favorably with that given for species of such well-known vertebrate animal groups as the reptiles and amphibians, birds, and mammals (see Mayr *et al.*, 1953). The numbers of genera and species have nearly doubled within the past 25 years. And it is probably unnecessary to point out the rather discouraging fact that many hundreds of ciliates still remain to be described!

Over 75% of the families, genera, and species of ciliates have been erected or named by fewer than half a hundred protozoologists. Major family-makers include Bütschli, Cépède, Claparède and Lachmann, Ehrenberg, Kahl, Kent, Kofoid and Campbell, and Stein. Regarding genera, Kahl alone, in a ten-year period, described over 75 new ones. The combined labors of such early workers as Bory de St. Vincent, Bütschli, Claparède and Lachmann, Dujardin, Ehrenberg, Kent, O. F. Müller, Schewiakoff, Stein, Stokes, and Wrzesniowski produced more than 150 ciliate genera named as new; the great majority of these are recognized today under their original names. In the present century the publications of Busch, Cépède, Chatton and colleagues, Collin, Colom, da Cunha and associates, Delphy, Dons, Fauré-Fremiet and students, Gajewskaja, Gassovsky, von Gelei, Hadži, Hsiung, Jörgensen, Kofoid and co-workers, Kopperi, Kozloff, Lauterborn, Lom, Meunier, Penard, de Puytorac, Raabe, and Swarczewsky have included over 300 new generic descriptions accepted in the present compilation.

---

*Including 18 questionable ones but not several additional ones which I reject entirely.

CHAPTER 12

PRINCIPLES AND PROCEDURES IN CLASSIFICATION AND NOMENCLATURE

THE existing International Rules of Zoological Nomenclature (Hemming, 1958) are, intentionally, quite neglectful of supra-generic taxa. A forthcoming revision of the *Code* is expected to be a little more concerned with familial names than the rules have been formerly, but no control of any kind over the nomenclature of the highest taxa is envisioned.

For the sake of uniformity and consistency, I have had to follow certain rules in working out the scheme of classification presented in the following pages. In general these conform with common practices among systematists of various protozoan groups.* Several of my nomenclatural principles, however, are stricter than those usually followed. Although I strongly favor the " law of conservation " over the " rule of priority," in appropriate situations, I also believe, on ethical grounds if nothing else, that credit should be given where credit is due. For example, authors of time-honored taxonomic names of the higher categories should not be forgotten merely because more recent workers have made slight emendations in the spelling of those names.

There are three general goals which act as guides in nomenclatural taxonomy: priority, consistency, and stability. The greatest of these, in my opinion, should be stability, and I have so favored it in the present work.

---

*And, indeed, of metazoan, including vertebrate, groups as well. For example, see Mayr *et al.* (1953), and various references cited therein, and the introductory sections of Simpson's (1945) classic, very recently brought up to date (see Simpson, 1961).

1. *Treatment of Names in General*

A. *Orthography.* I have uniformly ended all ordinal names with the suffix "-ida "; subordinal names with "-ina "; and, of course, familial names with "-idae." The worker who originally suggested the name, for a group at approximately the same taxonomic level as used here, is fully credited with the present name if the stem of the word has been derived from his name. Many old familial names ended in "-ina "; I cannot agree with those taxonomists who credit the first worker who subsequently spelled the name with "-idae " with legal authorship of the name. It seems to me that responsibility for the taxon to which the name is applied also should date from the time of the original worker, not from the time at which an emendation of the name was proposed.

Without comment other than here, I have arbitrarily inserted "-at-" between the "-stom " or "-som " termination of certain stems and the added suffixes "-ida," "-ina," or "-idae." This is in accordance with good etymological practice, and, for familial names formed from neuter (or considered neuter) type generic names, it is essentially required by the International Rules. Thus in my scheme Apostomea, an order, has become Apostomatida; among the several families involved, Condylostomatidae (for Condylostomidae) and Dendrosomatidae (for Dendrosomidae) may serve as examples. The original names, without the "-at-," are listed as synonyms in the case of families. Ordinal and sub-ordinal synonymies have been considered in detail in an earlier work (Corliss, 1957a); thus the names of those taxa which differ only in suffixes are not re-listed in the present treatment*.

I have been obliged, of course, to leave generic names untouched as far as etymological formations are concerned; and, with rare exceptions, corrections made by others are rejected in favor of the original spellings. With considerable reluctance I have made one particular change, however: all " ü's " have been changed to " ue " in accordance with a strong recommendation to be included in the revised International Rules (see Bradley, 1957). Thus all families and genera named in honor of Bütschli

---

*But conventional spellings of the names of the higher taxa may be noted in the left-hand column of Table I, in Chapter 1 (p. 21).

(and one invalid familial name honoring Lieberkühn) are affected; names spelled with umlauted " u " are not cited as synonyms.

Certain other automatic corrections in familial names, other than those just mentioned, have been made, all as directed by the Rules. To cite a few which seemingly have been controversial in the protozoological literature: the " i " is retained before the suffix "-idae " if the name of the type genus ends in " ia," " ius," or " ium "; insertion of an (extra) " i " is rejected when it is not part of the stem; the stem of "-corys " or "-coris " is considered to be "-coryth "; the stem of "-cylis," "-cylid "; of "-stylis," "-stylid "; of "-pelma," "-pelmat." Earlier misspellings are listed as synonyms in these and similar cases.

B. *Authorship.* As mentioned above, I have made responsible for the name of any higher taxon the worker who first employed the name basically still in use, irrespective of minor emendations in spelling, particularly of the suffix. However, creation of the *concept* of a group may be considered more important than formulation of its name. In this regard — for example, when a family-level group has been promoted to an order-level taxon — I credit the ordinal name to the person who made this significant shift in rank. But for changes *within* a group, such as the raising of a subfamily or suborder to the level of family or order, respectively, I hold that the original worker still should be considered responsible for the name of the taxon, even in its slightly changed position. For names within the family-group such a decision actually is required by the International Rules.

It does not need to be pointed out that new names proposed for homonyms obviously cannot be credited to the authors of the names which have had to be replaced. The general problem of homonyms among generic names of ciliates has been treated in some detail in a very recent paper (Corliss, 1960b).

2. *Treatment of Familial Names*

A. When there is no controversy or no special situation exists, familial names are given with authorship and date; and spellings are automatically corrected if required (see preceding section). Subfamilies, relatively uncommon in the protozoological literature as a whole and rather unstable among ciliate groups, anyway, with one or two exceptions, are deliberately omitted from the present scheme of classification*. Such omission, however, does not signify disapproval of their being recognized as valid taxa of the ciliates involved.

It should be mentioned that many careless errors exist in the literature with regard to both the authorship and date of familial names. Sometimes these are the fault of the original describer; more often, of subsequent writers. Unfortunately Kahl, whose authoritative taxonomic monographs are justly held in such high regard, was guilty of a rather large number of minor nomenclatural mistakes. One or two pertinent to the present section should be clarified here. Seven of Kahl's families — the Conchophthiridae, Condylostomatidae, Epistylididae, Mylestomatidae, Scyphidiidae, Spathidiidae, and Strobilidiidae — which were erected as " new " in parts of his culminating work (Kahl, 1930–1935) actually were described elsewhere at earlier dates. The Epistylididae and Scyphidiidae were erected by himself (Kahl, 1933a) two years before being described as new once again. (At the same time names of the two peritrich suborders, Mobilina and Sessilina, were treated similarly.) The other five familial groups listed above appeared in the 5th edition of Doflein and Reichenow (1927–1929) with brief diagnoses and credited to Kahl, but without mention of their newness to science. In his own later works Kahl published them as new, (re)describing them in greater detail with no citation of their previous appearance. In all of these cases the earlier dates must be cited. The authorship of Kahlian names appearing first, complete with diagnoses, in works of others should include all parties involved: e.g., " Condylostomatidae Kahl in Doflein and Reichenow, 1929."

B. When original names of type genera of families are now known to be *junior synonyms*, I have, in the interests of stability, acted with some inconsistency. When the familial name based on such a junior synonym has been well established in the literature and is well known, I have preserved it. In other cases if the familial name is well established but is based on the *senior* synonym, then here also I have not changed it, even if older

---

*Unless they are considered here as full *families,* which is the situation in several instances.

names for the same family, formed from any junior synonym, are available.

In both of the situations just described I have, for the sake of clarity, listed the date and authorship of all the familial names involved and supplied all pertinent generic names. Thus, even when the name which I have accepted for the family is based on a junior synonym, the type genus is readily identifiable by inspection of my list of included genera which, in such cases, contains both senior and junior synonyms.

C. When names of type genera are discovered to be *junior homonyms*, I have consistently rejected familial names formed from such names. In these cases I have accepted the familial names formed from the generic names proposed as replacements for the preoccupied names, acting completely within both the spirit and the law of the International Rules. In some instances of this kind it may be claimed that stability is being upset by rejection of a familial name originally quite inadvertently formed from such a homonym. But junior homonyms can never serve as a firm basis for stability of any duration.

D. When there is no relationship between the originally proposed name of the family and (any of) the name(s) of its type genus, I have uniformly rejected that familial name. For the dozen or so cases of this type which exist in the ciliate literature I have accepted only names correctly formed for such families by subsequent workers. Such a decision is demanded by the International Rules and is a reasonable one.

E. When more than one genus has been considered type of a single family by different authors at various times, I have again acted with stability foremost in mind. Nearly two dozen such cases exist in the ciliate literature! Sometimes the original type genus had been overlooked inadvertently. More often two or more families had been combined, or separate type genera moved into a single family, with subsequent selection of a single familial name for the amalgamated group without regard for priority among the several available familial names. When it has seemed to matter little (i.e., causing little present disruption and serving as no source of predictable confusion in the future), I have favored priority as the guiding principle: the oldest name available is chosen as the proper present name of the family concerned. But in nearly a dozen cases* I have acted with deliberate inconsistency and with disregard for priority, proposing retention of the best- or better-known name for the family even when it is not the oldest or senior name among the synonyms available. The other name(s), including the legally senior synonym, is (are) listed as (junior) synonym(s). It seems clear to me that nomenclatural stability is best served by such action in these situations. In every case I have included mention of all pertinent names, authorships, and dates for the sake of completeness of the record.

3. *Treatment of Generic Names*

A. Authorship is supplied for every generic name considered as a valid senior synonym. Dates are not given, in keeping with the abbreviated and simplified form adopted here, but I have checked such data in the preparation of this work. Direct citations to the literature also are thus generally not given here, but a great majority of the papers involved in original descriptions of new ciliate genera may be found to have been included in the references at the end of this book, the works having been referred to elsewhere than in the present section. They often will be recognizable by their titles under the appropriate author's name.

B. Junior synonyms, both objective and subjective, are included in parentheses following the name of the senior synonym, if they are well known or still in use by some workers. Generally neither authors nor dates are given for such names, although I have been obliged to check these data with care. I have made no attempt to include all the synonyms ever in existence for a given generic group; in fact, I have deliberately omitted a number of the long-forgotten ones of the early and mid-19th century literature.

C. Generic names of ciliates which are junior homonyms are never knowingly accepted as valid names in my lists of genera†.

---

*Attention is called to each of these in the place of its occurrence in the section on classification following this chapter.

†Except *Stentor*. But the preservation of *Stentor* Oken, 1815 (heterotrich ciliate), junior homonym of *Stentor* Saint-Hillaire, 1812 (monkey), is a special case sanctioned by recent action of the International Commission on Zoological Nomenclature (see Corliss, 1960b; Hemming, 1956; Kirby, 1954).

A replacement name is not considered necessary, however, if the preoccupied name itself has fallen as a junior synonym of an earlier name for the same genus.

D. Names of genera entirely insufficiently described originally, or never adequately redescribed or even accepted by subsequent workers, are omitted entirely from the present scheme of classification. Nothing is to be gained by perpetuation of such *nomina dubia*. As pointed out in the preceding chapter (see top of page 107), in my judgment such cases are, fortunately, exceedingly rare among the orders of ciliates.

E. Pre-Linnean authorships are abandoned. For example, Hill (1752) is no longer credited with such names as *Cyclidium*, *Enchelys*, and *Paramecium*, although his work remains important historically. This action is simply in accordance with a directive of the International Rules.

F. Subgeneric names, rather uncommon in protozoan taxonomy, anyway, are deliberately omitted from the present classificational scheme, with one or two major exceptions noted in the places of their occurrence. Taxa originally described as subgenera but now considered genera by some authorities are included here as full genera. The omission of subgenera from my lists does not imply disapproval of their being recognized as valid taxa of the ciliates involved.

Incidentally, the nearly universal habit among protozoologists of placing the *former* generic name of a transferred species in parentheses between its new generic name and its specific (trivial) name is to be deplored. The custom is widespread but very misleading and completely illegal. According to the International Rules this position, and exactly this way of writing the name, *must* be reserved for the name of a *sub*genus, if one exists. Thus the many hundreds of seemingly subgeneric names which appear in the monumental works of such taxonomists as Kahl are actually only former generic names of the species in question, i.e., merely synonyms of the generic names endorsed by him for those particular species. This malpractice can become particularly confusing in the numerous cases in which names of genera perfectly stable in their own right are seemingly being treated as names of subgenera of other recognized genera, and vice versa, because of the shifting about of a few individual species.

Taxonomic Innovations*

The innovations presented in the following section of this book are of several kinds and are not all concerned with the same level in the classificational hierarchy. A number of the changes have been discussed in preceding pages of this chapter and in Chapter 1 and thus need be mentioned only briefly here.

Ordinal and supraordinal levels. The taxa representing the major groups of ciliates are essentially arranged in accordance with the scheme proposed by Fauré-Fremiet (1950a). The principal changes over conventional systems of classification, such as consideration of suctorians, peritrichs, and chonotrichs as holotrich taxa, have been enumerated in Part I. Refinements of Fauré-Fremiet's original concise proposals include recognition of independent, equivalent status for the oligotrichous groups, the Oligotrichida, Tintinnida, and Entodiniomorphida, with support of Reichenow's name for the last of these three groups; acute appreciation of the heterogeneity and at least partial artificiality of the Astomatida; substitution of the name Odontostomatida for Ctenostomat(id)a; establishment of definite subordinal groups within the Gymnostomatida, Hymenostomatida, Thigmotrichida, and Heterotrichida; adoption of suffixes, "-ida " and "-ina," for all ordinal and subordinal names, respectively. Authorship and date of all names have been determined anew by inspection of the original publications involved, since such information often has been given incorrectly or not at all in previous, more superficial treatments of ciliate systematics.

Familial level. Little notice has been given to familial groups as a whole since the comprehensive works of Kahl (1926 through 1935); yet the number of ciliate families has increased by nearly 50% since that date. Although the attention of individual specialists is required for detailed revisions, I have made several taxonomic

---

*Some of these are not appearing in print for the first time in the present publication. See especially Corliss (1956a, 1957a, 1959b) for introduction of some changes at suprafamilial levels particularly, changes based primarily on suggestions made by Fauré-Fremiet (1950a). Recall that *Opalina* is dropped from the Ciliophora. Many name changes at the generic level, necessitated by discovery of neglected cases of junior homonymy, have been proposed in a separate paper (Corliss, 1960b).

I

decisions at this level in the present work. They may be considered briefly as follows:

(1) A few families established as new within the past 25 years have been rejected outright. And some eighteen, a third of which have been erected within the past decade, have been accepted only tentatively. These have been allocated to appropriate orders, and generally characterized; but, pending further investigation, they are not accorded full separate status. With few exceptions these families are monotypic, and further comparative study is needed to determine if they should be retained as independent taxa. The families are: Bursostomatidae, Ditoxidae, Grandoriidae, Kiitrichidae, Liliimorphidae, Nathellidae, Pleurotrichidae, Polycyclidae, Protohalliidae, Psilotrichidae, Sagittariidae, Spirofilidae, Stephanopogonidae, Sulcigeridae, Thecacinetidae, Thigmocomidae, Urostylidae, Zoothamniidae.

(2) A number of families have been shifted from conventional to new locations. Such transfers include: Balantidiidae from the order of heterotrichs to trichostomes; Clathrostomatidae, from trichostomes to cyrtophorine gymnostomes; Coelosomididae, from rhabdophorine gymnostomes to trichostomes; Nathellidae, from hymenostomes to rhabdophorine gymnostomes; Parameciidae, from trichostomes to hymenostomes.

(3) Several large families have been considered to be so heterogeneous that they should be broken up into smaller familial units. The task of carrying out such revisions in detail, however, is beyond the scope of the present work. The families particularly in need of such attention, in my opinion, are the Buetschliidae, Enchelyidae, Frontoniidae, and Oxytrichidae. Some suggestions are made and some actions taken, especially in the case of the hymenostome family Frontoniidae, at appropriate places in the classificational scheme.

(4) A number of innovations have been made at the nomenclatural level: emendation of spellings, correction of authorships, and change of dates from those often given in the literature (see discussion under " Treatment of Familial Names," p. 110 ff.). When type genera have fallen as junior homonyms, the familial names are changed to agree with the replacement names proposed. When type genera are junior synonyms, I have either used the older or oldest familial name available or endorsed the familial

name most firmly established in the ciliate literature. New names are proposed in the present work for two families: one in which the original name bore no relationship to the single included genus (Belaridae, being replaced by Stephanopogonidae); another in which the original name was based on a generic name falling as a junior homonym (Coelosom(at)idae, being replaced by Coelosomididae).

In controversial situations I have worked with nomenclatural *stability* foremost in mind, if it has been at all possible to apply it under the circumstances attending the problem. Occasionally well-known names have had to be rejected, but I have endeavored not to be guilty of " pochization." (See the interesting comments on this subject in Chatton and Pérard, 1921.) With few exceptions, my nomenclatural actions in any situation are in complete accord with directives found in the International Rules of Zoological Nomenclature.

Generic level. Occasionally genera have been shifted from their original positions to different familial groups, generally on the basis of published revisions by specialists. My own treatment of generic names (see pp. 113–114) has involved some innovation at the nomenclatural level. Indispensable sources of information concerning possible homonymies are Neave (1939–1950), Schulze *et al.* (1926–1954), and the *Zoological Record* (established in 1864). Replacement names for some thirty junior homonyms which cannot be disposed of as junior synonyms have been proposed in a very recent paper (Corliss, 1960b) and are used here without special comment.

THE CILIATE TAXA
INCLUDING FAMILIES AND THEIR GENERA

Explanation of Format and Abbreviations

1. Orders and suborders are arranged in the same sequence as they appear in Part I of this book.

2. Families are ordered according to the chronology of their most acceptable name. Families erected in the same year are listed in alphabetical order.

3. Genera are arranged alphabetically within what are considered to be their proper families. All taxonomic names, generic and suprageneric, incidentally, are included for convenience in a Systematic Index placed at the end of this book.

4. When junior synonyms, including invalid emendations of original spellings of generic names, are given, they are preceded by the abbreviation " syn." or " syns." and are placed in parentheses following the senior synonym of the taxon concerned. For example, *Telotrochidium* Kent (syn. *Opisthonecta*). If a junior synonym is also a junior homonym (*unreplaced*) of the name for some other animal genus, it is followed by the abbreviation "hom." in brackets. For example, *Loxodes* Ehr. (syn. *Drepanostoma* [hom.]).

5. When junior homonyms have been or have had to be replaced, the preoccupied generic name is given in parentheses following the replacement name and preceded by the word " for." For example, *Actinobolina* Strand (for *Actinobolus*). The name in parentheses is also a synonym, of course. Familial names formed without relationship of any kind to the name of the type genus are treated similarly. For example, Conidiophryidae Kirby, 1941 (for Pilisuctoridae).

6. When a spelling is controversial but common practice has established a single, more recent variant as " correct," the name as formerly spelled, preceded by the words " originally written," is placed in parentheses following the name in its presently preferred form. In these particular cases the author cited is the

worker who originally proposed the name for the group, not the person who made the emendation. For example, *Oxytricha* Bory (originally written *Oxitricha*).

7. Occasionally other comments, self-explanatory, appear after given names in my lists. Special comments may be added briefly at the end of the treatment of order- or family-groups which seem to require additional explanation.

8. At the generic level, in the interest of conciseness, names of authors commonly encountered or very lengthy are abbreviated according to the following legend: Bory = Bory de St. Vincent; Büt. = Bütschli; Ch. = Chatton; Ch. & Lw. = Chatton and Lwoff; Clap. = Claparède; Clap. & Lach. = Claparède and Lachmann; Corl. = Corliss; Duj. = Dujardin; Ehr. = Ehrenberg; F-F = Fauré-Fremiet; Gaj. = Gajewskaja; Jörg. = Jörgensen; K. = Kofoid; K. & C. = Kofoid and Campbell; K. & MacL. = Kofoid and MacLennan; MacL. = MacLennan; O.F.M. = O. F. Müller; Pen. = Penard; Schew. = Schewiakoff; St. = Stein; Swarc. = Swarczewsky; Wrzes. = Wrzesniowski. Names of authors of familial names are accompanied by dates and are never abbreviated. Workers' names in joint authorships are united by an ampersand (&); but in any direct citation of the papers of such persons the ampersand is replaced by " and," following the general practice elsewhere in this book.

9. Finally, it should be mentioned that technical terminology is inevitable in these abbreviated characterizations. But the basic vocabulary used here has been treated and illustrated to some extent in the early chapters of Part I of this book and has recently been defined in more detail elsewhere (Corliss, 1959b).

Subphylum CILIOPHORA Doflein, 1901
(syns. Ciliae, Cytoidea, Heterokaryota, Infusoria)

Protozoa which possess or exhibit: simple cilia, often in great numbers, or compound ciliary organelles in at least one stage of the life cycle; a subpellicularly located infraciliature; two types of nuclei; a homothetogenic mode of binary fission; sexual phenomena such as conjugation and autogamy rather than syngamy. Majority of species free-living. Modes of nutrition heterotrophic. Contains a single class.

Class **CILIATA** Perty, 1852
(syn. Euciliata)

With characteristics of the subphylum. Contains two subclasses: Holotricha (pp. 120–157) and Spirotricha (pp. 157–171).

Subclass I. **HOLOTRICHA** Stein, 1859
(syns. Aspirigera, Aspirotricha)

Ciliates typically with simple and uniform somatic ciliature. Buccal ciliature, if present, generally tetrahymenal in nature and inconspicuous, with exception of the order Peritrichida. Contains 18 orders and suborders, some 87 families, over 560 genera, and well over 3,500, acceptably described species.

Order 1. **GYMNOSTOMATIDA** Bütschli, 1889

Essentially no oral ciliature. Cytostome–cytopharyngeal complex, containing trichites, opens directly to the outside. Body morphology and ciliation generally simple. Mostly large, commonly encountered forms. Nearly 1,000 species.

Suborder (1) **Rhabdophorina** Fauré-Fremiet in Corliss, 1956
(syn. Prostomatina + Pleurostomatina)

Cytostome in apical or lateral position; cytopharynx with expansible armature of trichites. Body ciliation generally uniform. Commonly carnivorous forms.

Family COLEPIDAE Ehrenberg, 1838
Cytostome apical. Body barrel-shaped with armor of cortical plates. Uniform somatic ciliation also present. Two genera.

Coleps Nitzsch
(syns. *Cricocoleps, Dictyocoleps, Pinacocoleps*)

Tiarina Bergh
(syn. *Stappersia*)

Family ENCHELYIDAE Ehrenberg, 1838
(syns. Enchelidae, Enchelynidae, Holophryidae, Lacrymariidae, Prorodontidae, Stephanopogonidae [for Belaridae], Trachelophyllidae).

Cytostome at or near apical pole, often opening through a rounded elevation; occasionally located at distal end of long neck. Body ciliation uniform and complete. Thirty-six genera.

Balanion Wulff

Balanophrya Kahl (only a
 subgenus of *Holophrya*?
 syn. *Acaryophrya*)

Chaenea Quennerstedt
 (syn. *Chaenia*)

Chilophrya Kahl

Crobylura André

Enchelyodon Clap. & Lach.
 (syn. *Lagynus*)

Enchelys O. F. M. (originally
 written *Enchelis;*
 syn. *Balantidion*)

Gymnozoum Meunier

Haematophagus Woodcock
 & Lodge

Helicoprorodon F-F

Holophrya Ehr.

Holophryozoon Jírovec

Ileonema Stokes
 (syn. *Monomastix*)

Lacrymaria Bory (originally
 written *Lacrimatoria*)

Lagynophrya Kahl

Lagynurus Mansfeld

Longitricha Gaj.

Microregma Kahl

Nannophrya Kahl

Pithothorax Kahl (syns.
 Gymnopithus, Micropithus)

Placus Cohn (syns. *Spathidiopsis* Fabre-Domergue
 [*non* Kahl], *Thoracophrya*)

Plagiocampa Schew.

Plagiopogon St.

Platyophrya Kahl (syn. *Telo-
 stoma* [hom.])

Prorodon Ehr. (*Gymnopharynx*)

Quasillagilis Busch

Rhagadostoma Kahl (only a
 subgenus of *Prorodon*?)

Rhopalophrya Kahl

Schewiakoffia Corl.
 (for *Maupasia*)

Spasmostoma Kahl

Sphaerobactrum Schmidt

Stephanopogon Entz

Thalassiomastix Busch

Trachelophyllum Clap. & Lach.

Urochaenia Savi

Urotricha Clap. & Lach.
 (syn. *Balanitozoon*)

Comments: Holophryidae Perty, 1852, is the name in most popular use for this family at the present time, but Enchelyidae is also widely known and seems the proper choice to perpetuate. The family probably is in need of subdivision. The Stephanopogonidae nom. nov. (for Belaridae Lwoff, 1936), containing the single genus *Stephanopogon* G. Entz, Sr., might well be separated off once again; no doubt other family groups also could be formed and given independent status. Family Stephanopogonidae may be characterized as follows: Cytostome apical. Body flattened dorso-ventrally, with only ventral surface ciliated. Allegedly homokaryote. Single genus.

Family TRACHELIIDAE Ehrenberg, 1838

Cytostome circular, some distance from apical pole, often at base of a proboscis. Body completely ciliated. Five genera.

Branchioecetes Kahl
Dileptus Duj.
  (syn. *Phragelliorhynchus*)
Micruncus Delphy

Paradileptus Wenrich
  (syn. *Tentaculifera*)
Trachelius Schrank

Family TRACHELOCERCIDAE Kent, 1880

Cytostome apically located. Body often extremely elongate. Six genera.

Gruvelina Delphy
Nephrocerca Delphy
Protrichophora Delphy

Trachelocerca Ehr.
Trachelonema Dragesco
Tracheloraphis Dragesco

Comments: The exact systematic status of Delphy's (1939) genera is uncertain. Dragesco (1958) offers detailed treatment of the other three genera.

Family AMPHILEPTIDAE Bütschli, 1889
(syn. Litonotidae)

Cytostome slit-like, not at apex of body. Body often elongate and laterally compressed; uniformly ciliated. Seven genera.

Acineria Duj.

Amphileptus Ehr.

Bryophyllum Kahl

Heminotus Kahl

Hemiophrys Wrzes. (often considered subgenus of *Litonotus*)
Litonotus Wrzes. (for *Leionota*; syn. *Lionotus* [hom.])
Loxophyllum Duj.
  (syn. *Opisthodon*)

Comments: Litonotidae Kent, 1880, has priority as name of the family but it seldom has been employed in the literature of the past 50 years. Bütschli (1887–1889) is responsible for the incorrect changing of Wrzesniowski's *Litonotus* to " *Lionotus*," an emendation not only unjustified but impossible to retain (since *Lionotus* is preoccupied), in spite of its popularity today (Corliss, 1960b).

Family LOXODIDAE Bütschli, 1889
(syn. Drepanostomatidae)

Cytostome, slit-like, located on the slightly concave surface of the body. Body laterally compressed with only right side bearing cilia. Four genera.

Ciliofaurea Dragesco
(for *Faurea*)
Kentrophoros Sauerbrey (syns.
Centrophorus [hom.], *Centro-phorella*)

Loxodes Ehr. (syn.
Drepanostoma [hom.])
Remanella Kahl

Comments: Drepanostomatidae (generally spelled Drepanosto-midae) Diesing, 1866, is the older familial name, but poorly known. Formed from a preoccupied generic name, it could not be used anyway. The taxonomic position of *Kentrophoros*, widely but wrongly called *Centrophorella*, is uncertain.

Family BUETSCHLIIDAE* Poche, 1913
(for Prorotrichidae; syn. Protohalliidae [for Halliidae (for Rhipidostomatidae)])

Cytostome usually apically located. Body ovoid or pear-shaped. A " concretion-vacuole " typically present. Ciliation uniform in some genera, restricted in others. In digestive tract of such herbivores as camels and horses; one genus (*Meiostoma*) reported from the caecum of mole rats. Twenty-nine genera.

Alloiozona Hsiung
Ampullacula Hsiung
Amylophorus Pereira
& Almeida
Blepharocodon Bundle
Blepharoconus Gassovsky
Blepharomonas Kopperi
Blepharoplanum Kopperi
Blepharoprosthium Bundle
Blepharosphaera Bundle

Blepharozoum Gassovsky
Buetschlia Schuberg
Buissonella da Cunha
& Muniz
Bundleia da Cunha & Muniz
Didesmis Fiorentini
Hemiprorodon Strelkow
Holophryoides Gassovsky
Hydrochoerella da Cunha
& Muniz

*In this and other names based on the name of Bütschli the " ü " has been replaced, with reluctance on my part, by " ue." See Chapter 12 (p. 109) for brief discussion of this matter.

Kopperia Corl. (for
    Malacosoma)
Levanderella Kopperi
Meiostoma Sandon
Paraisotrichopsis Gassovsky
Pingius Hsiung
Polymorphella Corl. (for
    Polymorpha)
Prorodonopsis Gassovsky

Protohallia da Cunha &
    Muniz (for *Hallia* [for
    Rhipidostoma])
Protolutzia da Cunha &
    Muniz
Pseudobuetschlia Jírovec
    (for *Buetschliella* Jírovec
    [*non* Awerinzew])
Sciurula Corl. (for *Sciurella*)
Sulcoarcus Hsiung

Comments: This family is in need of revision. Possibly Protohalliidae da Cunha & Muniz, 1927, should be resurrected as a
separate family. Extensive comparative study with modern
techniques will be required before sound taxonomic changes can be
made; even the most recently added genera were described some
20 years ago (e.g., see Kopperi, 1937; Sandon, 1941; Strelkow,
1939).

Family DIDINIIDAE Poche, 1913
(for Cyclodinidae; syn. Liliimorphidae)

Cytostome apically located. Body essentially radially symmetri-
cal, with special circlets of ciliature at one or more levels. Retractable seizing organelle in some forms. Ten genera.

Acropisthium Perty (syns.
    Dinophrya, *Siagonophorus*)
Askenasia Blochmann
Choanostoma Wang
Ctenoctophrys Weill
Cyclotrichium Meunier
Didinium St.
Liliimorpha Gaj.
    (syn. *Liliomorpha*)

Mesodinium St.
    (syn. *Acarella*)
Monodinium
    Fabre-Domergue (often
    considered syn. of
    Didinium)
Zonotrichium Meunier

Comments: *Choanostoma*, of doubtful status, is placed in this
family by some workers. If the curious " polymeric " *Ctenoctophrys* is a protozoon at all (see description in Weill, 1946), it may
well be associated with this family of ciliates. The family Liliimorphidae Gajewskaja, 1933, containing the single genus

Liliimorpha, may be a legitimate separate family; only further study can determine this.

Family PYCNOTRICHIDAE Poche, 1913
(syns. Nathellidae, Nicollellidae, Pycnothricidae)

Cytostome subequatorial or at posterior pole. Body completely ciliated. In digestive tract of various mammals. Eight genera.

Buxtonella Jameson (syn. of *Infundibulorium?*)
Collinina Ch. & Pérard (for *Collinella*)
Infundibulorium Bozhenko

Muniziella da Fonseca
Nathella Singh
Nicollella Ch. & Pérard
Pycnothrix Schubotz
Taliaferria Hegner & Rees

Comments: As Poche (1913) realized, the correct spelling of the name of his new family is "Pycnotrichidae" not "Pycnothricidae," as some subsequent workers have written it. The family Nathellidae Singh, 1953 (originally, in error, spelled Nathelliidae), was considered by its creator (Singh, 1953) as a hymenostome family. In many respects the two species of its single genus, *Nathella,* resemble species of pycnotrichids. Restudy, with particular attention to structures in the oral area, will be required before final taxonomic disposition of Singh's interesting forms can be made.

Family METACYSTIDAE Kahl, 1926

Cytostome located at posterior pole. Body, uniformly ciliated, characteristically encased in a pseudochitinous lorica. Three genera.

Metacystis Cohn
Pelatractus Kahl

Vasicola Tatem
(syn. *Pelamphora*)

Family SPATHIDIIDAE Kahl in Doflein & Reichenow, 1929

Cytostome, slit-like, generally apically located on a non-ciliated ridge of the body. Somatic ciliation typically uniform. Fourteen genera.

Cranotheridium Schew.
Diceratula Corl. (for *Diceras*)
Enchelydium Kahl

Homalozoon Stokes (syns. *Craspedonotana* [for *Craspedonotus*], *Leptodesmus* [hom.])

Legendrea F-F
Micromidas Delphy
Penardiella Kahl
Perispira St.
Proboscidium Meunier
(not in this family?)
Spathidiodes Kahl (syn.
Spathidiella)

Spathidioides Brodsky
Spathidiosus Gaj.
Spathidium Duj. (syn.
Spathidiopsis Kahl
[*non* Fabre-Domergue])
Teutophrys Ch. & Beauchamp
(syns. *Teuthophrys*, *Triloba*
[hom.])

Comments: Kahl (1930–1935) unnecessarily proposed a new name, *Spathidiella*, for *Spathidiodes* Kahl, 1926, upon learning of the existence of *Spathidioides* Brodsky, 1925. Although it is unfortunate that the two generic names are nearly identical in spelling, the International Rules do not allow replacement of either name in such cases.

Family ACTINOBOLINIDAE Kahl, 1930
(syn. Actinobolidae)

Cytostome apical. Retractable tentacles in addition to uniform covering of somatic ciliature. Four genera.

Actinobolina Strand
(for *Actinobolus*)
Belonophrya André
(syn. of *Actinobolina*?)

Dactylochlamys Lauterborn
Enchelyomorpha Kahl

Comments: The time-honored familial name Actinobolidae Kent, 1880, must fall because it has been formed from a preoccupied generic name.

Family GELEIIDAE Kahl, 1933

Cytostome, small, on ventral surface near anterior end of body. Large, elongate, strongly contractile forms. Body uniformly ciliated. Numerous in sands of intertidal zones. Two genera.

Corlissia Dragesco
(for *Corlisia*)

Geleia Kahl

Family AMPHIBOTHRELLIDAE R. & L. Grandori, 1935
(for Amphibothridae; syn. Amphibotrellidae)

Cytostome in non-ciliated furrow near apical end of body.

Somatic ciliation fairly uniform. Single genus.

Amphibothrella R. & L. Grandori (syn. *Amphibotrella*)

Suborder (2) **Cyrtophorina** Fauré-Fremiet in Corliss, 1956
(syn. Hypostomatina)

Cytostome mid-ventral, anterior half of body; cytopharynx with fused armature of trichites. Body often flattened dorso-ventrally, with ciliation restricted to ventral surface. Commonly herbivorous forms.

Family DYSTERIIDAE Claparède & Lachmann, 1858
(syns. Erviliidae, Hartmannulidae [for Onychodactylidae])

Characteristically possessing a ventro-posteriorly located stylus used directly in attachment to the substrate or as a secretory organelle producing a filament for such usage. Ciliation essentially confined to ventral surface. Nine genera.

Dysteria Huxley (syns. *Aegyria*,   *Paratrochilia* Kahl
  Cypridium, Dysteropsis p.p.,   *Scaphidiodon* St.
  Ervilia [hom.], *Iduna* [hom.])   *Trichopodiella* Corl.
Dysterioides Matthes   (for *Trichopus*)
Hartmannula Poche   *Trochilia* Duj.
  (for *Onychodactylus*)   (syn. *Dysteropsis* p.p.)
Mirodysteria Kahl   *Trochilioides* Kahl

Comments: The earliest familial name, Erviliidae Dujardin, 1841, cannot be used because it has been formed from a preoccupied generic name. It has been long-forgotten, anyway.

Family CHLAMYDODONTIDAE Stein, 1859
(syns. Chilodonellidae [for Odontohypotrichidae], Chilodontidae)

Somatic ciliation essentially restricted to ventral surface of the body. Body form often rigid, with pronounced dorso-ventral flattening. Twelve genera.

Allosphaerium Kidder &   *Chilodonella* Strand
  Summers   (for *Chilodon*)
Atopochilodon Kahl   *Chlamydodon* Ehr. (originally
Chilodina Šrámek-Hušek   written *Chlamidodon*)
  (belongs in following family?)   *Cryptopharynx* Kahl

Gastronauta Engelmann
  (syn. *Gastronanta*)
Lophophorina Pen.
Lynchella Kahl

Odontochlamys Certes
  (syn. of *Chilodonella?*)
Phascolodon St.
Phyllotrichum Engelmann

Family NASSULIDAE de Fromentel, 1874
(for Odontoholotrichidae; syn. Liosiphonidae)

Body completely ciliated. Pellicle capable of considerable distension. Nine genera.

Archinassula Kahl
Chilodontopsis Blochmann
  (syn. *Chlamydodontopsis*)
Cyclogramma Perty
Eucamptocerca da Cunha
Nassula Ehr.
  (syns. *Acidophorus, Liosiphon*)

Nassulopsis F-F
Orthodonella Bhatia (for *Ortho-*
  don; syn. *Rhabdodon* [hom.])
Schistophrya Kahl
Stomatophrya Kahl

Comments: The name Liosiphonidae Diesing, 1866, has priority but seldom has been used during the past 75 years. Stability is best served by recognizing Nassulidae. A brief but important review of the family has appeared very recently (Fauré-Fremiet, 1959b).

Family CLATHROSTOMATIDAE Kahl, 1926
(syn. Clathrostomidae)

Body uniformly ciliated, not flattened dorso-ventrally. Cytostome apically or ventrally located, often in an oral atrium somewhat resembling the vestibulum of trichostomes. Three genera.

Clathrostoma Pen.
Paranassula Kahl

Ptyssostoma Hentschel

Comments: Both the composition and the taxonomic location of this family are controversial subjects. I consider that its members possibly have played a significant role in the evolution of the order Hymenostomatida from the cyrtophorine Gymnostomatida (see Corliss, 1958e). As usual, more comparative work needs to be carried out on the many forms involved.

Order 2. **TRICHOSTOMATIDA** Bütschli, 1889

Vestibular but no buccal ciliature in oral area. Body typically with uniform ciliation but sometimes highly asymmetrical. About 250 species.

Family COLPODIDAE Ehrenberg, 1838
(syn. Woodruffiidae)

Cytostome ventrally located, anterior half of body, typically at the base of a more or less extensive, well-ciliated vestibulum. Body often kidney-shaped, with ciliary rows forming an asymmetrical pattern. Fission characteristically within reproductive cysts. Seven genera.

Bresslaua Kahl
Bryophrya Kahl
Cirrophrya Gellért
Colpoda O.F.M. (originally
written *Kolpoda*)

Rhyposophrya Kahl
Tillina Gruber (syn. *Pseudo-colpoda*)
Woodruffia Kahl

Comments: It is interesting to note that von Gelei (1954) considered *Woodruffia* to be a *spirotrich* genus, placing it in a family Woodruffiidae (misspelled Woodruffidae) in the order Heterotrichida. I do not agree with this action.

Family MICROTHORACIDAE Wrzesniowski, 1870
(syns. Leptopharyngidae, Trichoderidae [for Trichopelmidae])

Vestibulum and cytostome at various levels along ventral surface. Body laterally compressed, with ribbed, firm pellicle. Somatic ciliature greatly reduced. Nine genera.

Conchophrys Ch.
Discotricha Tuffrau
Drepanomonas Fresenius
(syn. *Drepanoceras*)
Hexotrichia Conn
Kreyella Kahl
Leptopharynx Mermod (syns.
Trichoderum [for
Trichopelma], *Trochiliopsis*)

Microdiaphanosoma Wenzel
(for *Diaphanosoma*)
Microthorax Engelmann
(syn. *Hemicyclium*)
Stammeriella Wenzel

Comments: Although this family is in need of considerable restudy, there is no reason why its name should not be that given it by Wrzeniowski (1870). Leptopharyngidae Kahl, 1926, was unnecessarily changed to Trichopelmidae Kahl, 1931, by Kahl (a name, incidentally, which should have been spelled Trichopelmatidae). But the latter name must fall, since it is formed from the junior homonym *Trichopelma;* and the former name was never needed. Trichoderidae, proposed by Strand (1942), is a proper substitute for Trichopelmidae, but is similarly unnecessary. Furthermore, *Trichoderum* really never should have been proposed, since *Leptopharynx* was available as a replacement name for the preoccupied *Trichopelma* (see Corliss, 1960b). Preceding Kahl's works, Wrzeniowski's familial name was widely used. *Pseudomicrothorax*, long placed here, has been transferred to the hymenostomes in the present scheme of classification. *Leptopharynx* may well follow suit: an additional reason (if needed) for its rejection as type of this presumably trichostome family.

Family ISOTRICHIDAE Bütschli, 1887

Cytostome at or near apical pole of the body. Somatic ciliation uniform, complete. Characteristically found in the digestive tract of ungulate ruminants. Three genera.

Dasytricha Schuberg   *Protoisotricha* Kopperi
Isotricha St.

Family PLAGIOPYLIDAE Schewiakoff, 1896

Cytostome centrally located in anterior half of the body. Dorsoventrally flattened forms with uniform ciliation. Species known from fresh- and salt-water habitats and digestive tract of sea urchins. Five genera.

Lechriopyla Lynch   *Sonderia* Kahl
Plagiopyla St.   *Sonderiella* Kahl
Plagiopyliella Poljansky

Comments: Strelkow's (1959a) recent species of *Plagiopyliella* is removed to an entirely separate family, the Thyrophylaxidae (see p. 134). The genus *Schizocaryum*, listed under unassigned apostome genera at the present time (see p. 140), may well belong in this family, a view which Berger (1961a) also holds.

Family MARYNIDAE Poche, 1913

Vestibulum apically located. Aboral end foremost in swimming. Loricate; often colonial. Three genera.

Maryna Gruber   *Opisthostomatella* Corl. (for
Mycterothrix Lauterborn (syn.   *Opisthostomum*)
  Trichorhynchus [hom.])

Comments: The status of *Opisthostomatella* is questionable.

Family CYATHODINIIDAE da Cunha, 1914
(syn. Enterophryidae)

Cytostome at base of a triangular, peristomial-like, non-ciliated field. Somatic ciliation limited to the anterior half of the body. Process of fission is complex and rather enigmatic. Single genus.

Cyathodinium da Cunha (syns. *Cyathodinioides, Enterophrya*)

Comments: This group probably should be removed from the order. Possibly it belongs among the oligotrichs, in subclass Spirotricha?

Family PARAISOTRICHIDAE da Cunha, 1917

Cytostome near apical end of the body. Somatic ciliation uniform, complete; anterior tuft of longer cilia. Two genera.

Paraisotricha Fiorentini   *Protocaviella* Kopperi

Family SPIROZONIDAE Kahl, 1926

Band of closely set cilia, in area of ventrally located vestibulum, spirals posteriorly to the left. Otherwise uniform ciliation, with special tuft at posterior pole of the body. Single genus.

Spirozona Kahl

Family TRICHOSPIRIDAE Kahl, 1926

Band of closely set cilia, in area of ventrally located vestibulum, spirals posteriorly to the right. Uniform ciliation elsewhere, with no caudal bristles. Single genus.

Trichospira Roux

K

Family BLEPHAROCORYTHIDAE Hsiung, 1929
(syn. Blepharocoridae)

Cytostome anteriorly located.   Somatic ciliature reduced to widely separated fields or tufts at various locations on the surface of the body.   In digestive tract of horses and ruminants.   Four genera.

Blepharocorys Bundle   *Charonnautes* Strelkow
Charonina Strand (for *Charon;*   *Ochoterenaia* Chavarria
syn. *Charonella*)

Family BALANTIDIIDAE Reichenow in Doflein & Reichenow, 1929

Vestibulum near anterior end of the body; cytostome at its base. Uniform somatic ciliation.   In digestive tract of invertebrates and vertebrates, including man.   Single genus.

Balantidium Clap. & Lach. (syns. *Balantidiopsis* Büt. [*non* Pen.], *Balantioides;* possibly *Parabursaria?*)

Comments: This family has long been considered as belonging to the spirotrich order Heterotrichida.   Its transfer, made by Fauré-Fremiet (1955), is now gaining wide acceptance.

Family ENTORHIPIDIIDAE Madsen, 1931

Body flattened laterally, with frontal " lobe " overhanging the cytostome.   Uniform ciliation.   In digestive tract of various sea urchins.   Single genus.

Entorhipidium Lynch

Comments: Madsen (1931) insisted that Kahl should be the author of the familial name; but Kahl (1930–1935) had only suggested that a separate family be erected for Lynch's genus. Madsen named the family and first described it as such.   To date, incidentally, workers have included the genera *Biggaria* and *Entodiscus* in this family; but I consider these forms to be tetrahymenine hymenostomes in need of further study (also see Berger, 1961c).   In fact, Berger (personal communication) is now considering removal of *Entorhipidium* itself to the order Hymenostomatida.

Family TRIMYEMIDAE Kahl, 1933
(syn. Sciadostomatidae)

Cytostome near apical end of the body. Somatic ciliature restricted to several spirals, anteriorly located, plus prominent caudal bristle. Single genus.

Trimyema Lackey (syn. *Sciadostoma*)

Family CONIDIOPHRYIDAE Kirby, 1941
(for Pilisuctoridae)

Mature form non-ciliated and attached to exoskeletal hairs of certain crustaceans. Ciliated migratory larva, produced by budding, impaled upon fresh hair through its cytostome-cytopharyngeal opening. Single genus.

Conidiophrys Ch. & Lw.

Comments: The replacement name, Conidiophryidae, for Pilisuctoridae Chatton & Lwoff, 1934, generally is credited to Mohr and LeVeque (1948). But Kirby (1941a) first suggested the new name and should be considered responsible for it.

Family COELOSOMIDIDAE nom. nov.
(for Coelosomatidae)

Cytostome apically located but preceded by a definite vestibulum. Somatic ciliation complete and uniform. Four genera.

Bursellopsis Corl. (for *Bursella*)   *Paraspathidium* Noland
Coelosomides Strand   *Pseudoprorodon* Blochmann
(for *Coelosoma*)

Comments: The taxonomic status and exact composition of this family are not altogether clear. The replacement name, Coelosomididae, for Coelosomatidae (originally spelled Coelosomidae) Fauré-Fremiet, 1950, is required because of the fall of the earlier name of the type genus as a junior homonym. I have increased the size of the family considerably over Fauré-Fremiet's (1950d, p. 260) original description, which was a very brief one, but it is clear that a detailed investigation of all the forms possibly involved is necessary for a better understanding of the group.

Family THYROPHYLAXIDAE Berger, 1961

Prominent vestibulum with lateral ectoplasmic flanges. Body very large, laterally compressed. Carnivorous endocommensals in sea urchin *Strongylocentrotus*. Single genus.

Thyrophylax Berger

Comments: The genus and family are being created by Berger (1961b) for Strelkow's (1959a) *Plagiopyliella vorax* and a closely related new form. But Poljansky's (1951b) genus *Plagiopyliella* is still maintained, with its type species, in the family Plagiopylidae.

Trichostomes: Unassigned Genera

Bursostoma Vörösváry

Comments: Vörösváry (1950) considered this genus as type of a new family, Bursostomatidae (originally spelled Bursostomidae) Vörösváry, 1950. Although additional comparative studies should be carried out to verify the independent taxonomic status of the family, there appears to be little doubt but that the genus is a true trichostome. It probably belongs among the most evolved groups, since it seems to possess highly organized vestibular ciliature.

Grandoria Corl. (for *Lagenella*)

Comments: R. and L. Grandori (1934, 1935) considered this genus as type of the family Lagenellidae R. & L. Grandori, 1935 [for Centrostom(at)idae R. & L. G., 1934]. *Lagenella* R. & L. Grandori falls as a homonym of *Lagenella* Ehrenberg, an earlier name for a genus of flagellated protozoa (see Corliss, 1960b). Thus, if the family is to be accepted, it should be known by its replacement name, Grandoriidae Corliss, 1960. Kahl (1930–1935) considered the ciliate to be a trichostome; the original describers listed it as a hypotrich. Restudy of fresh material is strongly indicated before the exact systematic status can be determined with certainty. Tentative characterization of the family: Cytostome mid-ventrally located. Body fig-shaped with fairly uniform ciliation. A strong bristle and a curious, conspicuous gelatinous(?) structure, used in attachment to the substrate, are located at the posterior pole. Single genus.

Sigalasia Delphy

Comments: This rather poorly described genus erected by Delphy (1938) may well belong among the trichostomes, but it seems impossible to place it in any known family until it has been rediscovered and more adequately studied.

Sulcigera Gaj.

Comments: This curious ciliate, considered by Gajewskaja (1933) as type of a family, seems quite distinctive from other trichostome genera. The family Sulcigeridae (originally spelled Sulcigeriidae) Gajewskaja, 1933, should it be resurrected by future workers, may be characterized as follows: Cytostome subapical. Curious groove (vestibulum?) on ventral surface, coursing from cytostome to posterior end of the body. Four " cirri " at posterior pole. Body somewhat flattened dorso-ventrally; ciliation complete. Single genus.

Order 3. **CHONOTRICHIDA** Wallengren, 1895

No somatic ciliature on mature forms. Vestibular ciliature in the apical " funnel " is derived from the field of ventral cilia present on the migratory larval forms. Adults possess vase-shaped bodies, characteristically attached to crustaceans by a non-contractile stalk. Reproduction by budding. All but one genus marine. Only some two dozen species described to date.

Family SPIROCHONIDAE Stein, 1854

Stalkless, or with very short stalk. Apical funnel elaborately spiralled. Found in association with fresh-water amphipods or marine isopods. Two genera.

Spirochona St.   *Lobochona* Dons

Family CHILODOCHONIDAE Wallengren, 1895

Stalked. Apical funnel reduced to two conspicuous " lips." Marine forms. Single genus.

Chilodochona Wallengren

Family STYLOCHONIDAE Mohr, 1948

With or without stalk. Apical funnel well-developed but not in spirals. Marine forms. Five genera.

Heliochona Plate   *Stylochona* Kent
Kentrochona Rompel   *Trichochona* Mohr
Kentrochonopsis Doflein

Order 4. **SUCTORIDA** Claparède & Lachmann, 1858 (syns., in their original spelling: Acineta, Acinetae, Acinetaria, Acinetidea, Acinetina, Acinetoidea, Suctorea, Suctoria, Suctoriae, Tentaculifera, Tentaculiferiae, Tentaculiferida, and Actinifera + Actinosuctorifera + Suctorifera).

Mature stage without cilia and typically sessile, attached to the substrate by a non-contractile but scopula-produced stalk. Ingestion via suctorial tentacles, few to many in number. Somatic ciliature present in the mouthless, migratory larval stage. Reproduction by budding. Nearly 500 species.

Family ACINETIDAE Stein, 1859
(syns. Solenophryidae, Thecacinetidae)

With or without stalk. Capitate tentacles, typically arranged in groups. Often loricate. Endogenous budding characteristic. Twenty genera.

Acineta Ehr.   *Praethecacineta* Matthes
Acinetides Swarc.   *Pseudogemma* Collin
Acinetopsis Robin   *Pseudogemmides* Kormos
Actinocyathula Corl. (for   *Solenophrya* Clap. & Lach.
    Actinocyathus)   *Squalorophrya* Goodrich & Jahn
Allantosoma Gassovsky   (syn. *Squalophrya*)
Dactylophrya Collin   *Suctorella* Frenzel
Endosphaera Engelmann   *Tachyblaston* Martin
Loricophrya Matthes   *Thecacineta* Collin
Multifasciculatum G. & Jahn   *Tokophrya* Büt.
Pottsiocles Corl. (for *Pottsia*)   *Tokophryopsis* Swarc.

Comments: The family Thecacinetidae Matthes, 1956, was very recently established for the two genera *Praethecacineta* and

Thecacineta. This decision by Matthes (1956) probably should be reviewed by other specialists on the Suctorida before its final acceptance. The Thecacinetidae may be characterized as follows: Stalked forms. Tentacles numerous, clustered about apical end of body. Always loricate. Two genera.

Family DENDROCOMETIDAE Haeckel, 1866

Stalkless. Tentacles, capitate, often localized on extensions of body proper. Endogenous budding. Five genera.

Cometodendron Swarc.
.*Dendrocometes* St.
Dendrocometides Swarc.

Discosomatella Corl.
  (for *Discosoma*)
Stylocometes St. (syns. *Asellicola, Digitophrya, Pericometes*)

Family PODOPHRYIDAE Haeckel, 1866
(syns. Metacinetidae, Sphaerophryidae, Urnulidae)

With or without stalks and/or loricae. Exogenous budding typical. Eleven genera.

Lecanophrya Kahl
Metacineta Büt.
Mucophrya Gaj. (syn. of ?)
Ophryocephalus Wailes
Paracineta Collin
  (syn. *Hallezia* [hom.])

Parapodophrya Kahl
Podophrya Ehr.
Prodiscophrya Kormos
Spelaeophrya Stammer
Sphaerophrya Clap. & Lach.
Urnula Clap. & Lach.

Comments: By deliberate selection of *Hallezia multitentaculata* as type species, its problematic genus was caused to fall as a synonym of *Paracineta* (see Corliss, 1960b). Suctorian specialists must determine the fate of the species recently added by Sewell (1951).

Family OPHRYODENDRIDAE Stein, 1867

Stalked. Tentacles on ends of mobile " arms." Exogenous budding common. Six genera.

Collinophrya Kahl
Cucumophrya Kunz
Dendrosomides Collin

Hydrophrya Nozawa
Ophryodendron Clap. & Lach.
Rhabdophrya Ch. & Collin

Family DENDROSOMATIDAE Fraipont, 1878
(syns. Dendrosomidae, Trichophryidae)

Stalkless. Tentacles arranged in clusters. Endogenous budding common. Thirteen genera.

Astrophrya Awerinzew
Baikalodendron Swarc.
Baikalophrya Swarc.
Craspedophrya Rieder
Dendrosoma Ehr.
Erastophrya F–F
Gorgonosoma Swarc.

Lernaeophrya Pérez
Platophrya Gönnert
Staurophrya Zacharias
Stylophrya Swarc.
Tetraedrophrya Zykoff
Trichophrya Clap. & Lach.

Comments: This family, as is also true for many of the others in the order Suctorida, is in need of over-all, comparative review. Should *Dendrosoma* be removed to the Ophryodendridae, then Trichophryidae Fraipont, 1878, would become the familial name.

Family EPHELOTIDAE Kent, 1880
(syn. Hemiophryidae)

Stalked. Tentacles of two definite types: suctorial and so-called prehensile. Some species loricate. Exogenous budding typical. Four genera.

Ephelota Wright (syn. *Hemiophrya*)
Metephelota Willis

Podocyathus Kent
Spathocyathus Nie & Lu

Family DISCOPHRYIDAE Collin, 1912 [*non* Cépède, 1910]
(syn. Rhynchetidae)

With or without stalk. Never loricate. Endogenous budding characteristic. Fourteen genera.

Anarma Goodrich & Jahn
Caracatharina J. Kormos
  (for *Catharina*)
Choanophrya Hartog
Corynophrya Kahl
Cyclophrya Gönnert
Discophrya Lach. [*non* St.]
Echinophrya Swarc.

Heliophrya Saedeleer & Tellier
Periacineta Collin
Peridiscophrya Nozawa
Physaliella Pen.
Rhyncheta Zenker
Rhynchophrya Collin
  [*non* Raabe]
Thaumatophrya Collin

Comments: Rhynchetidae Kent, 1880, is the older name, but it has rarely been used during the past 75 years. For disposition of Discophryidae Cépède, 1910, see family Haptophryidae, order Astomatida.

Order 5. APOSTOMATIDA Chatton & Lwoff, 1928

Typically with unique rosette near inconspicuous cytostome. Polymorphic life cycles with marine crustaceans generally involved as hosts. Ciliation spirally arranged on bodies of mature forms. Fewer than 50 species known.

Family OPALINOPSIDAE Hartog, 1906
(syn. Chromidinidae)

Aberrant forms, often elongate. Chain formation possible through a budding type of fission. Hosts include cephalopods, coelenterates, and ctenophores. Two genera.

Chromidina Gonder

Opalinopsis Foettinger
  (syn. *Benedenia* [hom.])

Comments: The status and composition of this enigmatic group require additional, new studies. Some protozoologists use Chromidinidae Poche, 1913, as the preferred name; some separate the two genera at the familial level; others consider the two generic names synonymous, and attach the group to the following family.

Family FOETTINGERIIDAE Chatton, 1911

With characteristics of the order *sensu stricto*. Sixteen genera.

Calospira Ch. & Lw.

Cyrtocaryum F–F & Mugard

Foettingeria Caullery & Mesnil

Gymnodinioides Minkiewicz
  (syns. *Larvulina* p.p., *Oospira* [hom.], *Physophaga*)

Hyalospira Miyashita (syn. of *Gymnodinioides?*)

Metaphrya Ikeda

Ophiuraespira Ch. & Lw.

Pericaryon Ch.

Phoretophrya Ch., A. & M. Lw.

Phtorophrya Ch., A. & M. Lw.

Polyspira Minkiewicz

Spirophrya Ch. & Lw.

Synophrya Ch. & Lw.

Terebrospira Debaisieux
  (for *Chattonia*)

Traumatiophtora Ch. & Lw.
  (syn. *Traumatiophora*)

Vampyrophrya Ch. & Lw.

Apostomes: Unassigned Genera

Collinia Cépède   *Perezella* Cépède
Jeppsia Corl. (for *Chattonella*) *Schizocaryum* Poljansky &
Kofoidella Cépède   Golikowa

Comments: These five genera all are difficult to assign to particular apostome families until further study of their species has been carried out. Interestingly enough, the three described by Cépède (1910) were assigned by him to monotypic families (which I do not accept): the Colliniidae, Kofoidellidae, and Perezellidae. Certain phases in the incompletely known life cycle of *Jeppsia*, unassigned to any order by its original describer (Jepps, 1937), suggest an affinity with apostomes. *Schizocaryum* is considered " near the apostomes " by its describers (Poljansky and Golikowa, 1957); but it seems to me that it may well belong somewhere among the true trichostomes, probably in the family Plagiopylidae (see p. 130; also see Berger, 1961a).

Order 6.   **ASTOMATIDA** Schewiakoff, 1896
(syns. Anoplophryida, Anoplophrymorphida)

Mouthless forms, typically with uniform somatic ciliation and often of large size. Some species with endoskeletons and holdfast organelles. Catenoid " colonies " (chain-formation) typical of some groups. Found principally in oligochaete annelids. Some 200 species.

Comments: The reasonable proposal that this " order " should be entirely abandoned as a single high-level taxonomic group, with re-assignment of its species to other orders, has been considered in Part I of the present work; also see Corliss (1956a) and, especially, de Puytorac (1954a, 1959a).

Family ANOPLOPHRYIDAE Cépède, 1910
(syns. Herpetophryidae, Metastomatidae)

Body ovoid or elongate. Ciliation very uniform. Skeletal elements typically absent. With or without contractile vacuoles. Twelve genera.

Anoplophrya St. (syns.
    Eliptophrya, Macrophrya)
Anoplophryopsis de Puytorac
Corlissiella de Puytorac
Dogielella Poljansky
Herpetophrya Siedlecki
Herpinella de Puytorac

Lubetiella de Puytorac
Metastomum Georgévitch
Paranoplophrya Rohrbach
Perseia Rossolimo (syn. *Persea*)
Prototravassosia Artigas & Unti
Rhizocaryum Caullery & Mesnil

Comments: The taxonomic status of *Prototravassosia* Artigas & Unti, 1938, is uncertain. Georgévitch (1941a) erected a separate family " Metastomidae " for his genus *Metastomum*. But present-day astome specialists, with whom I agree, have not recognized the independence of Metastomatidae Georgévitch, 1941.

Family INTOSHELLINIDAE Cépède, 1910

Body elongate, with straight or spiral rows of cilia. Spiny holdfast apparatus. Catenoid " colonies " common. Generally numerous contractile vacuoles. Three genera.

Intoshellina Cépède   *Spirobuetschliella* Hovasse
Monodontophrya Vejdovsky

Comments: The genus *Spirobuetschliella*, described by Hovasse (1950), possibly should be considered a member of the family Hoplitophryidae (p. 143). Indeed, perhaps the entire present family, Intoshellinidae, should be reduced to a subfamilial rank within the Hoplitophryidae.

Family MAUPASELLIDAE Cépède, 1910

Body ellipsoidal in shape. Elaborate holdfast apparatus. Several contractile vacuoles. Two genera.

Maupasella Cépède   *Schultzellina* Cépède
                                        (syn. *Schulzellina*)

Comments: Some workers consider this entire group, like the preceding one, to comprise a subfamily within the larger family Hoplitophryidae (p. 143).

Family HAPTOPHRYIDAE Cépède, 1923
(for Discophryidae Cépède [*non* Collin])

Antero-ventral sucker characteristic of some genera. With or without hooks. Long contractile canal functionally replacing a series of contractile vacuoles. Body elongate and often large. Found in certain turbellarians, amphibians, and snails. Seven genera.

Annelophrya Lom   *Lachmannella* Cépède
Cepedietta Kay   *Proclausilocola* Lom
Clausilocola Lom   *Steinella* Cépède
Haptophrya St. (for *Discophrya* St.
    [*non* Lach.]; syn. *Sieboldiellina*)

Comments: There has been some confusion concerning the correct familial name for this family, but even more regarding the proper name of its type genus. The astome genus *Discophrya* Stein, 1860, was so named one year after the suctorian genus *Discophrya* Lachmann, 1859. Thus the Discophryidae of Cépède (1910), although predating the suctorian family Discophryidae Collin, 1912, by two years, became invalid, since the original name of its type genus had fallen as a junior homonym. In 1911, Collin proposed the name *Sieboldiellina* to replace the *Discophrya* of Stein; most workers have accepted this action. Indeed, a subfamily Sieboldiellininae, erected by Bishop (1926) as " Sieboldiellinae," has been widely endorsed (for the most recent paper involving this group see Lom, 1959b). However, Stein (1867) himself had replaced his *Discophrya* with *Haptophrya*, an action which made Collin's proposal altogether unnecessary (see Corliss, 1960b). Furthermore, in Stein's time there was but a single species, the organism from a planarian originally described as *Opalina planariarum* von Siebold, 1839. Ignorance of the *nomenclatural* background involved is excusable; but, curiously enough, most of the many writers who have accepted both *Haptophrya* and *Sieboldiellina* as names have attempted to separate them *taxonomically*, understandably with little success. Cépède (1923), himself, while correctly changing the name of the family from Discophryidae to Haptophryidae, accepted Collin's name as the name of a different genus. My own stand is essentially that of Cheissin (1930) who would neither endorse the genus and its name nor accept Bishop's subfamily.

Family HOPLITOPHRYIDAE Cheissin, 1930
(syn. Mesnilellidae)

Body often elongate. Holdfast apparatus quite elaborate. Catenoid " colonies " in some genera. Many to several contractile vacuoles. Twenty-four genera.

Acanthophrya Heidenreich
Akidodes Lom
Anglasia Delphy
Anthonyella Delphy
Buchneriella Heidenreich
Buetschliella Awerinzew
  [*non* Jírovec]
Buetschliellopsis de Puytorac
Desmophrya Raabe
Durchoniella de Puytorac
Eumonodontophrya Heidenreich
Georgevitchiella de Puytorac
Hoplitophrya St.
Hovasseiella de Puytorac

Jirovecella Lom
Juxtaradiophrya de Puytorac
  (syns. *Cheissinella*,
  Cheissiniella)
Mesnilella Cépède
Metaradiophrya Heidenreich
Mrazekiella Kijensky
Ochridanus Georgévitch
Protoradiophrya Rossolimo
Protoradiophryopsis Georgévitch
Radiophrya Rossolimo
Radiophryoides Lom
Radiophryopsis Georgévitch

Comments: Some workers would increase the size of this large family even more by incorporating such families as the Intoshellinidae and Maupasellidae (p. 141). Cépède's Mesnilellidae already is included. The name of such a combined family would have to be one of Cépède's names, if strict priority were followed. In the interests of stability I strongly favor Cheissin's name for the group, no matter what its size, as have modern astome specialists.

Order 7. **HYMENOSTOMATIDA** Delage & Hérouard, 1896

Buccal cavity, ventrally located, contains ciliary apparatus considered fundamentally as tetrahymenal in nature (undulating membrane on right, tripartite AZM on left). Body size often small, with uniform somatic ciliature. About 350 species.

Suborder (1) **Tetrahymenina** Fauré-Fremiet in Corliss, 1956

Oral ciliature generally inconspicuous, but clearly tetrahymenal in its organization. Vestibulum seldom present. Body size typically small.

Family OPHYROGLENIDAE Kent, 1880
(syn. Ichthyophthiriidae)

An enigmatic " watch-glass " organelle presumably is always present, located in the cytoplasm in the vicinity of the buccal cavity. Large forms, with multiple reproduction occurring within a cyst. Somatic ciliation uniform and complete. Stomatogenesis dependent on several post-oral rows of cilia. Four genera.

Cryptocaryon Brown   *Ophryoglena* Ehr.
Ichthyophthirius Fouquet   (syn. *Otostoma*)
  (syn. *Chromatophagus*)   *Protophryoglena* Mugard

Comments: Determination of the exact taxonomic status of *Cryptocaryon* Brown, 1951, must await full publication concerning the (single) species involved; only an abstract has appeared to date (Brown, 1951).

Family PHILASTERIDAE Kahl, 1931

Shallow, elongate buccal cavity with 3 membranellar bases, deltoid, trapezoid, and falciform in shape, from anterior to posterior; first membranelle pseudosegmented in one genus. Body elongate. Stomatogenesis more or less autonomous. Six genera.

Helicostoma Cohn   *Porpostoma* Möbius
Philaster Fabre-Domergue   (syn. *Porpostomum*)
Philasterides Kahl   *Pseudocristigera* Horváth
                                 Rhinodisculus Mansfeld

Comments: Horváth (1956) has suggested that *Pseudocristigera* shows several clearly defined characteristics of the subclass Spirotricha, but he assigns it tentatively to the present holotrich family.

Family COHNILEMBIDAE Kahl, 1933
(for Lembidae)

Slender forms with elongate buccal cavity. Membranelles thrown over to the right, against the undulating membrane. A director-meridian sometimes involved in stomatogenesis. Six genera.

Anophrys Cohn
Cohnilembus Kahl (for *Lembus;*
  syn. *Sparotricha?*)
Lembadionella Kahl

Paralembus Kahl
  (for *Lemboides*)
Pseuduronema Hoare
Uronema Duj.

Comments: This family, as well as the Pleuronematidae (in the third suborder of the Hymenostomatida), is in great need of revision. Hoare (1927b) placed *Cohnilembus* and *Uronema* in the Pleuronematidae, with *Pseuduronema* serving as the link between the two families involved. But today the solution does not appear so simple. A number of the genera listed as " unassigned " at the end of the present suborder also may be involved. New comparative studies are demanded.

Family TETRAHYMENIDAE Corliss, 1952
(syn. Leucophryidae)

Simple arrangement of tetrahymenal ciliary organelles. Body uniformly ciliated, generally small. One or two post-oral rows of cilia (i.e., kinetosomes from these meridians) are responsible for stomatogenesis. Nine genera.

Colpidium St.
Deltopylum F–F & Mugard
Dichilum Schew.
Glaucoma Ehr. (syns. *Dallasia,*
  Diplomastax, Diplomestoma)
Loxocephalus Eberhard
  (syn. *Dexiotricha*)
Monochilum Schew.
Sathrophilus Corl.
  (for *Saprophilus*)
Stegochilum Schew.

Tetrahymena Furgason (probable syns. include *Acomia,*
  Lambornella, Leptoglena, Leu-
  cophra, Leucophrydium, Leu-
  cophrys, Paraglaucoma Kahl,
  Paraglaucoma Warren [hom.],
  Protobalantidium, Ptyxidium,
  Tetrahymen, Trichoda, Tur-
  chiniella)

Comments: A family erected to partially relieve the heterogeneity of the peniculine family Frontoniidae. A detailed petition (Corliss and Dougherty, 1961) to the International Commission on Zoological Nomenclature treats the several major nomenclatural problems involved, especially with regard to preservation of the generic name *Tetrahymena* and the familial name Tetrahymenidae.

Tetrahymenine Hymenostomes: Unassigned Genera

Aristerostoma Kahl
Balanonema Kahl
Balantiophorus Schew.
Biggaria Kahl
Bizonula Corl. (for *Bizone*)
Blepharostoma Schew.
Cardiostomatella Corl.
   (for *Cardiostoma*)
Chasmatostoma Engelmann
Colpodopsis Gourret & Roeser
Cryptochilum Maupas (syn.
   Cryptochilidium)
Cryptostomina Fedele (for
   Cryptostoma)
Curinostoma Kozloff
Cyrtolophosis Stokes
Dexiotrichides Kahl
Entodiscus Madsen
Epimecophrya Kahl
Eurychilum André
Homalogastra Kahl

Larvulina Pen. (p.p.)
Lembadion Perty (syns. *Hymeno-
   stoma, Thurophora*)
Madsenia Kahl
Malacophrys Kahl
Pinchatia Shibuya
Platynematum Kahl
   (for *Platynema*)
Pleurochilidium St.
Pseudoglaucoma Kahl
Pseudomicrothorax Mermod
   (syns. *Chilodonopsis,
   Craspedothorax*)
Pseudoplatynematum Bock
Sagittaria R. & L. Grandori
Turaniella Corl. (for *Turania;*
   syn. *Tourania*)
Uronemopsis Kahl
Uropedalium Kahl
Urozona Schew.

Comments: Most of these 33 genera were included by Kahl (1930–1935) in his over-sized family Frontoniidae. Although exact disposition of them must await careful restudy, with particular attention to buccal structures, I believe that the many species involved generally will be found to belong to the present suborder. The interesting genus " *Cryptochilidium* Schouteden, 1906," as now comprised, should be known by the older name for the group, *Cryptochilum* Maupas, 1883. By a small but unfortunate error, Kahl (1930–1935, 1934a), Lucas (1940), and many others have supposed that *Cryptochilum* falls as a homonym of *Cryptochilus* Rafinesque, 1815, which it does not. *Curinostoma* is astomatous (Kozloff, 1954). *Biggaria* and *Entodiscus* have been considered trichostomes in the past. *Pseudomicrothorax*, formerly considered a member of the trichostome family Microthoracidae, may require establishment of a new suborder (Corliss, 1958d).

Sagittaria was considered type of the family Sagittariidae R. & L. Grandori, 1935 (for Proshymenidae R. & L. G., 1934) by its describers. Further study is necessary to determine the status of the family. If accepted, it may be characterized as follows: Conspicuous buccal area (the ciliary apparatus of which needs restudy) present at apical end of the body. Body small, with uniform but somewhat sparse somatic ciliation and single caudal bristle. Single genus.

Suborder (2) **Peniculina** Fauré-Fremiet in Corliss, 1956

Oral ciliature dominated by the presence of " peniculi " deep in the buccal cavity. An outer vestibulum, with uniform vestibular ciliature, often present. Body size usually large.

Family PARAMECIIDAE Dujardin, 1841

Conspicuous oral groove leads to the vestibulum which, in turn, opens into the buccal cavity. Buccal ciliary apparatus comprised of endoral membrane, two peniculi, and a quadrulus. Somatic ciliation complete. Prominent explosive trichocysts. Typically two contractile vacuoles. Single genus.

Paramecium O.F.M. (originally written *Paramaecium;*
    syns. *Paramaecidium, Paramoecium*)

Comments: Conventionally considered a trichostome family. But the recent shift by Fauré-Fremiet (1949b) appears to be gaining wide acceptance. I am excluding the rather poorly known genus *Physalophrya*, placing it in an unassigned position in the present suborder (see p. 148).

Family CINETOCHILIDAE Perty, 1852

Relatively inconspicuous buccal cavity. Body very small, oval to ellipsoid in shape. Somatic ciliation present only on the flattened ventral surface; several long caudal cilia. Single genus.

Cinetochilum Perty

Comments: This family is tentatively resurrected as part of my revision of the family Frontoniidae.

L

Family UROCENTRIDAE Claparède & Lachmann, 1858
(syn. Calceolidae)

Buccal cavity and cytostome subequatorial. Body short, cylindrical, with two broad encircling bands of closely set cilia and an eccentric posterior tuft. Stomatogenesis autonomous. Single genus.

Urocentrum Nitzsch (syns. *Calceolus, Turbinella* [hom.])

Comments: This family is tentatively resurrected as part of my revision of the family Frontoniidae.

Family FRONTONIIDAE Kahl, 1926
(for Chiliferidae)

Vestibulum shallow or absent. Number of compound ciliary organelles present in the buccal cavity. Cytostome expansive yet ill-defined in the herbivorous genera (e.g., *Frontonia*). Body size generally large; ciliation complete. Single contractile vacuole. Four genera.

Disematostoma Lauterborn	*Frontonia* Ehr. (syns. *Cyrtostomum,*
Espejoia Bürger	*Frontoniella, Panophrys*)
	Stokesia Wenrich

Comments: In this tentative revision of the family I have reduced the number of genera, perhaps too drastically, from some 36 to 4! But this has seemed advisable in view of the extreme heterogeneity of the family as constituted in Kahl (1930–1935). Most of the missing genera are included in my list of unassigned tetrahymenine hymenostomes (p. 146). Perhaps *Lembadion* belongs back in ?

Peniculine Hymenostomes: Unassigned Genera

Marituja Gaj.	*Sigmostomum* Gulati
Physalophrya Kahl	

Comments: Further study is needed to determine the proper familial associations of these three genera. *Marituja* has been listed as a rhabdophorine gymnostome by some and as a trichostome by other workers; but it may well belong here among the hymenostomes.

Suborder (3) **Pleuronematina** Fauré-Fremiet in Corliss, 1956

Oral ciliature dominated by the conspicuous, external undulating membrane; adoral zone of membranelles hardly recognizable. No vestibulum. Cytostome typically subequatorial. Somatic ciliation usually sparse, but a prominent caudal cilium common.

Family PLEURONEMATIDAE Kent, 1880
(for Aphthoniidae; syn. Cyclidiidae)

With characteristics of the suborder. Seven genera.

Calyptotricha Phillips (syns.
  Diplospyla, Diplostyla [hom.])
Cristigera Roux (syn. *Aulaxella*
  [for *Aulax*])
Ctedoctema Stokes

Cyclidium O.F.M.
  (syn. *Alyscum*)
Histiobalantium Stokes
Pleurocoptes Wallengren
Pleuronema Duj. (syn. *Glossa*)

Comments: Cyclidiidae Ehrenberg, 1838, is the older, but much less familiar, familial name for this group of hymenostomes. Thus, for the sake of stability, I urge continued acceptance of the better-known name.

Order 8. **THIGMOTRICHIDA** Chatton & Lwoff, 1922

Buccal ciliature, if present, located subequatorially on the ventral surface or at the posterior pole. Tuft of thigmotactic somatic ciliature commonly present near anterior end of body. Generally found in or on bivalve molluscs. Nearly 150 species known.

Suborder (1) **Arhynchodina** Corliss, 1957
(for Stomatina)

Oral ciliature and cytostome present. Somatic ciliature generally uniform.

Comments: Arhynchodina is a replacement name for the Stomatina (originally proposed as "tribe Stomatidae") of Chatton and Lwoff, unfortunately preoccupied by both Stomatina von Siebold and Stomatina Wenyon, names used for other protozoan groups (see Corliss, 1957a).

Family HYSTEROCINETIDAE Diesing, 1866
(syns. Ladidae, Ptychostomatidae)

Cytostome at posterior pole of the body, but a "sucker" located at the anterior end. Dorso-ventrally flattened forms, with dense, uniform ciliation. In digestive tract of certain snails and oligochaetes. Six genera.

Cotylothigma Raabe
Elliptothigma Meier
Hysterocineta Diesing
  (syn. *Ladopsis*)

Kysthothigma Raabe
Protoptychostomum Raabe
Ptychostomum St. (syn. *Lada*
  [hom.])

Comments: At one time a number of protozoologists favored the familial name Ptychostomatidae (usually spelled Ptychostomidae) Cheissin, 1932, over the older name, Hysterocinetidae. It is true that *Ptychostomum* is the oldest, largest, and best known of the genera. But today Diesing's familial name is widely accepted.

Family HEMISPEIRIDAE König, 1894
(syns. Ancistridae, Ancistrumidae, Boveriidae,
Orchitophryidae, Protophryidae, Thigmocomidae)

Cytostome at or near the posterior pole; buccal ciliature may extend anteriad on ventral surface. Thigmotactic ciliature near anterior pole. General somatic ciliature typically quite dense. Seventeen genera.

Ancistrella Cheissin
Ancistrospira Ch. & Lw.
Ancistrum Maupas (syns.
  Ancistruma, *Ancystrum*)
Ancistrumina Raabe (for
  Ancistrina)
Boveria Stevens
Cheissinia Ch. & Lw. (for
  Tiarella)
Eupoterion MacL. & Connell
Hemispeira Fabre-Domergue

Hemispeiropsis König
Isselina Cépède
Orchitophrya Cépède
Plagiospira Issel
Proboveria Ch. & Lw.
Protoanoplophrya Miyashita
  (syn. *Protanoplophrya*)
Protophrya K.
Protophryopsis Raabe
Thigmocoma Kazubski

Comments: As Raabe (1959a) and several other workers at earlier dates have noted, Strand's (1928) replacement name *Ancistruma* for Maupas' *Ancistrum* was unnecessary, since *Ancistrum* is *not* a junior homonym. The family name Ancistridae Issel, 1903, which does not need to be replaced by Ancistrumidae Kahl, 1931, is more popular with some workers than the older name (Hemispeiridae), which was originally proposed as a name at the subfamily-level. *Protoanoplophrya*, erected over 30 years ago by Miyashita (1929) as an astome genus, is still so classified by many protozoologists.

Kazubski (1958a) erected the family Thigmocomidae to contain his distinctive genus *Thigmocoma*. It is possible that other specialists will accept his action. A monographic treatment of these thigmotrichs is in preparation (Kazubski, personal communication). In such a case, the family Thigmocomidae Kazubski, 1958, may be characterized very briefly as follows: Cytostome nearly mid-ventral. Thigmotactic ciliature quite distinct. Ciliation reduced on posterior parts of the body. Single genus.

Family THIGMOPHRYIDAE Chatton & Lwoff, 1923

Cytostome posteriorly located. Anterior thigmotactic field composed of closely set cilia derived from several somatic rows. General body ciliature uniform. Two genera.

Conchophyllum Raabe   *Thigmophrya* Ch. & Lw.

Family CONCHOPHTHIRIDAE Kahl in Doflein & Reichenow, 1929 (syn. Conchophthiriidae)

Cytostome in posterior half of the body. Body laterally compressed. Ciliation uniform. Five genera.

Andreula Kahl   *Conchoscutum* Raabe
Cochliophilus Kozloff   *Myxophyllum* Raabe
Conchophthirus St. (syns. *Conchophthirius*;
  possibly *Kidderia* [hom.] and *Morgania* [hom.])

Comments: The original, and correct, spelling of both the name of the type genus and of the family is *without* an " i " following the " r " and preceding the termination (see Stein, 1861, and Corliss, 1960b). Spelling them *with* an " i " is an error commonly seen; it stems principally from misinformation given in Strand (1928). The exact taxonomic status of the genus *Conchophthirus* itself (and thus of its family) is, unfortunately, uncertain. Even less certain is the standing, both systematic and nomenclatural, of two additional, separate(?) " genera ": *Kidderia* Raabe, 1934, and *Morgania* Kahl, 1934. These were erected in the same year (*Kidderia* one month earlier than *Morgania*), and they share the same type species (*C. mytili*)! Furthermore, as a final complication, both names fall as junior homonyms (Corliss, 1960b).

Suborder (2) **Rhynchodina** Chatton & Lwoff, 1939

Cytostome replaced functionally by an anteriorly located sucker, sometimes on the end of a tentacle. Somatic ciliature often reduced; entirely absent in some forms.

Family HYPOCOMIDAE Bütschli, 1889

Suctorial tentacle located antero-dorsally. Body somewhat flattened, with ciliation restricted to the dorsal surface. Three genera.

Heterocoma Ch. & Lw.   *Parahypocoma* Ch. & Lw.
Hypocoma Gruber (syn. *Acinetoides*)

Family SPHENOPHRYIDAE Chatton & Lwoff, 1921

Short suctorial tentacle. Mature form without cilia, but budded larval form possesses several rows of somatic ciliature. Four genera.

Gargarius Ch. & Lw.   *Pelecyophrya* Ch. & Lw.
   (syn. *Rhynchophrya* [hom.])   *Sphenophrya* Ch. & Lw.
Lwoffia Kozloff

Family ANCISTROCOMIDAE Chatton & Lwoff, 1939
(syn. Cepedellidae)

Anterior suctorial tentacle. Body ovoid to pyriform in shape, with general somatic and thigmotactic ciliature often restricted to anterior portions. Twenty-one genera.

Ancistrocoma Ch. & Lw.   *Enerthecoma* Jarocki
Anisocomides Ch. & Lw.   *Goniocoma* Ch. & Lw.
Cepedella Poyarkoff   *Heterocineta* Mawrodiadi
Crebricoma Kozloff   *Heterocinetopsis* Jarocki

Holocoma Ch. & Lw.
Hypocomagalma Jarocki &
 Raabe
Hypocomatidium Jarocki &
 Raabe
Hypocomatophora Jarocki &
 Raabe
Hypocomella Ch. & Lw.

Hypocomides Ch. & Lw.
Hypocomidium Raabe
Hypocomina Ch. & Lw.
Insignicoma Kozloff
Isocomides Ch. & Lw.
Parachaenia K. & Bush
Raabella Ch. & Lw.
Syringopharynx Collin

Comments: Cepedellidae Cépède, 1910, is the older name, but, as is true for most of the many familial names created by Cépède (1910) for monotypic family groups (belonging to both the Thigmotrichida and the Astomatida), it has not been endorsed by subsequent workers. Thus, for stability, I have adopted the more popular, widely used name proposed by Chatton and Lwoff.

Order 9. **PERITRICHIDA** Stein, 1859
(syns. Dexiotricha, Stomatina [of von Siebold])

. Oral ciliature conspicuous, located predominantly at the " apical " pole of the body. Mature form, generally devoid of somatic ciliature, often attached to the substrate by a scopula-produced contractile stalk. Migratory larval form, produced by unequal fission, motile with posterior ciliary girdle. Colonial organization common. Over 1,000 species described to date: largest of all ciliophoran orders.

Suborder (1) **Sessilina** Kahl, 1933
(syn. Sedentaria)

Predominantly sessile, with contractile or non-contractile stalks. Solitary or colonial. Some forms loricate.

Family OPHRYDIIDAE Ehrenberg, 1838

With or without stalk. Vase-shaped, with oral end typically pulled out into a long contractile neck. Some species with symbiotic zoochlorellae; some, green or colorless, form gelatinous colonies (Winkler and Corliss, 1961). Two genera.

Ophrydiopsis Pen.
 (syn. *Ophridiopsis*)

Ophrydium Bory
 (syns. *Gerda*, *Ophionella*)

Comments: As Kahl (1930–1935) suggested, Penard's genus *Ophrydiopsis* might better be classified as a loricate member of the family Scyphidiidae (p. 155).

Family VORTICELLIDAE Ehrenberg, 1838
(syn. Zoothamniidae)

Sessile forms with contractile stalks. One genus exclusively solitary (*Vorticella*). Among the colonial forms, the zooids are independently contractile in one genus (*Carchesium*), but continuous myonemes are the rule in the remaining genera. Eight genera.

Carchesium Ehr.
Craspedomyoschiston Precht
Haplocaulus Precht
Intranstylum F–F
  (syn. *Intrastylum*)
Myoschiston Precht

Pseudocarchesium Sommer
Vorticella Linnaeus
  (syn. *Vorticellopsis*)
Zoothamnium Bory (originally written *Zoothamnia*)

Comments: Sommer (1951) has separated out all but two of these genera (*Carchesium* and *Vorticella*), several of which, incidentally, have conventionally been assigned to the neighboring family Epistylididae, into a new family. It is too early to know if this action will meet with general acceptance among the specialists. If it is adopted, the family Zoothamniidae Sommer, 1951, may be characterized as follows: Contractile stalks, with continuous myonemes in the colonial forms. Six genera.

Family VAGINICOLIDAE de Fromentel, 1874
(for Vaginiferidae)

Stalk often short. All species loricate, with entire oral end of the body protrusible beyond the opening of the lorica. Ten genera.

Caulicola Stokes
Cothurnia Ehr.
Cothurniopsis Stokes
  (syn. of *Cothurnia*?)
Nidula Gaj.
Pachytrocha Kent

Platycola Kent
Pseudothuricola Kahl
Pyxicola Kent
Thuricola Kent
  (syn. *Thuricolopsis*)
Vaginicola Lamarck

Family LAGENOPHRYIDAE Bütschli, 1889
(syn. Lagenophryiidae)

Stalk inconspicuous or absent. All species loricate, with only peristomial (buccal) ciliature protrusible through the opening of the lorica. Four genera.

Cyclodonta Matthes   *Lagenophrys* St.
Cystophrys Bresslau   *Stylohedra* Kellicott

Family EPISTYLIDIDAE Kahl, 1933
(syn. Epistylidae)

Characteristically stalked, but non-contractile. Some forms solitary, some colonial. Fourteen genera.

Ballodora Dogiel & Furssenko   *Orsomia* Baer
Campanella Goldfuss   *Orthochona* André
Entziella Stiller   *Pyxidiella* Corl. (for *Pyxidium;*
Epistylis Ehr.   syn. *Cochlearia* p.p.)
Opercularia St.   *Rhabdostyla* Kent
   (syn. *Cochlearia* p.p.)   *Systylis* Bresslau
Operculariella Stammer   *Telotrochidium* Kent
Opisthostyla Stokes   (syn. *Opisthonecta*)
Orbopercularia Lust

Comments: Following Sommer's (1951) revision, I have transferred Precht's (1938) three genera, conventionally placed in this family, to the Vorticellidae (or Zoothamniidae: see p. 154). Possibly the enigmatic genus *Entziella*, recently described by Stiller (1951), should be treated similarly.

Family SCYPHIDIIDAE Kahl, 1933

Sessile, but essentially stalkless; the scopula functions as a holdfast organelle. Aboral end of the body often broad and flattened. Ten genera.

Ambiphrya Raabe   *Glossatella* Büt. (syn. *Cordylo-*
Apiosoma Blanchard   *soma* [hom.]; possibly syn. of
Caliperia Laird   *Apiosoma?*)
Ellobiophrya Ch. & Lw.   *Gonzeella* Kufferath

Pachystomos Rudzinska (for   *Scyphidia* Duj.
  Pachystomus; possibly syn. of   *Termitophrya* Noirot & Noirot-
  Scyphidia?)   Timothée
Paravorticella Kahl

Family ASTYLOZOIDAE Kahl, 1935
(syns. Astylozooidae, Astylozoonidae)

Stalkless, non-sessile forms. Oral end directed foremost in locomotion. Three genera.

Astylozoon Engelmann   *Hastatella* Erlanger
Geleiella Stiller

Suborder (2) **Mobilina** Kahl, 1933
(syn. Natantia)

Without stalk; motile. Oral–aboral axis shortened, with prominent adhesive basal disc common at aboral pole of the body. Often found as episymbionts, occasionally causing considerable harm, on a variety of aquatic hosts.

Family URCEOLARIIDAE Dujardin, 1841
(syns. Polycyclidae, Trichodinidae, Trichodinopsidae)

With characteristics of the suborder. Thirteen genera and subgenera.

Acyclochaeta Zick   *Trichodina* Ehr.
Cyclochaeta Jackson   (syn. *Anhymenia*)
  (syn. *Cyclocyrrha*)   *Trichodinella* Šrámek-Hušek
Dogielina Raabe   (for *Brachyspira*)
Foliella Lom   *Trichodinopsis* Clap. & Lach.
Leiotrocha Fabre-Domergue   *Tripartiella* Lom
Polycycla Poljansky   *Urceolaria* Lamarck
Semitrichodina Kazubski   *Vauchomia* Mueller

Comments: In spite of a recent group of excellent papers concerned with various problems related to the systematics of the mobiline peritrichs (e.g., see Lom, 1958, 1959c; Raabe, 1959b,c; Raabe and Raabe, 1959; Uzmann and Stickney, 1954; and the up-to-date references cited in these comprehensive works), further over-all restudy and taxonomic revision are indicated. I have listed subgenera, as well as genera, for this particular family, without attempting to distinguish between them, because of uncertainty concerning the relative status of several of the groups.

Poljansky (1951a) recently has erected a new family for the single genus *Polycycla*, with species found in the gut of sea cucumbers. I tentatively accept the family Polycyclidae Poljansky, 1951, pending reconsideration of the entire suborder Mobilina by specialists of the group. Inspection of Poljansky's figures, however, suggests that possibly *Polycycla* is more closely related to the scyphidiids (p. 155) than to the urceolariids.

Subclass II. **SPIROTRICHA** Bütschli, 1889
(syn. Spirigera)

Ciliates generally with sparse somatic ciliature, with exception of the order Heterotrichida. Conspicuously developed buccal ciliature, with adoral zone typically composed of many membranelles. Cirri characteristic of one major group, the order Hypotrichida. Contains 8 orders and suborders, some 42 families, about 275 genera, and more than 2,200 acceptably described species: almost exactly one-half the size of subclass Holotricha at all taxonomic levels.

Order 1. **HETEROTRICHIDA** Stein, 1859

Somatic ciliature, when present, commonly uniform. Body size frequently large. Some species pigmented; a few loricate with migratory larval forms. Commonly encountered ciliates. About 450 species.

Suborder (1) **Heterotrichina** Stein, 1859

With characteristics of the order *sensu stricto*.

Comments: In 1957, I divided the order Heterotrichida into two very unequal parts, proposing names for these two subordinal groups which are used in the present work (Corliss, 1957a). Although the International Rules do not govern nomenclatural procedure at such high taxonomic levels, I have decided here to credit Stein with the name of the first group since, by my choice of names, it is a *nominate* suborder.

Family BURSARIIDAE Dujardin, 1841

Peristomial (buccal) cavity funnel-shaped and conspicuously large. Body, also large, covered uniformly with simple somatic ciliature. Four genera.

Bursaria O.F.M.
Bursaridium Lauterborn

Neobursaridium Balech
Thylakidium Schew.
  (syn. *Thylacidium*)

Family STENTORIDAE Carus, 1863

Prominent adoral zone of membranelles extends out of the buccal cavity around apical pole of the body. Body large, highly contractile, covered with uniform ciliation. Some species pigmented. Four genera.

Climacostomum St.
Fabrea Henneguy
  (syn. *Bursalinus*)
Stentor Oken (now a *nomen conservatum;* syns. *Stentorella, Stentorina*)

Stentoropsis Dogiel & Bychowsky

Family GYROCORYTHIDAE Stein, 1867
(syns. Caenomorphidae, Gyrocoridae, Gyrocorycidae, Metopidae)

Generally uniformly ciliated. Buccal membranelles often rather inconspicuous. Torsion of the body, especially anteriorly, characteristic of many species. Seven genera.

Bryometopus Kahl
Caenomorpha Perty
  (syns. *Gyrocoris, Gyrocorys*)
Copemetopus
  Villeneuve-Brachon
Ludio Pen.

Metopus Clap. & Lach. (syns.
  Bothrostoma, Caenomorphina,
  Metopides [hom.], *Spirorhyn-*
  chus, Trochella [hom.])
Palmarium Gaj.
Tropidoatractus Levander

Comments: There is considerable competition for the " correct " name of this family! Gyrocorythidae (spelled in various ways) is the oldest name and, generally as Gyrocoridae, has been widely used in the literature, until about 1930. Caenomorphidae Poche, 1913, seldom has been accepted. In fairness to Poche (1913), it should be mentioned that he proposed the name in good faith, since *Gyrocorys* had become a junior synonym of *Caenomorpha*. Metopidae Kahl, 1927, has been the name in most popular (textbook) usage for the past 25 years, purely because of the authoritative weight of Kahl's works. Kahl (1930–1935) should have chosen either Stein's or Poche's name; I can find no reason for his abrupt dropping of the type genus (*Caenomorpha*, syn. *Gyrocorys*) and selection of a different type, *Metopus*. Therefore I strongly advise return to the original type genus, endorsing the familial name based on the junior synonym (*Gyrocorys*) because of its far greater usage than the one based on the present senior synonym (*Caenomorpha*). The Rules are not contravened in any manner by such action. Incidentally, the genus *Metopus* has become unwieldy and quite heterogeneous; probably it should be subdivided into several separate genera.

Family PERITROMIDAE Stein, 1867

Cytostome mid-ventral, along left margin; buccal membranelles extend over anterior end of the body. Body dorso-ventrally flattened, with somatic ciliature confined to the ventral surface. Three genera.

Pediostomum Kahl   *Peritromus* St.
Peritromoides Bhatia

Family SPIROSTOMATIDAE Stein, 1867
(syn. Spirostomidae)

Large, often elongate forms, some highly contractile, some pigmented. Buccal membranelles sometimes inconspicuous. Somatic ciliation uniform, typically complete. Nine genera.

Blepharisma Perty   *Pseudoblepharisma* Kahl
  (syns. *Apgaria, Trichomecium*)   *Spirostomina* Gruber
Gruberia Kahl   *Spirostomum* Ehr.
Parablepharisma Kahl   *Transitella* Gellért
Phacodinium Prowazek
Protocruzia de Faria, da Cunha
  & Pinto (syns. *Diplogmus,
  Propygocirrus, Protocrucia*)

Family PLAGIOTOMIDAE Bütschli, 1887

Cytostome may be subequatorial; buccal membranelles prominent and extensive. Somatic ciliation dense and complete. Found in digestive tract of various invertebrates and vertebrates. Four genera.

Nyctotheroides Grassé (only a
   subgenus of *Nyctotherus?*)
Nyctotherus Leidy (syn.
   Parabursaria?)

Paranyctotherus Sandon
Plagiotoma Duj.

Family FOLLICULINIDAE Dons, 1914

Sessile, loricate forms attached to wide variety of predominantly marine plants and animals. Anteriorly the body is pulled out into two wings bearing extensions of the adoral zone of membranelles. Often pigmented. Migratory larval forms produced by fission within the lorica. Thirty genera.

Ampullofolliculina Hadži
Ascobius Henneguy
   (syn. *Semifolliculina* p.p.)
Atriofolliculina Hadži
Aulofolliculina Hadži
Claustrofolliculina Hadži
Diafolliculina Hadži
Donsia Hadži
   (syn. *Semifolliculina* p.p.)
Echinofolliculina Dons
Epifolliculina Hadži
Eufolliculina Hadži
Folliculina Lamarck (syn. *Freia*)
Folliculinopsis F-F
   (syn. *Alexandrina*)
Halofolliculina Hadži
Lagotia Wright
   (syns. *Angustofolliculina*,
     Semifolliculina p.p.)

Latifolliculina Hadži
Metafolliculina Dons
Mirofolliculina Dons
   (syn. *Microfolliculina*)
Pachyfolliculina Hadži
Parafolliculina Dons
Pebrilla Giard
Pedifolliculina Hadži
Perifolliculina Hadži
Planifolliculina Hadži
Platyfolliculina Hadži
Priscofolliculina Deflandre &
   Deunff
Pseudofolliculina Dons
Splitofolliculina Hadži
Stentofolliculina Hadži
Tapetofolliculina Andrews &
   Nelson (in Hadži, 1951)
Valletofolliculina Andrews

Family CONDYLOSTOMATIDAE Kahl in Doflein & Reichenow, 1929
(syn. Condylostomidae)

Buccal cavity near anterior pole of body; conspicuous adoral zone of membranelles, plus easily detectable right-hand undulating membrane. Body large, quite uniformly ciliated. Two genera.

Condylostoma Bory (originally   *Dellochus* Corl. (for *Lochus*)
written *Kondyliostoma;*
also, later, *Kondylostoma*)

Family REICHENOWELLIDAE Kahl, 1932

Slit-like cytostome, near anterior end of the body. Buccal membranelles quite prominent. Uniform somatic ciliation. Two genera.

Balantidioides Kahl (for *Balan-*   *Reichenowella* Kahl
tidiopsis Pen. [*non* Büt.])

Family CLEVELANDELLIDAE Kidder, 1938
(for Clevelandiidae)

Buccal cavity at posterior pole of the body. Uniformly ciliated body tapers anteriorly. Endocommensal in the Indonesian wood-feeding roach. Two genera.

Clevelandella Kidder (for   *Paraclevelandia* Kidder
Clevelandia; syn. *Emmaninius*)

Comments: Kidder's (1938) replacement name for his own originally preoccupied name was published just 16 days before appearance of *Clevelandella* Resser, 1938, name given to a fossil trilobite! As senior homonym, Kidder's name is the only one which can validly be retained. A year later, Yamasaki (1939), unaware of Kidder's papers, independently described the same interesting ciliates from the same host; but his new generic name, *Emmaninius*, must fall as a synonym on grounds of priority.

Family CHATTONIDIIDAE Villeneuve-Brachon, 1940

Buccal cavity at the anterior pole, ringed by prominent adoral zone of membranelles. Uniform somatic ciliation. Single genus.

Chattonidium Villeneuve

Suborder (2) **Licnophorina** Corliss, 1957

Somatic ciliature absent. Buccal membranelles conspicuous, adorning prominent oral disc. Basal disc serves as an organelle of attachment. Found almost exclusively as marine ectocommensals.

Family LICNOPHORIDAE Bütschli, 1887

With characteristics of the suborder. Single genus.

Licnophora Clap. (syn. *Lichnophora*)

Order 2. **OLIGOTRICHIDA** Bütschli, 1887

Somatic ciliature sparse or absent. Buccal membranelles conspicuous, often extending around the apical end of the body. Species, typically of small body size, most commonly found in marine habitats. About 100 species known.

Family HALTERIIDAE Claparède & Lachmann, 1858
(syns. Meseridae [for Lieberkuehnidae], Torquatellidae)

Buccal membranelles extend out of the buccal cavity. Somatic ciliature limited to bristles or tufts of simple cilia. Seven genera.

Cephalotrichium Meunier	*Strombidium* Clap. & Lach. (for
Halteria Duj.	*Strombidion;* syns. *Buehringa,*
Halterioforma Horváth	*Clypeolum* [hom.], *Conocylis,*
Meseres Schew.	*Laboea, Octocirrus, Torqua-*
Metastrombidium F–F	*tella* [hom.], *Woodania*)
	Tontonia F–F

Family STROBILIDIIDAE Kahl in Doflein & Reichenow, 1929

Buccal membranelles form a conspicuous spiral crown at the apical pole of the body. Typically marine forms. Six genera.

Ciliospina Leegaard	*Strobilidium* Schew. (syns.
Lohmanniella Leegaard	*Arachnella* and *Arachnidiumia*
Parastrombidium F-F	[both for *Arachnidium*],
Sphaerotrichium Wulff	*Strombilidium, Turbilina*)
	Strombidinopsis Kent

Comments: I have placed the curious fresh-water genus *Strombidinopsis* Kent, 1881, in this family. General protozoological accounts always consider it a tintinnid (the following order), but the tintinnid specialists seldom include it in their lists. Probably it is in need of careful restudy.

Order 3. **TINTINNIDA** Kofoid & Campbell, 1929

All loricate, but motile, with loricae exhibiting a variety of shapes, sizes, and composition. Typically marine, pelagic, although one species of the genus *Codonella* is widespread in large bodies of fresh water. Oral membranelles conspicuous when extended from the lorica. Intra-ordinal classification based entirely on characteristics of the lorica. Nearly 1,000 species now known, a number described only as fossils.

Family TINTINNIDAE Claparède & Lachmann, 1858

Lorica of various forms; oral end typically flared. Twenty-five genera.

Albatrossiella K. & C.	*Odontophorella* K. & C.
Amphorellina Colom	*Ormosella* K. & C.
Amphorellopsis K. & C.	*Proamphorella* K. & C.
Amphorides Strand (for	*Prostelidiella* K. & C.
Amphorella)	(syn. *Prostellidiella*)
Brandtiella K. & C.	*Rhabdosella* K. & C. (syns. *Epir-*
Bursaopsis K. & C.	*habdosella, Epirrhabdosella*)
Buschiella Corl. (for *Imperfecta*)	*Salpingacantha* K. & C.
Canthariella K. & C.	*Salpingella* Jörg.
Clevea Balech	*Salpingellina* Colom
Dadayiella K. & C.	*Salpingelloides* Campbell
Daturella K. & C.	*Steenstrupiella* K. & C.
Epicranella K. & C.	*Stelidiella* K. & C.
Eutintinnus K. & C.	*Tintinnus* Schrank

Family DICTYOCYSTIDAE Haeckel, 1873

Lorica with dense bowl and collar formed of arched frames; collar with one or two rows of windows. Three genera.

Dictyocysta Ehr.	*Wangiella* Nie
Luminella K. & C.	

M

Family CODONELLIDAE Kent, 1880

Lorica cup-shaped or tubular; with or without collar. Several species found in fresh water, e.g., *Codonella cratera*. Six genera.

Codonaria K. & C.
Codonella Haeckel
Codonopsis K. & C.

Rhizodomus Strelkow &
  Virketis
Tintinnopsella Colom
Tintinnopsis St.

Comments: The most appropriate taxonomic disposition of the recently discovered (Strelkow and Virketis, 1950) and rather unusual genus *Rhizodomus* is yet to be decided. Tentatively I place it here.

Family CODONELLOPSIDAE Kofoid & Campbell, 1929

Lorica top-shaped; collar with spiral turns. Seven genera.

Calpionella Lorenz
Calpionellites Colom
Calpionellopsis Colom
Codonellopsis Jörg.

Laackmanniella K. & C.
Stenosemella Jörg.
Stenosemellopsis Colom

Family COXLIELLIDAE Kofoid & Campbell, 1929

Lorica goblet-shaped or tubular; delicate. Six genera.

Climacocylis Jörg.
Coxliella Brandt
Coxliellina Colom
Helicostomella Jörg.

Metacylis Jörg.
  (syn. *Metacyclis*)
Stylicauda Balech

Family CYTTAROCYLIDIDAE Kofoid & Campbell, 1929
(syn. Cyttarocylidae)

Lorica bell- or kettle-shaped; collar flared and set off by constriction. Single genus.

Cyttarocylis Fol

Family PETALOTRICHIDAE Kofoid & Campbell, 1929

Lorica cup-shaped; one or two collars. Six genera.

Acanthostomella Jörg.
Ascampbelliella Corl.
  (for *Craterella*)
Luxiella Lecal

Niemarshallia Corl.
  (for *Marshallia*)
Petalotricha Kent
Wailesia K. & C.

Family PTYCHOCYLIDIDAE Kofoid & Campbell, 1929
(syn. Ptychocylidae)

Lorica bell- or kettle-shaped; bowl typically elongate. Six genera.

Cymatocylis Laackmann
(syn. *Cymatocyclis*)
Favella Jörg.
Favelloides Colom

Poroecus Cleve   (for *Porella;*
syn. *Porecus*)
Protocymatocylis K. & C.
Ptychocylis Brandt
(syn. *Ptychocyclis*)

Family RHABDONELLIDAE Kofoid & Campbell, 1929

Lorica conical to chalice-shaped. Five genera.

Epirhabdonella K. & C.
(syn. *Epirrhabdonella*)
Protorhabdonella Jörg.
(syn. *Protorrhabdonella*)

Rhabdonella Brandt
Rhabdonelloides Colom
Rhabdonellopsis K. & C.

Comments: The spelling with double " r's," in the first two generic names above and in *Epir(r)habdosella* (syn. of *Rhabdosella*) of the family Tintinnidae, was introduced by Campbell (1954). His emendations were made because of the etymological rule that the Greek letter *rho* is to be doubled when preceded by a vowel in formation of a compound word. According to the Rules of Nomenclature, however, the spellings of generic names used by the original describers must stand; thus Campbell's emended forms fall as synonyms.

Family TINTINNIDIIDAE Kofoid & Campbell, 1929
(syn. Tintinnididae)

Lorica tubular or saccular; collar typically absent. An occasional species of *Tintinnidium* found in fresh water. Two genera.

Leprotintinnus Jörg.   *Tintinnidium* Kent

Family UNDELLIDAE Kofoid & Campbell, 1929

Lorica goblet-shaped. Seven genera.

Amplectella K. & C.
Amplectellopsis K. & C.
Cricundella K. & C.
(syn. *Circundella*)
Micrundella Busch

Proplectella K. & C.
(syn. *Proplecta*)
Undella Daday
Undellopsis K. & C.

Family XYSTONELLIDAE Kofoid & Campbell, 1929

Lorica more or less chalice-shaped; elongate. Five genera.

Parafavella K. & C.   *Parundella* Jörg.
Parafavelloides Deflandre &   *Xystonella* Brandt
  Deflandre-Rigaud   *Xystonellopsis* Jörg.

Family EPIPLOCYLIDIDAE Kofoid & Campbell, 1939
(syn. Epiplocylidae)

Lorica acorn-shaped; short, stout. Four genera.

Epicancella K. & C.   *Epiplocylis* Jörg.
Epiorella K. & C.   *Epiplocyloides* K. & C.

Order 4. **ENTODINIOMORPHIDA** Reichenow
in Doflein & Reichenow, 1929

Simple somatic ciliature absent. Oral membranelles functional in feeding are restricted to a small area, but dorsal zones and other membranellar tufts are present in many species. Pellicle, firm, often drawn out posteriorly into spines. Exclusively endocommensal in herbivores, particularly ruminants. About 200 species.

Family OPHRYOSCOLECIDAE Stein, 1859

Ciliature limited to adoral plus, usually, a single dorsal zone of membranelles. Typically found in the rumen of cattle, sheep, and related forms. Twenty-one genera.

Amphacanthus Dogiel   *Epiplastron* K. & MacL.
Caloscolex Dogiel   *Eremoplastron* K. & MacL.
Cunhaia Hasselmann   *Eudiplodinium* Dogiel
Diplodinium Schuberg   *Metadinium* Awerinzew
  (syn. *Anoplodinium* p.p.)   & Mutafowa
Diploplastron K. & MacL.   *Ophryoscolex* St.
Elephantophilus K.   *Opisthotrichum* Buisson
Elytroplastron K. & MacL.   *Ostracodinium* Dogiel
Enoploplastron K. & MacL.   *Polydiniella* Corl.
Entodinium St.   (for *Polydinium*)
Eodinium K. & MacL.   *Polyplastron* Dogiel
  (syn. *Anoplodinium* p.p.)   *Thoracodinium* Latteur
Epidinium Crawley

Comments: Possibly the genera *Elephantophilus*, *Polydiniella*, and *Thoracodinium* belong in the following (or a new?) family.

Family CYCLOPOSTHIIDAE Poche, 1913
(syn. Ditoxidae)

Ciliation includes several groups of membranelles, often caudal in location, in addition to the adoral and dorsal zones. Found principally in horses, with a few species from such hosts as the rhinoceros, chimpanzee, and gorilla. Sixteen genera.

Bertolinella Carpano
Bozasella Buisson (syn. of ?)
Cochliatoxum Gassovsky
Cycloposthium Bundle
Ditoxum Gassovsky
Lavierella Buisson (syn. of ?)
Prototapirella da Cunha
  (syn. *Protoapirella*)
Spirodinium Fiorentini

Tetratoxum Gassovsky
Toxodinium da Cunha
Triadinium Fiorentini
Tricaudalia Buisson
  (syn. of *Tripalmaria?*)
Trifascicularia Strelkow
Tripalmaria Gassovsky
Triplumaria Hoare
Troglodytella Brumpt & Joyeux

Comments: Restudy and revision of the composition of this, as well as of the preceding, family are indicated. Strelkow (1939) erected a separate family for the single genus *Ditoxum;* but the family Ditoxidae Strelkow, 1939, apparently has not been widely accepted by specialists of the entire group.

Order 5. **ODONTOSTOMATIDA** Sawaya, 1940
(for Ctenostomatida)

Oral ciliature reduced to 8 membranelles. Somatic ciliation generally sparse. Body small, wedge-shaped, laterally compressed. Pellicle, or carapace, sometimes drawn out into spines. Polysaprobic forms. Fewer than three dozen species have been described to date.

Comments: The familiar Ctenostomatida (Ctenostomata Kahl, 1932: often miscredited to Lauterborn, 1908) is preoccupied by a name of a bryozoan order, Ctenostomata Busk, 1852, and thus it should be abandoned as the name for the protozoan order under present consideration. Sawaya (1940) realized this many years ago, but his observation, and well-chosen replacement name, went unnoticed until recently (Corliss, 1956a, 1957a).

Family MYLESTOMATIDAE Kahl in Doflein & Reichenow, 1929
(syn. Mylestomidae)

Somatic ciliation very limited. Posterior tufts sometimes fused into long " cirri." Two genera.

Atopodinium Kahl   *Mylestoma* Kahl

Family DISCOMORPHELLIDAE Corliss, 1960
(for Discomorphidae [for Ctenostomatidae])

Prominent dorsal keel. Somatic ciliation limited. Single genus.

Discomorphella Corl. (for *Discomorpha*)

Comments: The name Discomorphidae Poche, 1913, was quite well-established, but it had been formed from the preoccupied name *Discomorpha* Levander, 1893. Type generic names which are junior homonyms, unlike the case of a junior synonym, cannot be used as the basis of the familial name. The new familial name is thus based on the substitute generic name *Discomorphella* (see Corliss, 1960b).

Family EPALXELLIDAE Corliss, 1960
(for Epalxidae)

Posterior end of the body unarmored. Somatic ciliation fairly complete. Three genera.

Epalxella Corl. (for *Epalxis*)   *Saprodinium* Lauterborn
Pelodinium Lauterborn

Comments: See remarks made with respect to the preceding family. *Epalxis* Roux, 1899, original name of the type genus, has fallen as a junior homonym; thus the familial name Epalxidae (always erroneously written Epalcidae) Wetzel, 1928, also has had to be replaced (Corliss, 1960b).

Order 6. **HYPOTRICHIDA** Stein, 1859

Conspicuous somatic compound ciliature, the cirri, present in various patterns on the ventral surface of the body. Adoral zone of membranelles prominent in the oral area. Body, sometimes possessing a quite rigid pellicle, is flattened dorso-ventrally. Nearly 400 species are recognized.

Family ASPIDISCIDAE Ehrenberg, 1838

Reduced zone of adoral membranelles. Cirri limited to a small group of frontals and a group of anals. Two genera.

Aspidisca Ehr. (syns. *Aspidis-*   *Onychaspis* St.
  copsis, possibly *Monostylus?*)

Family EUPLOTIDAE Ehrenberg, 1838
(syn. Ploesconiidae)

Large peristomial (buccal) area, with well-developed membranelles. Cirri prominent but restricted to several well-defined locations on the ventral surface of the body. Eleven genera.

Certesia Fabre-Domergue   *Euplotidium* Noland
Cirrhogaster Ozaki & Yagiu   *Gastrocirrhus* Lepşi
Diophrys Duj. (syns. *Plani-*   *Gruberella* Corl. (for *Stylocoma*)
  plotes, Styloplotes,   *Lacazea* Dragesco
  Styloptotes)   *Swedmarkia* Dragesco
Discocephalus Ehr.   *Uronychia* St.
  (syn. *Polycoccon*)   (syn. *Campylopus* [hom.])
Euplotes Ehr. (syns. *Ploesconia,*
  possibly *Crateromorpha*
  [hom.])

Family OXYTRICHIDAE Ehrenberg, 1838
(syns. Keronidae, Kiitrichidae, Pleurotrichidae, Psilotrichidae, Spirofilidae, Urostylidae)

Buccal membranelles conspicuous, but body morphology dominated by the large array of cirri covering much of the ventral surface of the body in various arrangements. Fifty-six genera and subgenera, listed here without discrimination because of the uncertainty concerning the relative status of some of them, as the group is currently composed. Thus it is by far the largest family, above the species-level, in the entire subphylum Ciliophora.

Actinotricha Cohn   *Atractos* Vörösváry
Allotricha Sterki   *Balladinopsis* Ghosh
Amphisiella Gourret & Roeser   (syn. *Balladynopsis*)
  (syn. *Tetrastyla*)   *Balladyna* Kowalewski
Ancystropodium F-F   (syn. *Balladina*)

Banyulsella Dragesco
Caryotricha Kahl
Chaetospira Lachmann
   (syns. *Archimedea*,
   Stichospira)
Cladotricha Gaj.
Epiclintes St. (syn. *Claparedia*)
Eschaneustyla Stokes
Gastrostyla Engelmann
   (syn. *Nothopleurotricha*)
Gonostomum Sterki
   (syn. *Plagiotricha*)
Hemicycliostyla Stokes
Hemiholosticha von Gelei
Histriculus Corl. (for *Histrio*)
Holosticha Wrzes.
   (syn. *Amphisia*)
Hypotrichidium Ilowaisky
   (syn. *Spirofilum* von Gelei,
   1929)
Isosticha Kiesselbach
Kahliella Corl. (for *Kahlia*)
Kerona Ehr. (first, O.F.M.)
Keronopsis Pen.
Kütricha Nozawa
Micromitra Kahl (for *Mitra*)
Onychodromopsis Stokes
Onychodromus St.
Opisthotricha Kent
   (syn. *Opistotricha*)
Oxytricha Bory (originally
   written *Oxitricha*; syn.
   Rhabdotricha?)

Paraholosticha Kahl
Paruroleptus Kahl
Parurosoma von Gelei
Pleurotricha St.
Psilotricha St. (syn. *Pigostyla*)
Psilotrix Gourret & Roeser
Spiretta von Gelei
Spirofilopsis Corl. (for *Spiro-
   filum* von Gelei, 1944)
Steinia Diesing
Stichochaeta Clap. & Lach.
Stichotricha Perty
   (syn. *Schizosiphon*)
Strongylidium Sterki
Stylonethes Sterki
Stylonychia Ehr. (syns.
   Dipleurostyla, *Drepanina*,
   Prosopsenus?)
Tachysoma Stokes
Trachelochaeta Šrámek-Hušek
Trachelostyla Kahl
Trichotaxis Stokes
Uncinata Bullington
Uroleptoides Wenzel
Uroleptopsis Kahl
Uroleptus Ehr. (syns. *Platy-
   trichotus*, *Tricholeptus*)
Urosoma Kowalewski
   (syn. *Pseudostrombidium*)
Urospinula Corl. (for *Urospina*)
Urostrongylum Kahl
Urostyla Ehr. (syn. *Prooxy-
   tricha* [for *Trichogaster*]?)

Comments: As in the case of the holotrich family Frontoniidae, this family probably has become too heterogeneous in its great growth. As the list of synonyms indicates, attempts have been made by several workers in the past to remove a number of genera from the main group. Although Kahl (1930–1935) rejected recognition of the three families Pleurotrichidae Bütschli, 1889, Psilotrichidae Bütschli, 1889, and Urostylidae Bütschli, 1889 (considered only as subfamilies by Bütschli, 1887–1889, but as families by Calkins, 1926, and others), it is possible that they should be resurrected in future revisions of the order Hypotrichida. The family proposed by von Gelei (1929) for his interesting genus *Spirofilum** (a synonym of *Hypotrichidium*) might well be reconsidered: even the name Spirofilidae von Gelei, 1929, could be retained legitimately.

Special mention should be made of the family Kiitrichidae Nozawa, 1941, a group suggested since the monographic reviews by Kahl. In a paper generally overlooked, Nozawa (1941) considered his new genus *Kiitricha* plus *Caryotricha* Kahl to form a small assemblage of hypotrichs with very primitive characteristics. Although he did not definitively erect a new family, he proposed the name Kiitrichidae for it and offered data which would comprise its characterization. Pending further over-all study, I tentatively accept Kiitrichidae, as Nozawa's family, and offer the following distinctive diagnosis: Buccal ciliature moderately developed. Cirri quite uniformly distributed over the ventral surface of the body, with eight anal cirri representing the only specialized group. Two genera.

Family PARAEUPLOTIDAE Wichterman, 1942

Adoral zone of membranelles exceedingly well developed and extensive. Number of cirri, on the other hand, greatly limited and restricted to posterior end of the body. But several tufts or bands of free cilia appear on the anterior half of the ventral surface. Two genera.

Euplotaspis Ch. & Séguéla   *Paraeuplotes* Wichterman

---

*Not to be confused with a second genus *Spirofilum* mentioned in later works by von Gelei (1944, 1954), although the species involved seem to be quite closely related. See Corliss (1960b) for further discussion of this interesting matter, primarily a nomenclatural problem.

PART III

GUIDE TO THE LITERATURE

CHAPTER 13

MAJOR WORKS ON THE CILIATES

PROBABLY some 10,000 to 12,000 original papers appearing within the past 200 years have been directly concerned, in whole or in a significant part, with one or more species of ciliated protozoa. Such an estimated figure includes books, monographs, other papers, notes, and preliminary reports and refers to all kinds of investigations (descriptive, experimental, or theoretical) in these often overlapping areas of study: systematics, comparative morphology, cytology, physiology and biochemistry, genetics and cytogenetics, life cycles, morphogenesis, general ecology, and parasitology. One aim of the present book is to provide a selective guide to this great mass of literature. It has been a problem to decide how many direct citations of published works should be included in the reference-section following this chapter: too large a number decreases the usefulness of the bibliography and risks inclusion of numerous papers of doubtful significance; too small a number is frustrating to the reader desirous of being able to see first-hand the full titles of major contributions in areas of special interest to him. I strongly believe that only papers actually cited in the text should be included among the references, for a bibliography divorced from direct consideration elsewhere in a publication is of limited value.

Some 1,700 titles have finally been chosen for inclusion in this book. Not only would the combined bibliographies of these papers lead the reader to practically all works ever published on ciliates to date, but the cited papers themselves may be considered to represent the great majority of the sizeable and significant publications in the principal areas of research mentioned in the preceding paragraph. The following general comments, however, should be made concerning my selections.

(1) All major monographs, including protozoological textbooks,

are included, regardless of their date of publication. " Monographs " may be defined in a general way to mean extensive works, generally of considerable length (100 or more pages) which treat a major area of investigation, or some specific aspect of such an area, with a high degree of thoroughness. Monographs have been published in the fields of physiology, cytology, genetics, etc., but naturally they are more common in areas of systematics and comparative morphology.

(2) Works which I consider to be " classical " are included. These may be short as well as long papers, experimental or theoretical in nature as well as taxonomic or morphological. They do not need to be " old " to be recognized as classical. The prime criterion is that they are of outstanding significance and of predictably lasting value in the area of their coverage. It is to be understood that only a small fraction of the 1,700 papers cited merit assignment to this category.

(3) Papers are cited from all fields. Systematics is purposely favored with the greatest representation of works. But even in taxonomic areas an earnest attempt has been made to cover all major groups of ciliates equally well, particularly since some are commonly neglected in most textbooks or similar compendia. Nearly all original descriptions of valid familial groups, and of many of the generic taxa as well, are cited.

(4) The preponderance of citations is to modern works, with the papers of the past decade deliberately most favored and, next, those published in the period 1935–1950*. The reasons for this are obvious: the well-documented monographs of Bütschli (1887–1889) and Kahl (1930–1935), devoted exclusively to ciliates, are out of date yet cover the earlier literature well; the more recent papers include references to earlier works in the same fields; knowledge of up-to-date references in any major area is an important prerequisite to carrying out further research in that area.

(5) Particular attention is given to the literature concerned with the systematics and special biology of a selected group of genera

*A rough "break-down" of the total number of references, by arbitrarily chosen chronological periods, may be of passing interest. From 1565 through 1849: about 35 papers are cited; for the period 1850–1899: about 100; 1900–1935: nearly 500; 1935–1949: over 350; 1950 to date well over 700 (greater than 40% of the total bibliography).

For reasons explained in Chapter 5 of Part I, *Paramecium* and *Tetrahymena* are especially favored. Other genera direct citations to which are possibly disproportionately* numerous in comparison with those cited for the hundreds of remaining generic groups include: *Balantidium, Colpoda, Euplotes, Frontonia, Stentor, Trichodina,* and *Vorticella.* The families Ophryoscolecidae and Oxytrichidae also are somewhat favored bibliographically.

(6) Among techniques of study probably electron microscopy is relatively favored in numbers of papers cited. This is done deliberately, because electron microscopical investigations represent a modern area of significant specialized research, and the data being obtained through such studies may become of increasing value in future systematic considerations of the ciliates.

(7) Many papers very limited in scope, even if representing a worthwhile contribution to the protozoological literature, are not included. For example, works restricted to brief descriptions of new species are excluded in great numbers. Similarly numerous individual papers concerned with problems of an experimental nature (in physiology and biochemistry, genetics, etc.) are not cited unless they are of unusual significance. When a series of brief works has appeared on a particular topic, I have often referred only to the last paper, or the first and last, with a comment pointing out that earlier or intermediate publications by the same author do exist. Brief works culminating in a monograph also generally are not included. Abstracts are rarely cited unless they are particularly appropriate and/or represent a research problem of potential significance concerning which the investigator has not yet had an opportunity to publish a full report.

Location of Citations

The bulk of my direct references to the ciliate literature occurs in the chapters of Part I. Scattered new citations of pertinence appear in various " Comments " throughout Part II. Papers on taxonomic subjects are easily found by virtue of the general organization of the book. But references to other fields usually cannot appear in a single location, since no separate section is

*On the other hand, these very genera contain the best-known and most widely studied species of ciliates.

concerned strictly with the biology of ciliates. Generally, the reader interested in such areas must know the names of the experimental organisms. For example, papers concerned with parasitological considerations of *Balantidium*, genetics or infraciliature of *Tetrahymena* or *Paramecium*, morphogenesis of *Stentor*, ultrastructure of *Vorticella*, cytology of *Euplotes*, en- and excystment of *Colpoda*, etc., will be cited on pages devoted to these genera (see Systematic Index).

Major references to the important but rather neglected field of ciliate ecology are arbitrarily listed in a single location, under discussion of the order Gymnostomatida (Chapter 3). In such an extensive area of biological research as the field of sexuality I have made no attempt to include exhaustive citation to the literature. Here, as for other areas similarly of vast scope (such as biochemistry), I have relied heavily on citation of selected outstanding works, recent specialized reviews, and up-to-date books on the subject.

A large number of references appear only in the present chapter. This should not imply that such works are of any more or less significance than those cited in earlier chapters. They have been reserved for brief consideration here because they are either related to special topics not treated elsewhere or bear publication dates of more than a quarter of a century ago and thus generally have not been appropriate for inclusion in Part I.

Space does not permit critical comment on each and every reference cited. Fortunately authors' titles usually indicate clearly the subject matter of their papers, and my citation of the full reference, including total pagination*, should provide the reader with an adequate idea of the extensiveness of the work.

Ciliates and Parasitology

Among the major groups of protozoa the Ciliophora are of the least interest to the general parasitologist. Considering all kinds of hosts and all types of host–symbiont relationship, however, many species of ciliates can be implicated in symbiosis, if the phenomenon is treated in its broadest sense. Indeed, members of

*Often not available in books published today, to the exasperation and real inconvenience of the reader.

entire groups exhibit the symbiotic habit; for example, all of the Apostomatida, Astomatida, Entodiniomorphida, and Thigmo-trichida; hundreds of species of the Peritrichida and Suctorida (primarily as ectosymbionts); and scores of the Chonotrichida, Gymnostomatida, Heterotrichida, Hymenostomatida, and Tricho-stomatida.

A relationship between vertebrates and ciliates, on the other hand, is admittedly of relatively rare occurrence. Thus professional workers in the fields of medicine and veterinary science find few ciliates to be of direct concern to them. The trichostome *Balantidium* is the only genus found in man. The ophryoscolecids are well known because of their association with herbivorous mammals; the smaller neighboring family of cycloposthiids likewise is found exclusively in mammalian digestive tracts. Higher vertebrates also harbor gymnostomes of the families Buetschliidae and Pycnotrichidae and trichostomes of the families Balantidiidae, Blepharocorythidae, Cyathodiniidae, Isotrichidae, and Paraiso-trichidae, as well as very scattered representatives of other ordinal groups (such as members of the heterotrich genus *Nyctotherus*). Fishes are parasitized by a number of ciliates, but notably by species of the hymenostome genus *Ichthyophthirius* and the peritrich *Trichodina*.

The reader interested in veterinary protozoology is referred specifically to Cameron (1951), Curasson (1943), Lapage (1956), Levine (1961), Morgan and Hawkins (1948), Neveu-Lemaire (1943), and Richardson and Kendall (1957). More general references treating medical or parasitological matters some of which involve ciliates of direct concern to man and his domestic animals include: Doflein and Reichenow (1949–1953), Hall (1953), Hoare (1949), Kudo (1954), Thomson and Robertson (1929), and Wenyon (1926); not to mention the many standard texts and reference works on general and clinical parasitology, some of which have substantial sections on the protozoa (e.g., Belding, 1952; Brumpt, 1949; Cameron, 1956; Chandler and Read, 1961; Faust *et al.*, 1957; Piekarski, 1954). A number of treatises on specialized topics [for example, Steinhaus (1947) on insect microbiology] also should not be overlooked by the parasitologically oriented protozoologist.

Biological Abstracts and the *Zoological Record* are, of course,

N

very helpful continuing sources of protozoological–parasitological information. If the names of workers are known, the *Index-Catalogue of Medical and Veterinary Zoology*, an invaluable storehouse of titles of papers published on parasitological topics, can be used to great advantage. It should be noted, however, that the *ciliate* literature in areas of parasitological research, for the reasons given on the preceding page, is relatively very sparse.

20th Century Leaders in Ciliate Studies

The major concentrated work on the taxonomy of the Ciliophora published in the present century must be credited to Alfred Kahl of Hamburg, Germany (see portrait in Frontispiece, upper left). His culminating, profusely illustrated, well-documented monograph containing keys to the ciliates of the world (exclusive of suctorians, major symbiotic groups, and marine tintinnids) is properly the best known (Kahl, 1930–1935). His complementary undertakings, however, on endocommensal and parasitic forms, as well as on free-living and ectocommensal species, also should be recalled (Kahl, 1933a, 1934a). Kahl's important publications on the Suctorida, on species of several individual holotrich genera, and on " new or little-known " holotrichs and heterotrichs should be recognized as original productions of lasting importance as well (Kahl, 1926, 1927a,b, 1928, 1929, 1930, 1930–1931, 1931a,b, 1933b,c, 1934b). His painstaking attention to the comparative morphology and systematics of ciliates at the species-level has never been equalled in modern times.

Kahl's own prodigious output on ciliates is rivalled, however, by the impressive publication lists of three European contemporaries of his, only the last-mentioned of whom is still living: Édouard Chatton, of France, József von Gelei, of Hungary; and Emmanuel Fauré-Fremiet, of France.

Chatton, often in collaboration with his younger colleague André Lwoff (see portraits in Pl. XXII) and/or other members of his school, made major contributions in at least three areas of ciliate study: theoretical, technical, and taxonomic. Evidences of his work and influence in these areas are abundant in the references cited throughout Part I. Extensive though his detailed morphological and systematic papers, primarily on symbiotic ciliates, have been (Chatton and Lwoff, 1935a, 1936a, 1949, 1950; Chatton and Pérard, 1921; Chatton and Séguéla, 1940), and with due respect for his development of the nearly indispensable French silver impregnation technique and other improved methods of cytological study (Chatton, 1940; Chatton and Lwoff, 1930, 1935a, 1936c), Chatton may well be remembered longest for his stimulating hypotheses. Chattonian ideas of value in ciliate systematics include ones already considered in Chapter 1: the autonomy and genetic continuity of the kinety, the pluripotency of kinetosomes, the rule of desmodexy, the significance of stomatogenesis, the development of the concepts of homothetogenic and symmetrogenic modes of fission (see Figs. 1–5, Pl. V; Figs. 3, 4, Pl. VII). An appreciation of the extent of Chatton's protistological researches may be realized by consulting Chatton (1938), Corliss (1956a), and Lwoff (1948). Specific papers of pioneering importance not already cited elsewhere in this book include Chatton (1936), Chatton and Brachon (1935a,b), Chatton and Chatton (1929a,b, 1931), Chatton and Lwoff (1931, 1935b, 1936b), Chatton, Lwoff, and Lwoff (1931), Chatton, Lwoff, Lwoff, and Monod (1931a,b), Chatton, Lwoff, Lwoff, and Tellier (1929), Chatton and Villeneuve (1937b).

Von Gelei (see portrait in Pl. XXII, upper right) developed special cytological techniques, including variations of silver and gold impregnation methods, carried out numerous observations of ecological importance, and made a number of outstanding contributions of taxonomic value. His painstaking cytological investigations of contractile vacuoles, sensory bristles, and buccal ciliary organelles may be considered classical among modern protozoological research publications. Gellért and Müller (1954) have published a complete list of J.* von Gelei's papers which is thus available there to the interested reader. I consider his most important works to be the following, the titles of which will give an indication of the variety of major problems he attacked related to ciliated protozoa: von Gelei (1925, 1927, 1929, 1932a,b, 1934a–d, 1935a–c, 1938a–c, 1939a,b, 1940, 1944, 1950a–c, 1952,

---

*József von Gelei's son, Gabor, also published several very noteworthy papers on ciliates (e.g., see G. von Gelei, 1937, 1939, 1940). Half the age of his father at the time, he unfortunately passed away in the same year, 1952.

1954); von Gelei and Horváth (1931a,b); von Gelei and Szabados (1950).

Fauré-Fremiet (see portrait in Frontispiece, lower right), still very actively at work in Paris, has produced more papers on ciliates, and over a longer period of time, than any of the other investigators under discussion here. His impact on ciliophoran systematics has been made abundantly clear, I believe, in Part I of this book (also see Corliss, 1956a). His attention to morphogenesis, ecology, nuclear phenomena, and, most recently, ultrastructural details of protozoan organization has been much greater than his interest in taxonomic descriptions *per se*. Yet his contributions in the area of systematics, at descriptive as well as conceptual levels, have been considerable. Since 1903, Fauré-Fremiet has published over 400 papers the bulk of which has been concerned with ciliated protozoa! Some 75 of his principal works, including several reviews, are given in the reference-section following this chapter. All have been cited in preceding pages except these: Fauré-Fremiet (1904a,b, 1908, 1909, 1910b, 1935, 1952b, 1953a, 1954c, 1957d).

In America, during the first half of the present century, leaders in studies of ciliate systematics were G. N. Calkins at Columbia University, New York City, and C. A. Kofoid at the University of California, Berkeley. These men, plus their students and associates, produced a large number of outstanding taxonomic (and also other) publications cited in appropriate places in Part I or in later sections of the present chapter. The valuable papers of Beers, Kidder, Noland, and Wenrich also deserve special mention. In non-systematic areas of research the works of Hall, Jennings, Kidder (again: this time in biochemistry), Sonneborn, and Woodruff, and of their students, similarly represent major advances in ciliate protozoology.

Technical Advances of Greatest Importance

Along with the development of the microscope, the improvement in cytological staining techniques during the present century has done much to permit a refinement of protozoological studies previously unattainable. The value of methods of silver impregnation already has been stressed (Chapter 1). The discoverer of the technique or, at least, the first worker to apply it successfully to ciliated protozoa, was Bruno Klein of Vienna (see portrait in Pl. XXII, upper left). Klein has been eminently successful with his " dry " silver technique, studying scores of different species of free-living, fresh-water ciliates. Although the Austrian worker himself has not been primarily concerned with taxonomic problems, the silverline system as well as the infraciliature (both systems include the argentophilic basal granules or kinetosomes) has become nearly indispensable in modern systematic studies. Thus his major publications should be cited: Klein (1926a,b, 1927, 1928, 1929, 1930, 1932, 1933, 1943, 1958).

Other investigators have used Klein's technique to advantage, also the " wet " refinements by Chatton and Lwoff (1930: and see Corliss, 1953b) and von Gelei (see references given under his name in a preceding paragraph). Rio Hortéga's piridinated silver carbonate method has worked well in the hands of Fernández-Galiano (e.g., 1949, 1955, 1958) and Wessenberg (1957); and the Bodian activated protein silver or " Protargol " impregnation technique (Honigberg and Davenport, 1954; Kirby, 1945), so very useful for certain symbiotic zooflagellates, quite recently has been applied very successfully to ciliates (e.g., see Kozloff, 1955, 1957; Williams and Scherbaum, 1959).

Other cytological techniques especially adapted for use in study of ciliated protozoa are too numerous to cite individually, although particular mention might be made of such pioneering papers as those by Bresslau (1921a), von Gelei (1927, 1934d), Khainsky (1910), Reichenow (1928), and Sharp (1914); also see references in Taylor (1941) and Wichterman (1953). Within the past decade important techniques have been developed as new, or advantageously modified, by Alfert and Goldstein (1955), Banerjee (1958), Child and Mazia (1956), Dippell (1955), Ehret and Powers (1955), Fauré-Fremiet (1954, 1957b), Ganguly and Banerjee (1956), Mazia et al. (1953), McArdle (1959), Mugard (1957), Mugard and Lorsignol (1957), Nissenbaum (1953), Párducz (1952), Preer (1950), Preer and Stark (1953), Raikov (1958, 1959a,b), Ray (1956a,b), Schwartz (1957, 1958), Seshachar (1950), Thomas (1952), Turner (1954), Yusa (1957). Techniques other than cytological also have been advanced in recent years. These are generally described in the works in which they have been applied; occasionally they are published separately, such as the valuable " manual " by Sonneborn (1950) devoted to methods of culturing and handling species of *Paramecium* for use in genetic and cytogenetic investigations.

The following recent compilations are recommended to the reader in search of detailed technical information regarding general methods of culturing, fixing, and staining of ciliates (and other protozoa as well): Corliss (1961b), Kirby (1950), Mayer (1956), Wenrich and Diller (1950). To this brief list one must add the older but still unreplaced references on food preferences and techniques of culture by Sandon (1932) and Needham *et al.* (1937). The latter, containing a collection of papers by specialists, is now again available, having been reprinted in a paper-bound edition by Dover Publications in 1959.

Pre-20th Century References*

Discussion of the earliest literature is beyond the scope of the present work. Landmarks in the exciting discovery of protozoa of microscopic size†, including ciliates, by such " philosophers in little things " as Leeuwenhoek (1674 *et seq.*), Hooke (1678), Buonanni (1691), King (1693), Harris (1696), Joblot (1718), Trembley (1744), Hill (1752), Baker (1753), Rösel von Rosenhof (1755), Wrisberg (1765), and Ellis (1769) can only be mentioned by inclusion of their titles in the reference-section following this chapter. The reader is referred to the interesting historical accounts, and additional references, available in such works as Bütschli (1887–1889), Cole (1926), Dobell (1932), Kent (1880–1882), and Woodruff (1938, 1939a,b, and several earlier papers not cited here). Special citation should be made, however, of the great

---

*Young workers in ciliate systematics are particularly urged to acquaint themselves with the classical older literature: with surprising frequency it may be found that " new " observations have already been made, and often with considerable precision, in spite of the lack of " modern " techniques.

†Foraminiferidans (sarcodinids) visible to the naked eye were described by Gesner (1565) as molluscs and figured by Hooke (1665) one hundred years later. Large ciliates may have been noted before the second half of the 17th century, but we have no records of such observations.

pioneering works of O. F. Müller (1773, 1776, 1786). In spite of a large number of classificational errors, when his work is viewed in retrospect, his monographs represent the first comprehensive taxonomic treatment of all protozoan forms known at the time. Müller also made a number of precise observations of biological importance, such as his recognition of conjugation in *Paramecium*, a phenomenon incorrectly interpreted as longitudinal fission for some 90 years following his publications.

From a taxonomic-nomenclatural point of view it may be interesting to point out that the only generic name of extant protozoa included by Linnaeus (1758) in his celebrated 10th edition was *Volvox*. By the 12th edition (Linnaeus, 1766), the ciliate *Vorticella* joined *Chaos*, *Furia*, and *Volvox* in representing invertebrate categories which included protozoa (exclusive of Foraminiferida) as we know them today.

The 19th century produced scores of important publications on ciliated protozoa, as might be expected. Over a hundred of the principal books, monographs, or most significant experimental papers are cited in the following paragraphs. The specialist on any one group of ciliates or in any one field of research naturally will need to consult additional works, citation to which may be found in the combined bibliographies of those given below.

Monographs truly considered classical include the contributions of Balbiani (1888, 1892–1893), Bütschli (1876, 1887–1889), Claparède and Lachmann (1858–1861), Delage and Hérouard (1896), Dujardin (1838, 1841), Ehrenberg (1838), Hertwig (1889), Kent (1880–1882), Maupas (1881, 1883, 1888, 1889), Schewiakoff (1896), Stein (1854, 1859, 1867), Stokes (1888).

From the point of view of systematics, several of these deserve further special mention. Ehrenberg's monumental work* represents the first thorough and accurate over-all taxonomic treatment of the Protozoa and included descriptions of some 350 new species,

---

*Incidentally, immediately following publication of this magnificent over-sized tome (it measures 19 by 13 inches!), Mandl (1839) produced a very convenient " pocket-book " edition, extracting only the French from Ehrenberg's Latin–German–French accounts. At the same time Kutorga (1839) published an abbreviated Russian version, later translated into German (Kutorga, 1841).

many of them ciliates and many still recognized today. His ill-fated Polygastrica Theory, exploded principally by Dujardin, does not detract from other aspects of his work which remain of lasting value. Stein may justifiably be hailed as the father of the ciliate classificational scheme still generally in vogue today (see Chapter 1). Somewhat paralleling the situation just mentioned with regard to Ehrenberg, Stein's ill-conceived and erroneous Acineta Theory, overthrown by such thorough contemporaries as Lachmann, need not lessen our respect for his taxonomic work. Our debt to Bütschli, well named the " architect of protozoology " (Dobell, 1951), is a particularly great one.* He carried out important researches of a cytological and experimental nature as well as establishing a unified classificational scheme for all the major groups of protozoa which has undergone little modification during the past 75 years. Schewiakoff, concentrating his efforts on the holotrich ciliates, attempted to complete the series of systematic monographs produced earlier by Stein. His invaluable culminating work is written entirely in Russian and is not available in many libraries.†

Other important contributions of the nineteenth century may be listed as follows: Allman (1855), Balbiani (1861, 1898), Binet (1889), Blochmann (1866), Bory de St. Vincent (1826), de Bruyne (1888), Bundle (1895), Claparède (1867), Cohn (1866), von Daday (1887), Diesing (1865), Eberhard (1858, 1862), Ehrenberg (1832a,b, 1835, 1840), Eichwald (1844–1852), Engelmann (1876), G. Entz, Sr. (1884, 1892, 1893), Fabre-Domergue (1888a,b), Foettinger (1881), Fraipont (1877–1878), de Fromentel (1874), Gourret and Roeser (1886, 1888), Greeff (1888), Gruber (1884),

---

*Bütschli's impact on the whole field of 19th and 20th century zoology has been portrayed admirably in the enjoyable account by Goldschmidt (1956). At least his other taxonomic protozoological monographs must be cited here: Bütschli (1880–1882, 1883–1887). The most recent comparably detailed treatment of the non-ciliate groups, incidentally, is to be found in Grassé (1952, 1953).

†Schouteden (1906–1907) published a French version of Schewiakoff (1896) which, curiously enough, is even less easily obtainable. Fortunately Hoare (1927a) has produced a most accurate English translation of Schewiakoff's keys; his paper, however, is not widely known among protozoologists, judging from the rarity with which it is cited.

Gruby and Delafond (1843), Haeckel (1866, 1873), Henneguy (1890, 1898), Hertwig (1876, 1877), Huxley (1857, 1877), Jennings (1897), Johnson (1893), Keppen (1888), Kowalewski (1882), Lachmann (1856), Lanessan (1882), Lankester (1873, 1885), Le Dantec (1892), Levander (1893, 1894), Lillie (1896), Maskell (1886–1887), Maupas (1876), Mereschkowsky (1877, 1879), Möbius (1888), Moxon (1869), Perejaslawzewa (1886), Perty (1852), Plate (1886, 1889), Pritchard (1834–1861), von Prowazek (1898–1903), Quennerstedt (1865–1869), van Rees (1884), Rhumbler (1888), Roux (1899), Sand (1895, 1899–1901), Schewiakoff (1889, 1893a,b), Schuberg (1887, 1888, 1890), von Siebold (1848), Stein (1849, 1851, 1861), Sterki (1878), Stokes (1893, 1894), Verworn (1889), Wallengren (1894, 1895, 1897), Wrzesniowski (1870, 1877).

20th Century Works on Ciliates

The majority of protozoological papers concerned in whole or in part with investigations on ciliates has been published in the present century, with a larger number, on the average, appearing in each successive year. The reasons for this are obvious: an ever-increasing number of investigators and research laboratories, plus an increase in general in cellular and microscopical studies; the availability of a greater variety of specialized techniques and approaches without which certain problems would have to continue to be left to one side; a greater interest in experimental biological problems for the solution of which ciliates may be employed to distinct advantage; a growing number of scientific journals which serve as an outlet for numerous preliminary communications as well as full publications.

Many monographs or other papers of significance, particularly those of systematic importance and/or of post-Kahlian date (with emphasis, in fact, on those of the past decade) have been directly cited in preceding chapters of this book. Here I wish to list a limited number of works which were published between 1900 and 1940 but, for one reason or another, are *not* cited elsewhere. As inspection of the titles of these selected books, monographs, and papers will indicate, the emphasis is often on substantial research results in areas other than systematics: general biology, cytology,

PLATE XXII

Twentieth century leaders in the study of ciliates [also see Frontispiece].

Upper left: BRUNO KLEIN (1891–   ), discoverer of the eminently successful application of a method of silver impregnation to the study of subpellicular structures in ciliated protozoa. Major post-Kahlian revisions in the systematics of ciliates have stemmed

physiology, genetics, and miscellaneous considerations. These additional citations are grouped arbitrarily by decades.

Period 1900–1910. Brandt (1907), Bürger (1906, 1908), Buschkiel (1910), Calkins (1901a*, 1901b, 1902a,b), Calkins and Cull (1907), Conn (1905), von Daday (1910), Dale (1901), Doflein (1901†, 1902), Edmondson (1906), Enriques (1907), G. Entz, Jr. (1909), Gonder (1905), Griffin (1910), Hartog (1906), Hertwig (1902), Hickson (1903), Hickson and Wadsworth (1902, 1909), Jennings (1904), Lebedew (1908), Maier (1903)‡, Meunier (1910),

---

*Calkins' protozoological textbook was the first of its kind published in the English language. Greatly revised, it appeared twice later (Calkins, 1926, 1933).

†Doflein's textbook heavily emphasized parasitological aspects of protozoology but rapidly became an authoritiative model in the field. Six editions have spanned the period covering the first half of the present century (Doflein, 1901, 1909, 1911, 1916; Doflein and Reichenow, 1927–1929, 1949–1953). Doflein himself passed away in 1924, but Reichenow has carried on the tradition. [*N.B.* While this book was in preparation, Reichenow passed away, in March, 1960.]

‡The reader's attention is directed to this precise, yet often neglected, piece of cytological work. Maier made accurate observations of ciliary and infraciliary structures the presence of some of which has been confirmed only in very recent years with such techniques as silver impregnation and electron microscopy!

---

principally from precise comparative studies of scores of species treated with the nearly indispensable silver techniques. *Upper right:* JÓZSEF VON GELEI (1885–1952), producer of many important works on the cytology, ecology, and taxonomy of ciliates. Von Gelei also was responsible for development of a number of refined techniques, including modifications of Klein's " dry " silver method.

Lower left: ÉDOUARD CHATTON (1883–1947), tireless investigator of many major protozoological problems and responsible for establishment of the independence of a number of ciliate groups at the ordinal–subordinal level. Chatton's contributions in both technical and conceptual areas also were of great significance. *Lower right:* ANDRÉ LWOFF (1902–   ), co-author with É. Chatton of major systematic monographs and important hypotheses of outstanding theoretical value. For many years his *patron*'s closest associate, Lwoff also helped develop the invaluable Chatton–Lwoff silver impregnation technique, a refinement of the original Klein method.

Morgan (1901), Neresheimer (1903), Nirenstein (1905), Pearl (1907), Popoff (1909a), Powers and Mitchell (1910), Prandtl (1906), Roux (1901), Schröder (1906), Schuberg (1905), Simpson (1901), Statkewitsch (1904–1907), Stevens (1903b), Thon (1905), Wallengren (1900, 1902), Woodruff (1905).

Period 1911–1920. André (1912), Anigstein (1912, 1913), Behrend (1916), Bresslau (1919), von Buddenbrock (1920), Calkins (1911a,b, 1912), Conn and Edmondson (1918), da Cunha (1914b,c, 1919), Dehorne (1920), Dobell (1911)*, Edmondson (1920), Fermor (1913), Goodey (1913), Hamburger and von Buddenbrock (1911, 1913), Hance (1917), Hirsch (1914), Jennings (1920), Koltzoff (1912), Lauterborn (1916), Mast (1911), Minchin (1912†, 1915), Minkiewicz (1912, 1914), Peebles (1912), Penard (1914b, 1917, 1920), Plough (1916), Metalnikow (1912), A. Prenant (1913–1914), Root (1914), Rousseau (1912), Russo (1914), Savi (1915), Smith (1914), Vieweger (1912), Weber (1912), Woodruff (1911, 1912, 1913), Yocom (1918), Zweibaum (1912).

Period 1921–1930. Andrews (1921), Ball (1925, 1927), Becker and Hsiung (1929), Becker *et al.* (1930), Bělař (1926), Bhatia and Gulati (1927), Bhatia and Mullick (1930), Bishop (1923, 1927), Blättner (1926), Bogdanowicz (1930), Bozler (1924), Bresslau (1921b, 1922), Brodsky (1925), Bullington (1925), Calkins (1925, 1929, 1930a,b), Causey (1926), Chambers and Dawson (1925), Clark (1927), Cleveland (1927), da Cunha and Muniz (1927a, 1930), Darby (1929), Dawson and Mitchell (1929), De Morgan (1924), Diller (1928), Dogiel (1928), Enriques (1924), Finley (1930), Furssenko (1929), Glaser and Coria (1930), Gray (1928), Haye (1930), Hegner and Andrews (1930), Jennings (1929), Jollos (1921), Kalmus (1929), ten Kate (1927, 1928), Keiser (1921), Klee (1926), Koehler (1922, 1930), Krüger (1930), Landis (1925), Lepşi (1926c, 1929), Ludwig (1930), MacDougall (1925, 1928,

---

*It is in this trenchant essay on " principles of protistology " that Dobell, at the rather tender age of twenty-five, scathingly attacked the cell theory and its supporters and formulated his celebrated acellularity hypothesis, a notion still popular among some biologists (see Corliss, 1957c).

†Minchin's textbook deserves special mention because of its value, in spite of its age, as a source of original information still of applicable pertinence in many areas of protozoology.

1929a,b), Mansfeld (1923), Michelson (1928), Moore (1924a,b), Mudrezowa-Wyss (1929), Nadler (1929), Nassonov (1924), Noble (1929), Noland (1927), Ostroumow (1929), Percy (1929), Pertzewa (1929), Peschkoff (1929), Peschkowsky (1927, 1929), Philpott (1930), Pringsheim (1928), Rees (1922), Rhumbler (1925), Robertson (1927), Sassuchin (1928), Sauerbrey (1928), Schmähl (1926), Schmidt (1921), Schoenichen (1927)*, Shapiro (1927), Stolte (1922, 1924), Studitsky (1930), Swarczewsky (1929), Tannreuther (1926), Taylor (1923, 1928), Taylor and Farber (1924), Visscher (1923, 1926, 1927), Wang (1925), Weatherby (1929), Wenrich (1926, 1928a, 1929b,c), Wermel (1928), Wetzel (1925), Woodruff (1921b), Woodruff and Spencer (1922, 1924), D. B. Young (1922), Zick (1928), Zinger (1929).

Period 1931–1940. Adolph (1931), Artigas and Unti (1938), Baumeister (1932), Beers (1933, 1937, 1938a,b), Bretschneider (1934), Brown *et al.* (1933), Calkins (1934), Child (1934), Cohen (1934), Cosmovici (1933), Dawson and Hewitt (1931), Deflandre (1938), De Garis (1935), Diller (1940), Frisch (1939), Giese (1938), Giese and Alden (1938), Hall and Alvey (1933), Hayes (1938), Hetherington (1933), Horváth (1936b), Ivanić (1933a,b, 1938), Jennings (1931), Jollos (1934), Kalmus (1931), King and Beams (1937, 1941), Krüger (1934), Kudo (1931)†, Lepşi (1932), Losina-Losinsky (1931), Lund (1933) Luyet and Gehenio (1935), MacDougall (1931, 1935), MacLennan (1939), MacLennan and Connell (1931), Merton (1935), Moore (1934), Müller (1932), Noble (1940), Penard (1938)‡, Peschkowsky (1931), Pestel (1932), Philpott (1932), Pratt (1935), M. Prenant (1935), Rammelmeyer

*An interesting treatise completely neglected by subsequent workers, probably because it has been thoroughly overshadowed by Kahl's publications which appeared at about the same time.

†This is the first edition of a well-known, authoritative, and widely used American textbook of protozoology (later editions: Kudo, 1939, 1946, 1954). A fifth edition is now in preparation (personal communication from Dr. Kudo).

‡One of the last papers by Penard, a Swiss investigator with remarkable eyesight who made many important protozoological contributions, particularly in his studies on rhizopods and ciliates from Lake Geneva, during the 98 years of his very active life (see Corliss, 1956c, and Deflandre, 1958).

(1931), Rees (1931), Reynolds (1932), Rose (1936), D. Sokoloff (1931), Stranghöner (1932), Summers and Hughes (1940), Summers and Kidder (1936), Taylor *et al.* (1933), Tchang-Tso-Run (1931), Tittler (1938), Turner (1933), Wang (1940), Wang and Nie (1933, 1935), Worley (1933, 1934), Yocom (1934), D. Young (1939).

Recent Books and Review Papers

One is particularly indebted today, in face of the sometimes nearly overwhelming mass of original papers in the literature, to current textbooks and similar recent compendia, including comprehensive review papers, which serve as invaluable sources of consolidated information on both the general and the specific biology and bionomics of ciliated (as well as other) protozoa. An abbreviated list of such helpful works should include at least the following:

Beale (1954), an up-to-date treatment of the genetics of *Paramecium;* Bhatia (1936), a thorough book, with an extensive bibliography, on the ciliates of India; Brachet (1957) and De Robertis *et al.* (1960), modern treatises on cytology with scattered references to ciliates: the classic in cytology remains Wilson's (1928) " The Cell "; Calkins and Summers (1941), a weighty volume containing excellent chapters by a score of the leading American protozoologists of the time*; Canella (1957), a review of the biology of suctorians with some 800 references to ciliate literature; Carter (1951), third edition of an excellent general zoology of the invertebrates with emphasis on physiological considerations; Copeland (1956), a novel, well-documented, but certainly controversial, treatment of the systematics of all " lower " organisms; Corliss (1954a), a review of the literature on *Tetrahymena* with direct and full citation of nearly 300 papers; Corliss (1956a), a treatment of some of the major hypotheses related to problems of ciliate evolution, phylogeny, and systematics; Corliss (1957a), a detailed consideration of the nomenclatural history of higher ciliate taxa;

---

*Of the twenty chapters eighteen are concerned in large part with the physiology, cytology, morphogenesis, symbiosis, sexuality, or life cycles of ciliates; five of these have been specifically cited elsewhere in the present book: Kirby (1941a,b), Summers (1941), Taylor (1941), and Turner (1941). No chapter is devoted to problems of systematics. Nine of the twenty contributors are now no longer living.

Corliss (1959b), an illustrated key to the ordinal groups of ciliates, with modern definitions of terminology employed; Corliss (1960a), a review of the involvement of ciliates in their rather uncommon (considering the entire subphylum) exhibition of the phenomenon of facultative parasitism.

Doflein and Reichenow (1949–1953), the most recent edition of the established leader in the field of protozoological textbooks; Dogiel (1951), first protozoological textbook in Russian; Dragesco (1960), a 356-page monograph on the systematics, comparative morphology, and ecology of sand-dwelling ciliates, including accounts of over 250 species, half of which are described as new, belonging to some seven orders; Ehret and Powers (1959), a short but helpful review paper concerned with the exact nature and organization of pellicular and subpellicular structures in *Paramecium;* Fauré-Fremiet (1953a), a brief review work packed with original ideas particularly pertinent to the main theme of the present book; Grell (1956), a book which favors experimental and cytogenetic aspects of modern protozoology; Grimstone (1961), a significant and most timely critical review of studies on ultrastructure and morphogenesis in protozoa; Hall (1953), a thorough textbook very rich in bibliographical references, with detailed taxonomic considerations limited, in the Bütschlian style, to familial and suprafamilial levels; Hanson (1958), a provocative well-documented discussion, and extension, of the Hadži (1953) hypothesis of the origin of Eumetazoa from ciliophoran-like protozoa; Hawes (1961), a refreshing and very much up-to-date consideration of the ciliates as a group; Hutner (1961), Hutner and Lwoff (1955), and Lwoff (1951), a timely set of volumes on the biochemistry and physiology of protozoa with sections by experts in selected fields; Hyman (1940), brought up to date in a " retrospect " chapter of Hyman (1959), a well-considered general treatment of the biology of protozoa; Jahn and Jahn (1949), a handy illustrated guide to the most common species of protozoa; Jírovec *et al.* (1953), first protozoological textbook in Czechoslovakian, rich in references to work published in Slavic languages; Kerkut (1958), an invaluable invertebrate textbook brought up to date.

Kudo (1954), 4th edition of the standard American textbook of protozoology, an excellent source of references and a book unusually rich in descriptions and figures of individual species; Manwell (1961), a new introductory textbook of protozoology with some different approaches to the subject; Noland (1959), the ciliate part of the long-awaited revision of the popular "Ward and Whipple" volume on fresh-water biology; Pennak (1953), another fresh-water biology book with good coverage of the protozoa; Picken (1960), a discussion of cellular organization in macro-molecular terms, with inclusion of up-to-date references to ultrastructural work on ciliates; Robertson (1958), a brief considera-tion of modern trends in protozoology by an experienced person well qualified to make such a review; Sonneborn (1957), an elegant consideration of the species problem in protozoa; Tartar (1961), a most thorough compilation and analytical review of the biology of the experimentally popular genus *Stentor;* Wenrich (1954), the most recent well-documented review of sexuality in protozoa, with excellent information on ciliates in several chapters; Wichterman (1953), a work primarily restricted to the genus *Paramecium* but containing, among its 2,000 references, citation of a considerable number of research papers concerned with other ciliates as well.

REFERENCES*

ADAM, K. M. G. (1951, 1953) [Please see p. 287]

ADOLPH, E. F. (1931) The Regulation of Size as Illustrated in Unicellular Organisms. Thomas, Springfield, Illinois. 233 pp.

ALBACH, R. A. and J. O. CORLISS (1959) Regeneration in *Tetrahymena pyriformis*. *Trans. Amer. micr. Soc.*, 78: 276–284.

ALFERT, M. and W. BALAMUTH (1957) Differential micronuclear polyteny in a population of the ciliate *Tetrahymena pyriformis*. *Chromosoma*, 8: 371–379.

ALFERT, M. and N. O. GOLDSTEIN (1955) Cytochemical properties of nucleoproteins in *Tetrahymena pyriformis;* a difference in protein composition between macro- and micronuclei. *J. exp. Zool.*, 130: 403–421.

ALLEN, S. L. and D. L. NANNEY (1958) An analysis of nuclear differentiation in the selfers of *Tetrahymena*. *Amer. Nat.*, 92: 139–160.

ALLMAN, G. J. (1855) On the occurrence among the infusoria of peculiar organs resembling thread-cells. *Quart. J. micr. Sci.*, 3: 177–179.

ANDRÉ, É. (1912) Catalogue des Invertébrés de la Suisse. Infusoires. Fasc. 6, pp. 1–228. Mus. Hist. nat. Genève, Georg et Cie., Genève.

ANDREWS, E. A. (1914) The bottle-animalcule, *Folliculina:* oecological notes. *Biol. Bull.*, 26: 262–285.

———— (1921) American folliculinas: taxonomic notes. *Amer. Nat.*, 55: 347–367.

———— (1923) *Folliculina:* case making, anatomy and transformation. *J. Morph.*, 38: 207–277.

———— (1945) Stentor's anchoring organs. *J. Morph.*, 77: 219–232.

———— (1946) Ingestion organs in folliculinids and in stentors. *J. Morph.*, 79: 419–444.

———— (1953) *Valletofolliculina bicornis*, a unique new genus and species of folliculinid (Ciliata: Heterotricha) from California. *J. Wash. Acad. Sci.*, 43: 189–194.

———— (1955) More folliculinids (Ciliata: Heterotricha) from British Columbia. *J. Fish. Res. Bd. Canada*, 12: 143–146.

ANIGSTEIN, L. (1912) Über zwei neue marine Ciliaten. *Arch. Protistenk.*, 24: 127–141.

*With few exceptions, titles of journals are given in accordance with the abbreviations found in the 3rd edition of the *World List of Scientific Periodicals*, published by Butterworths, London, and Academic Press, New York, in 1952. Also practically without exception, all works cited here have been examined first-hand in order that dates, titles, names of journals or books, and complete pagination could be given with accuracy.

———— (1913) Über *Strombidium testaceum* nov. spec. eine marine oligotriche Ciliate. *Arch. Protistenk.*, 32: 79–110.

APPLEBY, J. C., EADIE, J. M., and A. E. OXFORD (1956) Interrelationships between ciliate protozoa and bacteria in the sheep's rumen. *J. appl. Bact.*, 19: 166–172.

ARTIGAS, P. DE T. and O. UNTI (1938) Novo ciliado encontrado no escarro humano: *Prototravassosia costai* g. n., sp. n. (Ciliata). *Livr. jub. Travassos*, Rio de Janeiro, 1938, pp. 47–50. [In Portuguese with English summary]

AUERBACH, E. (1953) A study of *Balantidium coli* Stein 1863, in relation to cytology and behavior in culture. *J. Morph.*, 93: 405–445.

AWERINZEW, S. W. (1936) Zur Biologie des Infusors *Lagenophrys*. *Arch. Protistenk.*, 87: 131–141.

AX, P. and R. AX (1960) Experimentelle Untersuchungen über die Salzgehaltstoleranz von Ciliaten aus dem Brachwasser und Süsswasser. *Biol. Zbl.*, 79: 7–31.

BACQ, Z. M., MUGARD, H., and A. HERVE (1952) Infusoires, rayons X et cyanure. *Arch. int. Physiol.*, 60: 117–118.

BAKER, H. (1753) Employment for the Microscope. Dodsley, London. 442 pp.

BAKER, J. R. (1948) The status of the protozoa. *Nature*, 161: 548–551, 587–589.

BALAMUTH, W. (1940) Regeneration in protozoa: A problem of morphogenesis. *Quart. Rev. Biol.*, 15: 290–337.

———— (1941) Studies on the organization of ciliate protozoa. I. Microscopic anatomy of *Licnophora macfarlandi*. *J. Morph.*, 68: 241–277.

———— (1942) Studies on the organization of ciliate protozoa. II. Reorganization processes in *Licnophora macfarlandi* during binary fission and regeneration. *J. exp. Zool.*, 91: 15–43.

BALBIANI, É. G. (1861) Recherches sur les phénomènes sexuels des infusoires. *J. Physiol.* (Brown-Sequard), 4: 102–130; 194–220; 431–448; 465–520.

———— (1888) Recherches expérimentales sur la mérotomie chez les infusoires ciliés. Contribution à l'étude du rôle physiologique du noyau cellulaire. *Rec. zool. suisse*, 5: 1–72.

———— (1892–1893) Nouvelles recherches expérimentales sur la mérotomie des infusoires ciliés. I, II. *Ann. Microgr.*, 4: 369–407, 449–489; 5: 1–25, 49–84, 113–137.

———— (1895) Sur la structure et la division du noyau chez le *Spirochona gemmipara*. *Ann. Microgr.*, 7: 241–265, 289–312.

———— (1898) Études sur l'action des sels sur les infusoires. *Arch. Anat. micr.*, 2: 518–600.

BALECH, E. (1941) *Neobursaridium gigas* n. gen. n. sp. de ciliado heterotrico. *Physis, B. Aires*, 19: 29–35.

——— (1959) Tintinnoinea del Mediterraneo. *Trab. Inst. esp. Oceanogr.*, No. 28, pp. 1–88.

BALL, G. H. (1925) Studies on *Paramecium*. I. Experiments on the action of various endocrine substances, of liver, and of glycogen on the division rate of *Paramecium*. II. The behavior of a conjugating race of *Paramecium caudatum*. *Univ. Calif. Publ. Zool.*, 26: 353–383, 387–433.

——— (1927) Studies on *Paramecium*. III. The effects of vital dyes on *Paramecium caudatum*. *Biol. Bull.*, 52: 68–78.

BAMFORTH, S. S. (1958) Ecological studies on the planktonic protozoa of a small artificial pond. *Limnol. Oceanogr.*, 3: 398–412.

BANERJEE, S. K. (1958) Preliminary observations of some cytochemical tests on *Nyctotherus ovalis* Leidy (Ciliophora). *Arch. Protistenk.*, 102: 309–320.

BARBIER, M., FAURÉ-FREMIET, E., and E. LEDERER (1956) Sur les pigments du cilié *Stentor niger*. *C. R. Acad. Sci.*, *Paris*, 242: 2182–2184.

BARTHELMES, D. (1960) [Please see p. 287]

BARY, B. M. (1950a) Studies on the freshwater ciliates of New Zealand. Part I. A general morphology of *Bursaria truncatella* Müller. *Trans. roy. Soc. N. Z.*, 78: 301–323.

——— (1950b) Studies on the freshwater ciliates of New Zealand. Part II. An annotated list of species from the neighbourhood of Wellington. *Trans. roy. Soc. N. Z.*, 78: 311–323.

——— (1950c) Four new species of fresh-water ciliates from New Zealand. *Zool. Publ. Victoria Univ. Coll.*, 2: 1–19.

——— (1953) Sea-water discoloration by living organisms. *N. Z. J. Sci. Tech.*, 34: 393–407.

BARY, B. M. and R. G. STUCKEY (1950) An occurrence in Wellington Harbour of *Cyclotrichium meunieri* Powers, a ciliate causing red water, with some additions to its morphology. *Trans. roy. Soc. N. Z.*, 78: 86–92.

BAUMEISTER, W. (1932) Das Infusor *Tropidoatractus acuminatus* Levander. *Arch. Protistenk.*, 77: 360–378.

BEADLE, L. C. and J. R. NILSSON (1959) [Please see p. 287]

BEALE, G. H. (1954) The Genetics of *Paramecium aurelia*. Cambridge Univ. Press, Cambridge. 179 pp.

——— (1957) The antigen system of *Paramecium aurelia*. *Int. Rev. Cytol.*, 6: 1–23.

BEALE, G. H. and A. JURAND (1960) [Please see p. 287]

BECKER, E. R. and T. S. HSIUNG (1929) *Buxtonella sulcata* Jameson, 1926 (Protozoa, Ciliata): cysts and cyst formation. *Parasitology*, 21: 266–268.

BECKER, E. R., SCHULZ, J. A., and M. A. EMERSON (1930) Experiments on the physiological relationships between the stomach infusoria of ruminants and their hosts, with a bibliography. *Iowa St. Coll. J. Sci.*, 4: 215–251.

Becker, E. R. and M. Talbott (1927) The protozoan fauna of the rumen and reticulum of American cattle. *Iowa St. Coll. J. Sci.*, 1: 345–373.

Beers, C. D. (1933) The relation of density of population to rate of reproduction in the ciliates *Didinium nasutum* and *Stylonychia pustulata*. *Arch. Protistenk.*, 80: 36–64.

——— (1937) The viability of ten-year-old *Didinium* cysts (Infusoria). *Amer. Nat.*, 71: 521–525.

——— (1938a) *Hysterocineta eiseniae* n. sp., an endoparasitic ciliate from the earthworm *Eisenia lönnbergi*. *Arch. Protistenk.*, 91: 516–525.

——— (1938b) Structure and division in the astomatous ciliate *Metaradiophrya asymmetrica* n. sp. *J. Elisha Mitchell sci. Soc.*, 54: 111–125.

——— (1945) The excystment process in the ciliate *Didinium nasutum*. *J. Elisha Mitchell sci. Soc.*, 61: 264–275.

——— (1946a) *Tillina magna:* micronuclear number, encystment and vitality in diverse clones; capabilities of amicronucleate races. *Biol. Bull.*, 91: 256–271.

——— (1946b) Excystment in *Didinium nasutum*, with special reference to the role of bacteria. *J. exp. Zool.*, 103: 201–232.

——— (1946c) History of the nuclei of *Tillina magna* during division and encystment. *J. Morph.*, 78: 181–200.

——— (1947) The relation of density of population to encystment in *Didinium nasutum*. *J. Elisha Mitchell sci. Soc.*, 63: 141–154.

——— (1948a) Excystment in the ciliate *Bursaria truncatella*. *Biol. Bull.*, 94: 86–98.

——— (1948b) The ciliates of *Strongylocentrotus dröbachiensis:* Incidence, distribution in the host, and division. *Biol. Bull.*, 94: 99–112.

——— (1952) Observations on the ciliate *Bursaria ovata*, n. sp. *J. Elisha Mitchell sci. Soc.*, 68: 184–190.

——— (1954) *Plagiopyla minuta* and *Euplotes balteatus*, ciliates of the sea urchin *Strongylocentrotus dröbachiensis*. *J. Protozool.*, 1: 86–92.

——— (1959) Some observations on the autecology of the ciliate *Conchophthirus mytili*. *J. Elisha Mitchell sci. Soc.*, 75: 3–10.

Behrend, K. (1916) Zur Conjugation von *Loxocephalus*. *Arch. Protistenk.*, 37: 1–5.

Bělař, K. (1926) Der Formwechsel der Protistenkerne. *Ergbn. Fortschr. Zool.*, 6: 1–420. G. Fischer, Jena.

Belding, D. L. (1952) Textbook of Clinical Parasitology. 2nd ed. Appleton-Century-Crofts, New York. 1139 pp.

Berger, J. (1959) The comparative morphology of two species of *Cyclidium* (Ciliata: Hymenostomatida). (Abstr.) *J. Protozool.*, 6 (Suppl.): 13.

——— (1960) Holotrich ciliates entocommensal in the sea urchin *Strongylocentrotus echinoides* from San Juan County, Washington. *J. Parasit.*, 46: 164.

—— (1961a?) The morphology and systematic position of *Schizocaryum dogieli*, a ciliate entocommensal in strongylocentrotid echinoids (Ciliata: Trichostomatida). [In preparation]

—— (1961b,c?) [Please see p. 287]

BERGER, J. and J. C. THOMPSON, Jr. (1960) A redescription of *Cyclidium glaucoma* O.F.M., 1786 (Ciliata: Hymenostomatida), with particular attention to the buccal apparatus. *J. Protozool.*, 7: 256–262.

BERNSTEIN, T. (1931) Pelagic protists of the northwest part of the Kara Sea. *Trans. arct. Inst. Leningr.*, 3: 1–23. [In Russian with English summary]

BEYERSDORFER, K. and J. DRAGESCO (1952a) Microscopie électronique des trichocystes de *Frontonia*. *Rev. Opt.*, pp. 655–660.

—— (1952b) Étude comparative des trichocystes de sept espèces de paramécies. *Rev. Opt.*, pp. 661–671.

BHANDARY, A. V. (1959) Cytology of an Indian race of *Blepharisma undulans* (Stein). *J. Protozool.*, 6: 333–339.

—— (1960) Conjugation in *Blepharisma undulans americanum*. *J. Protozool.*, 7: 250–255.

BHATIA, B. L. (1936) Protozoa: Ciliophora. *In* SEWELL, R. B. S., editor, The Fauna of British India, including Ceylon and Burma, pp. 1–493. Taylor and Francis, London.

BHATIA, B. L. and A. N. GULATI (1927) On some parasitic ciliates from Indian frogs, toads, earthworms and cockroaches. *Arch. Protistenk.*, 57: 85–120.

BHATIA, B. L. and B. K. MULLICK (1930) On some fresh-water ciliates from Kashmir. *Arch. Protistenk.*, 72: 390–403.

BICK, H. (1958) Ökologische Untersuchungen an ciliaten Fallaubreicher Kleingewässer. *Arch. Hydrobiol.*, 54: 506–542.

—— (1960) Ökologische Untersuchungen an Ciliaten und anderen Organismen aus verunreinigten Gewässern. *Arch. Hydrobiol.*, 56: 378–394.

BICZÓK, F. (1957) Physiology of the cystment examined on the *Colpoda fastigata*. *Acta Biol. szeged.*, (N. S.) 3: 109–122.

BIEGEL, M. (1954) Beitrag zur Peritrichenfauna der Umgebung Erlangens. *Arch. Protistenk.*, 100: 153–182.

BINET, A. (1889) The Psychic Life of Micro-Organisms: a Study in Experimental Psychology. Open Court Pub. Co., Chicago. 120 pp. [A 2nd reprint edition appeared in 1910. Originally published in 1888, in French, by Octave Doin, Paris.]

BIOCCA, E. (1957) Alcune considerazioni sulla sistematica dei protozoi e sulla utilitè di creare una nuova classe di protozoi. *Rev. bras. Malariol.*, 8 (yr. 1956): 91–102. [In Italian with brief summaries in English, French and Portuguese]

—— (1958) Essai de classification de *Toxoplasma*, *Sarcocystis* et organismes voisins. *Česk. Parasit.*, 5: 37–44.

BISHOP, A. (1923) Some observations upon *Spirostomum ambiguum* (Ehrenberg). *Quart. J. micr. Sci.*, 67: 391–434.

——— (1926) Notes upon *Sieboldiellina planariarum* (Siebold), a ciliate parasite of *Planaria torva*. *Parasitology*, 18: 187–194.

——— (1927) The cytoplasmic structures of *Spirostomum ambiguum* (Ehrenberg). *Quart. J. micr. Sci.*, 71: 147–172.

BISHOP, E. L., Jr. (1943) Studies on the cytology of the hypotrichous infusoria. I. The relation of structure to regeneration. *J. Morph.*, 72: 441–472.

BLANCKART, S. (1957) Die Oberflächenstrukturen von *Paramecium* spec. und *Opalina ranarum*. *Z. wiss. Mikr.*, 63: 276–287.

BLÄTTNER, H. (1926) Beiträge zur Reizphysiologie von *Spirostomum ambiguum* Ehrenberg. *Arch. Protistenk.*, 53: 253–311.

BLOCHMANN, F. (1886) Die Mikroskopische Thierwelt des Süsswassers. *In* KIRCHNER, O. and F. BLOCHMANN, Die Mikroskopische Pflanzen- und Thierwelt des Süsswassers, Vol. II, pp. 1–122. Braunschweig.

BOCK, K. J. (1952 a,b, 1953) [Please see p. 287]

BOGDANOWICZ, A. (1930) Über die Konjugation von *Loxodes striatus* und *Loxodes rostrum*. *Zool. Anz.*, 87: 209–222.

BONNER, J. T. (1954) The development of cirri and bristles during binary fission in the ciliate *Euplotes eurystomus*. *J. Morph.*, 95: 95–108.

BORY DE ST. VINCENT, J. B. (1826) Essai d'une Classification des Animaux Microscopiques. Paris. 104 pp.

BOVEE, E. C. (1957) *Euplotes leticiensis*, n. sp., from the Letician drainage into the Amazon River. *J. Protozool.*, 4: 124–128.

——— (1960) [Please see p. 287]

BOZLER, E. (1924) Über die Morphologie der Ernährungsorganelle und die Physiologie der Nahrungsaufnahme bie *Paramaecium caudatum* Ehrb. *Arch. Protistenk.*, 49: 163–215.

BRACHET, J. (1957) Biochemical Cytology. Academic Press, New York. 516 pp.

BRADFIELD, J. R. G. (1955) Fibre patterns in animal flagella and cilia. *Symp. Soc. exp. Biol.*, 9: 306–334.

BRADLEY, J. C. (1957) Draft of the English text of the *International Code of Zoological Nomenclature* as amended by the Paris (1948) and Copenhagen (1953) Congresses. *Bull. zool. Nom.*, 14: 11–285.

BRAND, T. VON (1923) Die Enzystierung bei *Vorticella microstoma* und hypotrichen Infusorien. *Arch. Protistenk.*, 47: 59–100.

BRANDT, K. (1907) Die Tintinnodeen der Plankton-Expedition. System-atischer Teil. *Ergbn. Plankton-Exped. Humboldt-Stiflung.*, 3 L.a.: 1–488. [Atlas published in 1906].

BRESSLAU, E. (1919) *Systylis hoffi* n. gen. n. spec., eine neue Vorticellide. *Biol. Zbl.*, 39: 41–59.

——— (1921a) Die Gelatinierbarkeit des Protoplasmas als Grundlage eines Verfahrens zur Schnellanfertigung gefärbter Dauerpräparate von Infusorien. *Arch. Protistenk.*, 43: 467–480.

—— (1921b) Neue Versuche und Beobachtungen über die Hüllenbildung und Hüllsubstanz der Infusorien. *Verh. dtsch. zool. Ges.*, 26: 35–37.

—— (1922) Zur Systematik der Ciliatengattung *Colpidium*. *Zool. Anz.*, 55: 21–28.

BRETSCHNEIDER, L. H. (1934) Beiträge zur Strukturlehre der Ophryoscoleciden. II. *Arch. Protistenk.*, 82: 298–330.

—— (1950) Elektronemikroskopische Untersuchung einiger Ziliaten. *Mikroskopie*, 5: 257–269.

—— (1959) [Please see p. 287]

BRIDGMAN, A. J. (1948) Studies on some aspects of cystment in the ciliate *Tillina magna*. *J. exp. Zool.*, 108: 21–44.

—— (1957) Studies on dried cysts of *Tillina magna*. *J. Protozool.*, 4: 17–19.

BRIDGMAN, A. J. and R. F. KIMBALL (1954) The effects of X-rays on division rate and survival of *Tillina magna* and *Colpoda* sp. with an account of delayed death. *J. cell. comp. Physiol.*, 44: 431–445.

BRODSKY, A. (1908) Observations sur la structure intime de *Frontonia leucas* Ehrbg. *Rev. suisse Zool.*, 16: 75–130.

—— (1924) Die Trichocysten der Infusorien. *Arch. russes Protist.*, 3: 23–37.

—— (1925) Deux infusoires holotriches nouvelles du Turkestan. *Bull. Univ. Asie cent.*, 8: 40–44. [In Russian with French summary]

BROOK, A. J. (1952) Some observations on the feeding of protozoa on freshwater algae. *Hydrobiologia*, 4: 281–293.

BROUARDEL, J. (1951) Recherches sur la biologie d'un infusoire péritriche commensal des patelles: *Urceolaria patellae* (Cuénot). *Ann. Inst. océanogr.*, *Monaco*, 26: 115–254.

BROWN, E. M. (1951) [A new parasitic protozoan the causal organism of a white spot disease in marine fish . . . *Cryptocaryon irritans* gen. et sp. n.] *Agenda sci. Mtgs. zool. Soc. Lond.*, 1950, No. 11, pp. 1–2.

BROWN, M. G. (1939) The blocking of excystment reactions of *Colpoda duodenaria* by absence of oxygen. *Biol. Bull.*, 77: 382–390.

BROWN, M. G., LUCK, J. M., SHEETS, G., and C. V. TAYLOR (1933). The action of X-rays on *Euplotes taylori* and associated bacteria. *J. gen. Physiol.*, 16: 397–406.

BROWN, M. G. and C. V. TAYLOR (1938) The kinetics of excystment in *Colpoda duodenaria*. *J. gen. Physiol.*, 21: 475–500.

BRUMPT, E. (1949) Précis de Parasitologie. Vol. I. 6th ed. Masson et Cie, Paris. 1,042 pp.

BRUYNE, C. DE (1888) Contribution à l'étude de la vacuole pulsatile. *Bull. Acad. Belg. Cl. Sci.* (sér. 3), 15: 718–749.

BUDDENBROCK, W. VON (1920) Beobachtungen über einige neue oder wenig bekannte marine Infusorien. *Arch. Protistenk.*, 41: 341–364.

BUHSE, H. E., Jr. (1960) [Please see p. 287]

Buisson, J. (1923) Les infusoires ciliés du tube digestif de l'homme et des mammifères. *Trav. Lab. Parasit., Fac. Med., Paris*, pp. 1–201.

Bullington, W. E. (1925) A study of spiral movement in the ciliate infusoria. *Arch. Protistenk.*, 50: 219–274.

—— (1930) A further study of spiraling in the ciliate *Paramecium*, with a note on morphology and taxonomy. *J. exp. Zool.*, 56: 423–449.

—— (1939) A study of spiraling in the ciliate *Frontonia* with a review of the genus and a description of two new species. *Arch. Protistenk.*, 92: 10–66.

—— (1940) XIII. Some ciliates from Tortugas. *Pap. Tortugas Lab.*, 32: 179–221.

Bundle, A. (1895) Ciliate Infusorien im caecum des Pferdes. *Z. wiss. Zool.*, 60: 284–350.

Buonanni, F. (1691) Observationes circa Viventia, quae in rebus non viventibus reperiunter. Cum Micrographia curiosa. Herculis, Romae. 342 pp.

Burbanck, W. D. and J. D. Eisen (1960) The inadequacy of monobacterially-fed *Paramecium aurelia* as food for *Didinium nasutum*. *J. Protozool.*, 7: 201–206.

Bürger, O. (1905) Estudios sobre protozoos chilenos del agua dulce. *An. Univ. Chile*, 117: 403–449.

—— (1908) Nuevos estudios sobre protozoos chilenos del agua dulce. *An. Univ. Chile*, 122: 137–204.

Burt, R. L. (1940) Specific analysis of the genus *Colpoda* with special reference to the standardization of experimental material. *Trans. Amer. micr. Soc.*, 59: 414–432.

—— (1945) Narcosis and cell division in *Colpoda steinii*. *Biol. Bull.*, 88: 12–29.

Burt, R. L., Kidder, G. W., and C. L. Claff (1941) Nuclear reorganization in the family Colpodidae. *J. Morph.*, 69: 537–561.

Busch, W. (1930) Ueber marine *Strombidium*-Arten aus der antarktischen allgemein Ostströmung. *Abh. Mus. Nat. u. Heimatk. Magdeburg*, 6: 83–87.

—— (1948) Mitteilung von Beobachtungen an marinen Tintinnoinea. *Mitt. Mus. Naturk. Vorgesch. Magdeburg*, 1: 121–135.

Buschkiel, A. L. (1910) Beiträge zur Kenntnis des *Ichthyophthirius multifiliis* Fouquet. *Arch. Protistenk.*, 21: 61–102.

Bush, M. (1934) The morphology of *Haptophrya michiganensis* Woodhead, an astomatous ciliate from the intestinal tract of *Hemidactylium scutatum* (Schlegel). *Univ. Calif. Publ. Zool.*, 39: 251–276.

Bush, M. and C. A. Kofoid (1948) Ciliates from the Sierra Nevada bighorn, *Ovis canadensis sierrae* Grinnell. *Univ. Calif. Publ. Zool.*, 53: 237–261.

Bütschli, O. (1876) Studien über die ersten Entwicklungsvorgange der Eizelle, der Zellteilung und die Conjugation der Infusorien. *Abh. Senckenberg. naturforsch. Ges. Frankfurt*, 10: 1–250.

—— (1880–1882) Protozoa. Abt. I. Sarkodina und Sporozoa. *In* Bronn, H. G., Klassen und Ordnung des Thier-Reichs, Vol. I, pp. 1–616. C. F. Winter, Leipzig.

—— (1883–1887) Protozoa. Abt. II. Mastigophora. *In* Bronn, H. G., Klassen und Ordnung des Thier-Reichs, Vol. I, pp. 617–1097. C. F. Winter, Leipzig.

—— (1887–1889) Protozoa. Abt. III. Infusoria und System der Radiolaria. *In* Bronn, H. G., Klassen und Ordnung des Thiers-Reichs, Vol. I, pp. 1098–2035. C. F. Winter, Leipzig.

BUTZEL, H. M., Jr., BROWN, L. H., and W. B. MARTIN, Jr. (1960) Effects of detergents upon electromigration of *Paramecium aurelia*. *Physiol. Zoöl.*, 33: 39–41.

CALKINS, G. N. (1901a) The Protozoa. Macmillan, New York. 347 pp.

—— (1901b) Some protozoa of especial interest from Van Cortlandt Park, New York. *Amer. Nat.*, 35: 645–658.

—— (1902a) Marine protozoa from Woods Hole. *Bull. U.S. Fish Comm.*, year 1901, pp. 413–468.

—— (1902b) Studies on the life-history of protozoa. I. The life-cycle of *Paramoecium caudatum*. *Arch. EntwMech. Org.*, 15: 139–186.

—— (1911a) Regeneration and cell division in *Uronychia*. *J. exp. Zool.*, 10: 95–116.

—— (1911b) Effects produced by cutting *Paramecium* cells. *Biol. Bull.*, 21: 36–72.

—— (1912) The paedogamous conjugation of *Blepharisma undulans* St. *J. Morph.*, 23: 667–691.

—— (1919) *Uroleptus mobilis*, Engelm. I. History of the nuclei during division and conjugation. *J. exp. Zool.*, 27: 293–357.

—— (1925) *Uroleptus mobilis*. V. The history of a double organism. *J. exp. Zool.*, 41: 191–213.

—— (1926) The Biology of the Protozoa. 1st ed. Lea and Febiger, Philadelphia. 623 pp.

—— (1929) *Uroleptus halseyi*, n. sp. I. The effect of ultraviolet rays. *Biol. Bull.*, 57: 59–68.

—— (1930a) *Uroleptus halseyi* Calkins. II. The origin and fate of the macronuclear chromatin. *Arch. Protistenk.*, 69: 151–174.

—— (1930b) *Uroleptus Halseyi* Calkins, III. The kinetic elements and the micronucleus. *Arch. Protistenk.*, 72: 49–70.

—— (1933) The Biology of the Protozoa. 2nd ed. Lea and Febiger, Philadelphia. 607 pp.

—— (1934) Factors controlling longevity in protozoan protoplasm. *Biol. Bull.*, 67: 410–431.

CALKINS, G. N. and R. BOWLING (1928) Studies on *Dallasia frontata* Stokes. I. Polymorphism. *Biol. Bull.*, 55: 101–112.

—— (1929) Studies on *Dallasia frontata* Stokes. II. Cytology, gametogamy and conjugation. *Arch. Protistenk.*, 66: 11–32.

CALKINS, G. N. and S. W. CULL (1907) The conjugation of *Paramaecium aurelia (caudatum)*. *Arch. Protistenk.*, 10: 375–415.

CALKINS, G. N. and F. M. SUMMERS, editors (1941) Protozoa in Biological Research. Columbia Univ. Press, New York. 1,148 pp.

CAMERON, T. W. M. (1951) The Parasites of Domestic Animals. 2nd ed. Black, London. 420 pp.

—— (1956) Parasites and Parasitism. Methuen, London, Wiley and Sons, New York. 322 pp.

CAMPBELL, A. S. (1926) The cytology of *Tintinnopsis nucula* (Fol) Lachmann with an account of its neuromotor apparatus, division, and a new intranuclear parasite. *Univ. Calif. Publ. Zool.*, 29: 179–236.

—— (1927) Studies on the marine ciliate *Favella* (Jörgensen), with special regard to the neuromotor apparatus and its role in the formation of the lorica. *Univ. Calif. Publ. Zool.*, 29: 429–452.

—— (1942) The oceanic Tintinnoina of the plankton gathered during the last cruise of the Carnegie. *Publ. Carneg. Instn.*, No. 537, pp. 1–63.

—— (1954) Tintinnina. *In* Moore, R. C., Treatise on Invertebrate Paleontology, Part D, Protista 3, pp. 166–180. Univ. Kansas Press, Lawrence.

CANELLA, M. F. (1951a) Contributi alla conoscenza dei Ciliati.
  I. Gimnostomi dei generi *Holophrya*, *Amphileptus* e *Lionotus* predatori di *Carchesium polypinum* e di altri peritrichi fissi. *Ann. Univ. Ferrara* (N.S., Sect. III), 1: 1–80.

—— (1951b) Contributi alla conoscenza dei Ciliati. II. Osservazioni morfologiche, biologiche e sistematiche su *Paradileptus estensis* sp. n. e su altri Trachiliidae (Holotricha). *Ann. Univ. Ferrara* (N.S., Sect. III), 1: 81–170.

—— (1954) Ricerche sulla microfauna delle acque interne ferraresi. Introduzione allo studio dei ciliati e dei rotiferi. *Pub. Civ. Mus. St. Nat. Ferrara*, 4: 1–154.

—— (1957) Studi e ricerche sui tentaculiferi nel quadro della biologia generale. *Ann. Univ. Ferrara* (N.S., Sect. III), 1:259–716.

CARTER, G. S. (1951) A General Zoology of the Invertebrates. 3rd ed. Sidgwick and Jackson, London. 421 pp.

CAUSEY, D. (1926) Mitochondria in ciliates with especially reference to *Paramecium caudatum* Ehr. *Univ. Calif. Publ. Zool.*, 28: 231–250.

CÉPÈDE, C. (1910) Recherches sur les infusoires astomes. Anatomie, biologie, éthologie parasitaire, systématique. *Arch. Zool. exp. gén.* (sér. 5), 3: 341–609.

—— (1923) Note taxonomique sur les infusoires astomes (Haptophryidae Cépède nom. nov. pro Discophryidae Cépède 1910). *Bull. Soc. zool. Fr.*, 48: 105–108.

CHAMBERS, R. and J. A. DAWSON (1925) The structure of the undulating membrane in the ciliate *Blepharisma*. *Biol. Bull.*, 48: 240–242.

CHANDLER, A. C. and C. P. READ (1961) Introduction to Parasitology, with Special Reference to the Parasites of Man. 10th ed. Wiley and Sons, New York. 799 pp.

CHATTON, É. (1936) Les migrateurs horizontalement polarisés de certain péritriches. De leur signification. *Mém. Mus. Hist. nat. Belg.* (sér. 2), 3: 913–940.

—— (1938) Titres et Travaux Scientifiques (1906–1937). Impr. Sottano, Sète. 406 pp.

—— (1940) Sur une méthode rapide d'imprégnation à l'argent réduit par hydroquinone. *C. R. Soc. Biol., Paris,* 134: 229–232.

—— (1942) Le problème de la continuité du cinétome chez les hypotriches. Nouvelles recherches sur l'*Euplotes crassus. Bull. biol. France Belg.,* 76: 314–335.

CHATTON, É. and S. BRACHON (1935a) Discrimination, chez deux infusoires du genre *Glaucoma,* entre système argentophile et infraciliature. *C. R. Soc. Biol., Paris,* 118: 399–403.

—— (1935b) Les relations du chondriome avec l'infraciliature chez divers ciliés. Mitochondries ciliaires et parabasaux. *C. R. Soc. Biol., Paris,* 118: 958–962.

CHATTON, É. and M. CHATTON (1929a) Les conditions de la conjugaison du *Glaucoma scintillans* en cultures léthobactériennes. Action directe et spécifique de certains agents zygogènes. *C. R. Acad. Sci., Paris,* 188: 1315–1317.

—— (1929b) L'état de jeûne, condition nécessaire, mais non suffisante de la conjugaison expérimentale de l'infusoire *Glaucoma scintillans. C. R. Acad. Sci., Paris,* 189: 59–62.

—— (1931) La conjugaison du *Paramoecium caudatum* déterminée expérimentalement par modification de la flore bactérienne associée. Races dites conjugantes et non conjugantes. *C. R. Acad. Sci., Paris,* 193: 206–208.

CHATTON, É. and A. LWOFF (1927) *Pottsia infusoriorum* n. g., n. sp., acinétien parasite des folliculines et des cothurnies. *Bull. Inst. océanogr. Monaco,* No. 489. 12 pp.

—— (1929) Contribution à l'étude de l'adaptation *Ellobiophrya donacis* Ch. et Lw., péritriche vivant sur les branchies de l'acéphale *Donax vittatus* da Costa. *Bull. biol. France Belg.,* 63: 321–349.

—— (1930) Imprégnation, par diffusion argentique, de l'infraciliature des ciliés marins et d'eau douce, après fixation cytologique et sans dessication. *C. R. Soc. Biol., Paris,* 104: 834–836.

—— (1931) La conception des ciliés apostomes (Foettingeriidés + Opalinopsidés). Preuves de sa validité. *C. R. Acad. Sci., Paris,* 193: 1483–1485.

—— (1935a) Les ciliés apostomes. I. Aperçu historique et général; étude monographique des genres et des espèces. *Arch. Zool. exp. gén.,* 77: 1–453.

—— (1935b) La constitution primitive de la strie ciliaire des infusoires. La desmodexie. *C. R. Soc. Biol., Paris*, 118: 1068–1072.

——— (1936a) Les Pilisuctoridae Ch. et Lw. Ciliés parasites des poils sécréteurs des crustacés édriophthalmes. Polarité, orientation, et desmodexie chez les infusoires. *Bull. biol. France Belg.*, 70: 86–144.

—— (1936b) Les remaniements et la continuité du cinétome au cours de la scission chez les thigmotriches ancistrumidés. *Arch. zool. exp. gén.*, 78 (*Notes et Rev.*): 84–91.

—— (1936c) Technique pour l'étude des protozoaires, spécialement de leurs structures superficielles (cinétome et argyrome). *Bull. Soc. franç. Micr.*, 5: 25–39.

——— (1939) Sur le suçoir des infusoires thigmotriches rhynchoidés (Hypocomidae et Sphenophryidae) et sa genèse. *C. R. Acad. Sci., Paris*, 209: 333–336.

—— (1949) Recherches sur les ciliés thigmotriches. I. *Arch. Zool. exp. gén.*, 86: 169–253.

—— (1950) Recherches sur les ciliés thigmotriches. II. *Arch. Zool. exp. gén.*, 86: 393–485.

CHATTON, É., LWOFF, A., and M. LWOFF (1931) La dualité figurée, substantielle et génétique, des corps basaux des cils chez les infusoires. Granule infraciliaire et corpuscule ciliaire. *C. R. Soc. Biol., Paris*, 107: 560–564.

CHATTON, É., LWOFF, A., LWOFF, M., and J. L. MONOD (1931a) La formation l'ébauche buccale postérieure chez les ciliés en division et ses relations de continuité topographique et génétique avec la bouche antérieure. *C. R. Soc. Biol., Paris*, 107: 540–544.

—— (1931b) Sur la topographie, la structure et la continuité génétique du système ciliaire de l'infusoire *Chilodon uncinatus*. *Bull. Soc. zool. Fr.*, 56: 367–374.

CHATTON, É., LWOFF, A., LWOFF, M., and L. TELLIER (1929) L'infraciliature et la continuité génétique des blépharoplastes chez l'acinétien *Podophrya fixa* O. F. Müller. *C. R. Soc. Biol., Paris*, 100: 1191–1196.

CHATTON, É. and C. PÉRARD (1921) Les Nicollellidae, infusoires intestinaux des gondis et des damans et le " cycle évolutif " des ciliés. *Bull. biol. France Belg.*, 55: 86–151.

CHATTON, É. and J. SÉGUÉLA (1936) Un hypotriche de la branchie de *Ciona intestinalis* L., intermédiaire entre les Euplotidae et les Aspidiscidae: *Euplotaspis cionaecola* n. g., n. sp. *Bull. Soc. zool. Fr.*, 61: 332–340.

—— (1940) La continuité génétique des formations ciliaires chez les ciliés hypotriches. Le cinétome et l'argyrome au cours de la division. *Bull. biol. France Belg.*, 74: 349–442.

CHATTON, É. and S. VILLENEUVE (1937a) La division de la bouche et la formation du péristome chez les péritriches (*Cyclochaeta astropectinis*, n. sp.). Leur continuité génétique immédiate. *C. R. Acad. Sci., Paris*, 204: 538–541.

—— (1937b) *Gregarella fabrearum* Chatton et Brachon, protiste parasite du cilié *Fabrea salina* Henneguy. La notion de dépolarisation chez les flagelles et la conception des apomastigines. *Arch. Zool. exp. gén.*, 78 (*Notes et Rev.*): 216–237.

CHEISSIN, E. (1930) Morphologische und systematische Studien über Astomata aus dem Baikalsee. *Arch. Protistenk.*, 70: 531–618.

CHEISSIN, E. M. and E. M. PICK-LEVONTIN (1946) [Introduction of various lines of *Balantidium coli* from man and pig into the intestine of a new host (the rat).] *Zool. Zh.*, 25: 219–224. [In Russian]

CHEN, T. T. (1951) Conjugation in *Paramecium bursaria*. IV. Nuclear behavior in conjugation between old and young clones. *J. Morph.*, 88: 293–359.

—— (1956) Varieties and mating types in *Paramecium bursaria*. II. Variety and mating types found in China. *J. exp. Zool.*, 132: 255–268.

CHILD, C. M. (1934) The differential reduction of methylene blue by *Paramecium* and some other ciliates. *Protoplasma*, 22: 377–394.

CHILD, F. M. (1959) The characterization of the cilia of *Tetrahymena pyriformis*. *Exp. Cell Res.*, 18: 258–267.

CHILD, F. M. and D. MAZIA (1956) A method for the isolation of the parts of ciliates. *Experientia*, 12: 161–162.

CHRISTENSEN, E. and A. C. GIESE (1956) Increased photoreversal of ultraviolet injury by flashing light. *J. gen. Physiol.*, 39: 513–526.

CLAFF, C. L., DEWEY, V. C., and G. W. KIDDER (1941) Feeding mechanisms and nutrition in three species of *Bresslaua*. *Biol. Bull.*, 81: 221–234.

CLAPARÈDE, É. (1867) Miscellanées zoologiques. VI. Sur les *Licnophora*, nouveau genre voisin de la famille des Urcéolariens. *Ann. Sci. nat.* (sér. 5, Zool.), 8: 30–34.

CLAPARÈDE, É. and J. LACHMANN (1858–1861). Études sur les infusoires et les rhizopodes. *Mém. Inst. nat. Genèvois*, 5: 1–260; 6: 261–482; 7: 1–291.

CLARK, A. M. (1946) The reactions of isolated parts of *Spirostomum*. *Aust. J. exp. Biol. med. Sci.*, 23: 317–322.

CLARK, H. (1927) A theoretical consideration of the action of X-rays on the protozoan *Colpidium colpoda*. *J. gen. Physiol.*, 10: 623–636.

CLEVELAND, L. R. (1927) The encystment of *Paramoecium* in the recta of frogs. *Science*, 66: 221–222.

—— (1949) The whole life cycle of chromosomes and their coiling systems. *Trans. Amer. phil. Soc.*, 39: 1–100.

COHEN, A. I. (1957) Electron microscopic observation of *Amoeba proteus* in growth and inanition. *J. biophys. biochem. Cytol.*, 3: 859–865.

COHEN, B. M. (1934) On the inheritance of body form and of certain other characteristics, in the conjugation of *Euplotes patella*. *Genetics*, 19: 40–61.

COHN, F. (1866) Neue Infusorien in Seeaquarium. *Z. wiss. Zool.*, 16: 253–302.

COLE, F. J. (1926) The History of Protozoology. Univ. London Press, London. 64 pp.

COLEMAN, G. S. (1960) The cultivation of sheep rumen oligotrich protozoa in vitro. *J. gen. Microbiol.*, 22: 555–563.

COLLIN, B. (1911) Étude monographique sur les acinétiens. I. Recherches expérimentales sur l'étendue des variations et les facteurs tératogènes. *Arch. Zool. exp. gén.*, 48: 421–497.

——— (1912) Étude monographique sur les acinétiens. II. Morphologie, physiologie, systématique. *Arch. Zool. exp. gén.*, 51: 1 457.

COLOM, G. (1948) Fossil tintinnids: loricated infusoria of the order Oligotricha. *J. Paleont.*, 22: 233–263.

COLWIN, L. H. (1944) Binary fission and conjugation in *Urceolaria synaptae*(?) type II (Protozoa, Ciliata) with special reference to the nuclear phenomena. *J. Morph.*, 75: 203–249.

CONN, H. W. (1905) A preliminary report on the protozoa of the fresh waters of Connecticut. *Bull. Conn. geol. nat. Hist. Survey*, No. 2, pp. 5–69.

CONN, H. W. and C. H. EDMONDSON (1918) Flagellate and ciliate protozoa (Mastigophora et Infusoria). *In* Ward, H. B. and G. C. Whipple, Fresh-Water Biology, pp. 238–300. Wiley and Sons, New York.

COPELAND, H. F. (1956) The Classification of Lower Organisms. Pacific Books, Palo Alto, California. 302 pp.

CORBETT, J. J. (1958) Factors influencing substrate utilization by *Tetrahymena pyriformis*. *Exp. Cell Res.*, 15: 512–521.

CORLISS, J. O. (1952a) Comparative studies on holotrichous ciliates in the *Colpidium–Glaucoma–Leucophrys–Tetrahymena* group. I. General considerations and history of strains in pure culture. *Trans. Amer. micr. Soc.*, 71: 159–184.

——— (1952b) Le cycle autogamique de *Tetrahymena rostrata*. *C. R. Acad. Sci.*, Paris, 235: 399–402.

——— (1952c) Characterization of the family Tetrahymenidae nov. fam. (Abstr.) *Proc. Soc. Protozool.*, 3: 4.

——— (1952d) Review of the genus *Tetrahymena*. (Abstr.) *Proc. Soc. Protozool.*, 3: 3.

——— (1953a) Comparative studies on holotrichous ciliates in the *Colpidium–Glaucoma–Leucophrys–Tetrahymena* group. II. Morphology, life cycles, and systematic status of strains in pure culture. *Parasitology*, 43: 49–87.

——— (1953b) Silver impregnation of ciliated protozoa by the Chatton-Lwoff technic. *Stain Tech.*, 28: 97–100.

——— (1953c) " Naturally-occurring " cases of homopolar doublets in *Tetrahymena pyriformis*. (Abstr.) *Proc. Soc. Protozool.*, 4: 4.

—— (1953d) Protozoa and systematics. *Yale sci. Mag.*, 28: 14–17, 36, 38, 40.

—— (1954a) The literature on *Tetrahymena*: its history, growth, and recent trends. *J. Protozool.*, 1: 156–169.

—— (1954b) The buccal apparatus and systematic status of *Glaucoma frontata* (" *Dallasia frontata* Stokes "). *J. Morph.*, 94: 199–220.

—— (1955a) The opalinid infusorians: flagellates or ciliates? *J. Protozool.*, 2: 107–114.

—— (1955b) Proposed uniformity in naming " mouth parts " in ciliates. (Abstr.) *J. Protozool*, 2 (Suppl.): 12.

—— (1956a) On the evolution and systematics of ciliated protozoa. *Syst. Zool.*, 5: 68–91, 121–140.

—— (1956b) Occurrence and study of autogamy in diverse strains of *Tetrahymena rostrata*. (Abstr.) *J. Protozool.*, 3 (Suppl.): 3.

—— (1956c) Eugène Penard [Obituary Notice]. *Proc. Linn. Soc. Lond.*, yr. 1953–1954, pts. 1–2, pp. 42–44.

—— (1957a) Nomenclatural history of the higher taxa in the subphylum Ciliophora. *Arch. Protistenk.*, 102: 113–146.

—— (1957b) *Tetrahymena paravorax* n. sp., the first caudal-ciliated member of the genus referable to the *vorax–patula* complex. (Abstr.) *J. Protozool.*, 4 (Suppl.): 13.

—— (1957c) Concerning the " cellularity " or acellularity of the protozoa. *Science*, 125: 988–989.

—— (1957d) The literature on *Tetrahymena*: 1954 through 1956. (Abstr.) *J. Protozool.*, 4 (Suppl.): 15–16.

—— (1958a) Proposed type genera for higher taxa within the subphylum Ciliophora (phylum Protozoa). *Bull. zool. Nom.*, 15: 520–522.

—— (1958b) Order/class names: Problems in the selection of type genera. *Bull. zool. Nom.*, 15: 1073–1079.

—— (1958c) Problems in selection of types for higher categories within the subphylum Ciliophora. (Abstr.) *J. Protozool.*, 5 (Suppl.): 17.

—— (1958d) The systematic position of *Pseudomicrothorax dubius*, ciliate with a unique combination of anatomical features. *J. Protozool.*, 5: 184–193.

—— (1958e) The phylogenetic significance of the genus *Pseudomicrothorax* in the evolution of holotrichous ciliates. *Acta biol. Acad. sci. hung.*, 8: 367–388.

—— (1959a) Some basic problems in the study of evolution of the ciliated protozoa. *Proc. XV int. Congr. Zool.*, London, 1958, pp. 179–182.

—— (1959b) An illustrated key to the higher groups of the ciliated protozoa, with definition of terms. *J. Protozool.*, 6: 265–281.

—— (1959c) Current composition of the genus *Tetrahymena* Furgason, 1940. (Abstr.) *J. Protozool.*, 6 (Suppl.): 24.

—— (1959d) *Glaucoma chattoni* n. sp., an experimental organism which has been confused with the type species of the genus, *G. scintillans* Ehrbg., 1830. (Abstr.) *J. Protozool.*, 6 (Suppl.): 24.

—— (1960a) *Tetrahymena chironomi* sp. nov., a ciliate from midge larvae, and the current status of facultative parasitism in the genus *Tetrahymena. Parasitology*, 50: 111–153.

—— (1960b) The problem of homonyms among generic names of ciliated protozoa, with proposal of several new names. *J. Protozool.*, 7: 269–278.

—— (1960c) Comments on the systematics and phylogeny of the protozoa. *Syst. Zool.*, 8 (yr. 1959): 169–190.

—— (1961a,b) [Please see p. 287]

CORLISS, J. O. and E. C. DOUGHERTY (1961?) An appeal for stabilization of certain names in the family Tetrahymenidae (Protozoa, Ciliophora), with special reference to the generic name *Tetrahymena* Furgason, 1940. [In final preparation for *Bull. zool. Nom.*]

CORLISS, J. O. and M. P. DYSART (1959) Some problems in approaching the study of senescence in *Tetrahymena rostrata.* (Abstr.) *J. Protozool.*, 6 (Suppl.): 24–25.

—— (1960) [Please see p. 287]

COSMOVICI, N. L. (1933) La nutrition et le rôle physiologique du vacuome chez les infusoires. La théorie canaliculaire du protoplasma. *Ann. sci. Univ. Jassy*, 17: 294–336.

COURTEY, B. and H. MUGARD (1958) Observations sur la régéneration et la division simultanées de *Paramaecium caudatum. Bull. biol. France Belg.*, 92: 210–232.

CRAWLEY, H. (1923) Evolution in the ciliate family, Ophryoscolecidae. *Proc. Acad. nat. Sci. Phil.*, 75: 393–412.

CUNHA, A. M. DA (1914a) Sobre os ciliados do estomago dos ruminantes domesticos do Brasil. *Mem. Inst. Osw. Cruz*, 6: 58–68. [In Portuguese and German]

—— (1914b) Contribuiçao para o conhecimento da fauna de protozoairos do Brazil. II. *Mem. Inst. Osw. Cruz*, 6: 169–179. [In Portuguese and German]

—— (1914c) Sobre os ciliados intestinaes dos mammiferos. *Mem. Inst. Osw. Cruz*, 6: 212–215. [In Portuguese and German]

—— (1917) Sobre os ciliados do tubo digestivo dos mammiferos. *Conf. Soc. sul-amer. Hyg., Buenos Aires*, 1916, pp. 383–390. [In Portuguese]

—— (1919) Sobre os ciliados intestinaes dos mammiferos. *Mem. Inst. Osw. Cruz*, 11: 1–9. [In Portuguese and French]

CUNHA, A. M. DA and G. DE FREITAS (1941) Ensaio monográfico da familia Cyathodiniidae. *Mem. Inst. Osw. Cruz*, 35: 457–494. [In Portuguese with English summary]

CUNHA, A. M. DA and J. MUNIZ (1925) Contribution to the knowledge of ciliata parasitic in mammalia of Brazil. *Sci. Med., Rio de J.*, 3: 732–747. [In Portuguese and English]

—— (1927a) Ciliés parasites de mammifères du Brésil. *C. R. Soc. Biol., Paris*, 97: 825–827.

—— (1927b) Nota solve o genero *Prototapirella, Tripalmaria* e *Tricaudalia. Bol. biol., Fac. Med., S. Paulo*, No. 6, pp. 40–42. [In Portuguese]

—— (1927c) Trois nouvelles espèces du genre *Cycloposthium. C. R. Soc. Biol., Paris*, 96: 494–495.

—— (1930) On the endomixis phenomenon in ciliata of the genus *Balantidium.* Observations concerning the encystment of these ciliata and description of a new parasitic species of *Macacus rhesus. Mem. Inst. Osw. Cruz*, 23: 189–235. [In Portuguese (pp. 189–212) and English (pp. 213–235)]

CURASSON, G. (1943) Traité de Protozoologie Vétérinaire et Comparée. Paris. Vols. I (445 pp.), II (330 pp.), III (493 pp.)

DADAY, E. VON (1887) Monographie der Familie der Tintinnodeen. *Mitt. Zool. Stat. Neapel*, 7: 473–591.

—— (1910) Die Süsswasser-Mikrofauna Deutsch-Ost-Afrikas. *Zoologica, Stuttgart*, 23: 1–314.

DAIN, L. (1930) Die Conjugation von *Cryptochilum echini* Maupas. *Arch. Protistenk.*, 70: 192–216.

DALE, H. H. (1901) Galvanotaxis and chemotaxis of ciliate infusoria. Part 1. *J. Physiol.*, 26: 291–361.

DANIELOVÁ, V. (1959) Faunistische Skizze der Gattung *Paramecium* aus der Tschechoslowakei. *Mém. Soc. zool. tchécosl.*, 23: 230–246. [In Czechoslovakian with German summary]

DARBY, H. H. (1929) The effect of the hydrogen ion concentration on the sequence of protozoan forms. *Arch. Protistenk.*, 65: 1–37.

DAS, S. M. (1953) Indian Folliculinidae (Ciliata, Heterotricha). *Ann. Mag. nat. Hist.*, 6: 235–240.

DASS, C. M. S. (1953a) Studies on the nuclear apparatus of peritrichous ciliates. Part I. The nuclear apparatus of *Epistylis articulata* (From.). *Proc. nat. Inst. Sci. India*, 19: 389–404.

—— (1953b) Evolution of sex in ciliate protozoa. *Bull. nat. Inst. Sci. India*, No. 7 (Symp. Organic Evol.), pp. 173–177.

—— (1954a) Studies on the nuclear apparatus of peritrichous ciliates. Part II. The nuclear apparatus of *Carchesium spectabile* Ehrbg. *Proc. nat. Inst. Sci. India*, 20: 174–186.

—— (1954b) Studies on the nuclear apparatus of peritrichous ciliates. III. The nuclear apparatus of *Epistylis* sp. *Proc. nat. Inst. Sci. India*, 20: 703–715.

P

DAVIS, H. S. (1942) A suctorian parasite of the smallmouth black bass, with remarks on other suctorian parasites of fishes. *Trans. Amer. micr. Soc.*, 61: 309–327.

—— (1947) Studies on protozoan parasites of fresh-water fishes. *Fishery Bull., U. S.*, 51: 1–29.

DAWSON, J. A. (1919) An experimental study of an amicronucleate *Oxytricha*. I. Study of the normal animal, with an account of cannibalism. *J. exp. Zool.*, 29: 473–514.

—— (1920) An experimental study of an amicronucleate *Oxytricha*. II. The formation of double animals or " twins." *J. exp. Zool.*, 30: 129–158.

DAWSON, J. A. and D. C. HEWITT (1931) The longevity of encysted colpodas. *Amer. Nat.*, 65: 181–186.

DAWSON, J. A. and W. H. MITCHELL (1929) The viability of certain infusorian cysts. *Amer. Nat.*, 63: 476–478.

DEBAISIEUX, P. (1957) Foettingeride à migration transcuticulaire. *Bull. Acad. Belg. Cl. Sci.* (sér. 5), 43: 98–105.

—— (1959) *Lagenophrys lunatus*, Ima. (Ciliate, péritriche). *Cellule*, 59: 359–383.

—— (1960) Ciliates apostomes parasites de palaemon. *Cellule*, 60: 331–352.

DEFLANDRE, G. (1938) Les corpuscules biréfringents des ciliés et des cryptomonadines. *Bull. Soc. franç. micr.*, 7: 110–129.

—— (1958) Eugène Penard (1855–1954). Correspondence et souvenirs. Bibliographie et bilan systématique de son oeuvre. *Hydrobiologia*, 10: 2–37.

DEFLANDRE, G. and J. DEUNFF (1957) Sur la présence de ciliés fossiles de la famille des Folliculinidae dans un silex du Gabon. *C. R. Acad. Sci., Paris*, 244: 3090–3093.

DE GARIS, C. F. (1935) Heritable effects of conjugation between free individuals and double monsters in diverse races of *Paramecium caudatum*. *J. exp. Zool.*, 71: 209–256.

DEHORNE, A. (1920) Contribution à l'étude comparée de l'appareil nucléaire des infusoires ciliés (*Paramecium caudatum* et *Colpidium truncatum*), des euglènes et des cyanophycées. *Arch. Zool. exp. gén.*, 60: 47–176.

DELAGE, Y. and E. HÉROUARD (1896) La Cellule et les Protozoaires. *Traité Zoologie Concrète*, Vol. I, pages 1–584. Schleicher Frères, Paris.

DELPHY, J. (1938) Études de morphologie et de physiologie sur la faune d'Arcachon. *Bull. Sta. biol. Arcachon*, 35: 49–75.

—— (1939) *Gruvelina* nov. gen. *longissima* nov. sp. et quelques autres protozoaires ciliés observés à Dinard. *Bull. Lab. mar. Dinard*, 20: 52–55.

DEMBOWSKA, W. (1938) Körperreorganisation von *Stylonychia mytilus* beim Hungern. *Arch. Protistenk.*, 91 : 89–105.

DE MORGAN, W. (1924) *Foettingeria actiniarum* (parasitic in anemones). *Quart. J. micr. Sci.*, 68 : 343–360.

—— (1925) Some marine ciliates living in the laboratory tanks at Plymouth, with a description of a new species, *Holophrya coronata*. *J. mar. biol. Ass. U. K.* (N.S.), 13 : 600–658.

—— (1926) Further observations on marine ciliates living in the laboratory tanks at Plymouth. *J. mar. biol. Ass. U. K.* (N.S.), 14 : 23–53.

DE ROBERTIS, E. D. P., NOWINSKI, W. W., and F. A. SAEZ (1960) General Cytology. 3rd ed. Saunders, Philadelphia. 571 pp.

DE TERRA, N. (1960a,b) [Please see p. 287]

DEVIDÉ, Z. (1951) Chromosomes in ciliates (Euciliata and Opalinidae). *Bull. int. Acad. yougosl. Sci.* (N.S.), 3 : 75–114.

DEVIDÉ, Z. and L. GEITLER (1947) Die Chromosomen der Ciliaten. *Chromosoma*, 3 : 110–136.

DEWEY, V. C., HEINRICH, M. R., and G. W. KIDDER (1957) Evidence for the absence of the urea cycle in *Tetrahymena*. *J. Protozool.*, 4 : 211–219.

DEWEY, V. C. and G. W. KIDDER (1958) Amino acid antagonisms in *Tetrahymena*. *Arch. Biochem. Biophys.*, 73 : 29–37.

—— (1960a) The influence of folic acid, threonine and glycine on serine synthesis in *Tetrahymena*. *J. gen. Microbiol.*, 22 : 72–78.

—— (1960b) Serine synthesis in *Tetrahymena* from non-amino acid sources; compounds derived from serine. *J. gen. Microbiol.*, 22 : 79–92.

DIERKS, K. (1926) Untersuchungen über die Morphologie und Physiologie des *Stentor coeruleus* mit besonderer Berücksichtigung seiner kontraktilen und konduktilen Elemente. *Arch. Protistenk.*, 54 : 1–91.

DIESING, K. M. (1866) Revision der Prothelminthen. Abtheilung: Amastigen. I. Amastigen ohne Peristom. *S. B. Akad. Wiss. Wien*, 52 : 505–579.

DILLER, W. F. (1928) Binary fission and endomixis in the *Trichodina* from tadpoles (Protozoa, Ciliata). *J. Morph.*, 46 : 521–561.

—— (1936) Nuclear reorganization processes in *Paramecium aurelia*, with descriptions of autogamy and "hemixis". *J. Morph.* 59 : 11–67.

—— (1940) Nuclear variation in *Paramecium caudatum*. *J. Morph.*, 66 : 605–633.

—— (1954) Autogamy in *Paramecium polycaryum*. *J. Protozool.*, 1 : 60–70.

—— (1958) Studies on conjugation in *Paramecium polycaryum*. *J. Protozool.*, 5 : 282–292.

DILLER, W. F. and P. R. EARL (1958) *Paramecium jenningsi*, n. sp. *J. Protozool.*, 5 : 155–158.

DIPPELL, R. V. (1954) A preliminary report on the chromosomal constitution of certain variety 4 races of *Paramecium aurelia. Proc. IX int. Congr. Genetics*, Bellagio, Italy, 1953, published in *Caryologia*, 6 (Suppl.): 1109–1111.

———— (1955) A temporary stain for *Paramecium* and other ciliate protozoa. *Stain Tech.*, 30: 69–71.

———— (1958) The fine structure of kappa in killer stock 51 of *Paramecium aurelia*. Preliminary observations. *J. biophys. biochem. Cytol.*, 4: 125–128.

DJORDJEVIC, M. S. (1959) Individual differences in *Paramecium. Proc. XV int. Congr. Zool.*, London, 1958, pp. 182–183.

DOBELL, C. (1911) The principles of protistology. *Arch. Protistenk.*, 23: 269–310.

———— (1932) Antony van Leeuwenhoek and his " Little Animals." Swets and Zeitlinger, Amsterdam. 435 pp.

———— (1951) In Memoriam. Otto Bütschli (1848–1920), " Architect of Protozoology." *Isis*, 42: 20–22.

DOBRZAŃSKA, J. (1959) The occurrence of ciliates of the genus *Tetrahymena* Furgason, 1940, in fresh-water mussels. *Bull. Acad. polon. Sci., sér. Sci. biol.*, 7: 377–382.

DOFLEIN, F. (1901) Die Protozoen als Parasiten und Krankheitserreger nach biologischen Gesichtspunkten dargestellt. G. Fischer, Jena. 274 pp. [Subsequently considered as the 1st edition of Doflein's, and then Doflein and Reichenow's, " Lehrbuch der Protozoenkunde "]

———— (1902) Das System der Protozoen. *Arch. Protistenk.*, 1: 169–192.

———— (1909) Lehrbuch der Protozoenkunde. Eine Darstellung der Naturgeschichte der Protozoen mit besonderer Berücksichtigung der parasitischen und pathogenen Formen. 2nd ed. G. Fischer, Jena. 914 pp.

———— (1911) Lehrbuch der Protozoenkunde . . . 3rd ed. G. Fischer, Jena. 1,043 pp.

———— (1916) Lehrbuch der Protozoenkunde . . . 4th ed. G. Fischer, Jena. 1,190 pp.

DOFLEIN, F. and E. REICHENOW (1927–1929) Lehrbuch der Protozoenkunde . . . 5th ed. G. Fischer, Jena. 1,262 pp.

———— (1949–1953) Lehrbuch der Protozoenkunde . . . 6th ed. G. Fischer, Jena. 1,214 pp.

DOGIEL, V. A. (1925) Die Geschlechtsprozesse bei Infusorien (speciell bei den Ophryoscoleciden), neue Tatsachen und theoretische Erwägungen. *Arch. Protistenk.*, 50: 283–442.

———— (1927) Monographie der Familie Ophryoscolecidae. I. *Arch. Protistenk.*, 59: 1–288.

———— (1928) Über die Conjugation von *Bütschlia parva. Arch. Protistenk.*, 62: 80–95.

—— (1929) Die sog. " Konkrementvacuole " der Infusorien als eine Statocyste betrachtet. *Arch. Protistenk.*, 68: 319–348.

—— (1932) Beschreibung einiger neurer Vertreter der Familie Ophryoscolecidae aus afrikanischer Antilopen nebst Revision der Infusorienfauna africanischer Wiederkäuer. *Arch. Protistenk.*, 77: 92–107.

—— (1934) Angaben über die Ophryoscolecidae des Wildschafes aus Kamtschatka, des Elches und des Yaks, nebts deren zoogeographischen Verwertung. *Arch. Protistenk.*, 82: 290–297.

—— (1946) Phylogeny of the family Ophryoscolecidae from a palaeontological and parasitological standpoint. *Zool. Zh.*, 25: 395–402.

—— (1951) [General Protistology.] Moscow. 603 pp. [In Russian]

DOGIEL, V. A. and T. FEDOROWA (1929) Ueber die Zahl der Infusorien im Wiederkäuermagen. *Zbl. Bakt. (I Abt. Orig.)*, 112: 135–142.

DONS, C. (1913–1914) *Folliculina*–Studien IV. Vorläufige Bemerkungen über die Systematik der Folliculiniden nebts Beschreibung neuer norwegischen Arten. *Tromsø Mus. Aarsh.*, yrs. 1912–1913, 35–36: 59–92.

—— (1928) Neue und wenig bekannte Protozoen. *K. Norske Vidensk. Selsk. Skr., Trondhjem*, yr. 1927, pp. 1–17.

—— (1948) On some marine sedentary protozoans from Tristan da Cunha. *Res. Norw. Scient. Exped. Tristan da Cunha*, 1937–1938, Oslo. No. 16, pp. 1–16.

DOWNS, L. E. (1952) Mating types in *Stylonychia putrina*. *Proc. Soc. exp. Biol. Med.*, 81: 605–607.

—— (1956) The breeding system in *Stylonychia putrina*. *Proc. Soc. exp. Biol. Med.*, 93: 586–587.

—— (1959) Mating types and their determination in *Stylonychia putrina*. *J. Protozool.*, 6: 285–292.

DRAGESCO, J. (1952) Sur la structure des trichocystes toxiques des infusoires holotriches gymnostomes. *Bull. Micr. appl.*, 2: 92–98.

—— (1954) Contribution à la connaissance d'un infusoire commensal de l'*Amphioxus: Frontonia branchiostomae* (Codreanu). *Vie et Milieux*, 4: 605–607.

—— (1958) Les Ciliés Mésopsammiques Littoraux (Systématique, Morphologie, Écologie). 300 pp. Doctoral Dissertation, Faculty of Sciences, Paris. [See Dragesco (1960), below]

—— (1959) Adaptations morphologiques des ciliés mésopsammiques. *Proc. XV int. Congr. Zool.*, London, 1958, pp. 332–334.

—— (1960) [Published form of Dragesco (1958). Please see p. 287]

DRAGESCO, J., BLANC-BRUDE, R., and Y. SKREB (1955) Morphologie et biologie d'un tentaculifère peu connu: *Heliophrya erhardi* (Rieder) Matthes. *Bull. Micr. appl.*, 5: 105–112.

DRAGESCO, J. and Y. GUILCHER (1950) Sur la structure et le fonctionnement des tentacules d'acinétiens. *Microscopie*, 2: 17–25.

DUCOFF, H. S. (1956) Radiation-induced fission block in synchronized cultures of *Tetrahymena pyriformis* W. *Exp. Cell Res.*, 11: 218–220.

DUJARDIN, F. (1838) Mémoire sur l'organisation des infusoires. *Ann. Sci. nat.* (sér. 2, Zool.), 10: 230–315.

—— (1841) Histoire Naturelle des Zoophytes. Infusoires. Paris. 678 pp.

DYSART, M. P. (1959) Macronuclear chromatin extrusion in the ciliate genus *Tetrahymena*. (Abstr.) *J. Protozool.*, 6 (Suppl.): 17–18.

—— (1960) [Please see p. 287]

DYSART, M. P. and J. O. CORLISS (1960) [Please see p. 287]

EBERHARD, E. F. (1858) Infusorienforschungen. Programm d. Realschule zu Coburg, pp. 21–50.

—— (1862) Zweite Abhandlung über die Infusorienwelt. Programm d. Realschule zu Coburg, pp. 1–26.

EDMONDSON, C. H. (1906) The protozoa of Iowa. *Proc. Davenport Acad. Sci.*, 11: 1–124.

—— (1920) Protozoa of Devil's Lake complex, North Dakota. *Trans. Amer. micr. Soc.*, 39: 167–198.

EGELHAAF, A. (1955) Cytologisch-entwicklungsphysiologische Untersuchungen zur Konjugation von *Paramecium bursaria* Focke. *Arch. Protistenk.*, 100: 447–514.

EHRENBERG, C. G. (1832a) Beiträge zur Kenntniss der Organisation der Infusorien und ihrer geographischen Verbreitung, besonders in Siberien. *Abh. Akad. Wiss. Berlin*, yr. 1830, pp. 1–88.

—— (1832b) Über die Entwicklung und Lebensdauer der Infusionsthiere; nebst ferneren Beiträgen zu einer Vegleichung ihrer organischen Systeme. *Abh. Akad. Wiss. Berlin*, yr. 1831, pp. 1–154.

—— (1835) Dritter Beiträgen zur Erkenntniss der grosser Organisation in der Richtung des kleinsten Raumes. *Abh. Akad. Wiss. Berlin*, yr. 1833, pp. 145–336.

—— (1838) Die Infusionsthierchen als Vollkommene Organismen. Leipzig. 612 pp. [Diagnoses given in Latin, French, and German]

—— (1840) Diagnosen von 274 neuen Infusorien. *Mber. Preuss. Akad. Wiss. Berlin*, pp. 197–219.

EHRET, C. F. (1953) An analysis of the role of electromagnetic radiations in the mating reaction of *Paramecium bursaria*. *Physiol. Zoöl.*, 26: 274–300.

—— (1958) Information content and biotopology of the cell in terms of cell organelles. *In* Yockey, H. P., Platzman, R. L., and H. Quastler, editors, Symposium on Information Theory in Biology, pp. 218–229. Pergamon Press, London.

—— (1959a) Induction of phase shift in cellular rhythmicity by far ultraviolet and its restoration by visible radiant energy. *In* Withrow, R. B., editor, Photoperiodism and Related Phenomena in Plants and Animals, pp. 541–550. AAAS Pub., Washington, D.C.

—— (1959b, 1960) [Please see p. 287]

EHRET, C. F. and E. L. POWERS (1955) Macronuclear and nucleolar development in *Paramecium bursaria. Exp. Cell Res.*, 9: 241–257.

—— (1957) The organization of gullet organelles in *Paramecium bursaria. J. Protozool.*, 4: 55–59.

—— (1959) The cell surface of *Paramecium. Int. Rev. Cytol.*, 8: 97–133.

EICHWALD, E. (1844–1852) Beitrag zur Infusorienkunde Russlands. *Bull. Soc. impér. nat. Moscou*, 17: 480–587, 653–706; 20: 285–366; 22: 400–548; 25: 388–536.

ELLIOTT, A. M. (1959a) A quarter century exploring *Tetrahymena. J. Protozool.*, 6: 1–7.

—— (1959b) Biology of *Tetrahymena. Ann. Rev. Microbiol.*, 13: 79–96.

ELLIOTT, A. M., ADDISON, M. A., and S. E. CAREY (1960) [Please see p. 287]

ELLIOTT, A. M. and G. M. CLARK (1957) Further cytological studies on haploid and diploid strains of *Tetrahymena pyriformis* with special reference to univalent spindles. *Cytologia*, 22: 355–359.

—— (1958a) Genetic studies of the pyridoxine mutant in variety two of *Tetrahymena pyriformis. J. Protozool.*, 5: 235–240.

—— (1958b) Genetic studies of the serine mutant in variety nine of *Tetrahymena pyriformis. J. Protozool.*, 5: 240–246.

ELLIOTT, A. M. and D. F. GRUCHY (1952) The occurrence of mating types in *Tetrahymena*. (Abstr.) *Biol. Bull.*, 103: 301.

ELLIOTT, A. M. and R. E. HAYES (1953) Mating types in *Tetrahymena. Biol. Bull.*, 105: 269–284.

ELLIOTT, A. M. and D. L. NANNEY (1952) Conjugation in *Tetrahymena. Science*, 116: 33–34.

ELLIS, J. (1769) Observations on a particular manner of increase in the animalcula of vegetable infusions. *Phil. Trans. roy. Soc.*, 59: 138–152.

ELLIS, J. M. (1937) The morphology, division, and conjugation of the salt-marsh ciliate *Fabrea salina* Henneguy. *Univ. Calif. Publ. Zool.*, 41: 343–388.

ENGELMANN, T. W. (1876) Ueber Entwicklung und Fortpflanzung der Infusorien. *Morph. Jb.*, 1: 573–635.

ENRIQUES, P. (1907) La coniugazione e il differenziamento sessuale negli infusorî. *Arch. Protistenk.*, 9: 195–296.

—— (1924) La Riproduzione nei Protozoi. Sonzogno, Milano. 210 pp.

ENTZ, G., Jr. (1909) Studien über Organisation und Biologie der Tintinniden. *Arch. Protistenk.*, 15: 93–226.

ENTZ, G., Sr. (1884) Ueber Infusorien des Golfes von Neapel. *Mitt. Zool. Stat. Neapel*, 5: 289–444.

—— (1892) Die elastischen und contractilen Elemente der Vorticellen. *Math. naturwiss. Ber. ung. Akad. Wiss.*, 10: 1–48.

EPSTEIN, H. (1926) Infektion des Nervensystems von Fischen durch Infusorien. *Arch. russes Protist.*, 5: 169–180. [In Russian with German summary]

EVANS, F. R. (1944) A study of nuclear reorganization in the ciliate *Woodruffia metabolica. J. Morph.*, 74: 101–129.

—— (1953) Reactions of *Paramecium multimicronucleatum* to suctorian toxin. *Trans. Amer. micr. Soc.*, 72: 171–174.

—— (1958) Competition for food between two carnivorous ciliates. *Trans. Amer. micr. Soc.*, 77: 390–395.

EVANS, F. R. and R. C. PENDLETON (1952) A study of radiophosphate uptake in *Paramecium multimicronucleatum. Biol. Bull.*, 103: 190–194.

FABRE-DOMERGUE, P. L. (1888a) Recherches anatomiques et physiologiques sur les infusoires ciliés. *Ann. Sci. nat.* (sér. 7, Zool.), 5: 1–140.

—— (1888b) Étude sur l'organisation des urcéolaires et sur quelques genres d'infusoires voisins de cette famille. *J. Anat. Physiol.*, 23: 214–260.

FANTHAM, H. B. and A. PORTER (1945) The microfauna, especially the protozoa, found in some Canadian mosses. *Proc. zool. Soc. Lond.*, 115: 97–174.

FAURÉ-FREMIET, E. (1904a) Note sur un groupe nouveau d'*Opercularia. Arch. Anat. micr.*, 7: 181–197.

—— (1904b) Sur le pédoncule de quelques vorticelles. *C. R. Acad. Sci., Paris*, 138: 994–997.

—— (1905) La structure de l'appareil fixateur chez les Vorticellidae. *Arch. Protistenk.*, 6: 207–226.

—— (1908) Le *Tintinnidium inquilinum. Arch. Protistenk.*, 11: 225–251.

—— (1909) L'*Ancystropodium Maupasi* (nov. gen. nov. sp.). *Arch. Protistenk.*, 13: 121–138.

—— (1910a) La fixation chez les infusoires ciliés. *Bull. sci. France Belg.*, 44: 27–50.

—— (1910b) Étude sur les mitochondries des protozoaires et des cellules sexuelles. *Arch. Anat. micr.*, 2: 457–648.

—— (1912) Études cytologiques sur quelques infusoires des marais salants du Croisic. *Arch. Anat. micr.*, 13: 401–479.

—— (1922) Le cycle de croissance des colonies de vorticellides. *Bull. biol. France Belg.*, 56: 427–453.

—— (1924) Contribution à la connaissance des infusoires planktoniques. *Bull. biol. France Belg.*, Suppl. No. 6, pp. 1–171.

—— (1925) La Cinétique du Développement. Presses Univ. France, Paris. 335 pp.

—— (1930) Growth and differentiation of the colonies of *Zoothamnium alternans* (Clap. and Lachm.). *Biol. Bull.*, 58: 28–51.

—— (1932) Division et morphogenèse chez *Folliculina ampulla* O. F. Müller. *Bull. biol. France Belg.*, 66: 78–110.

—— (1935) La famille des Philasteridae Kahl (Ciliata holotricha). *Bull. Soc. zool. Fr.*, 40: 127–143.

—— (1936) La famille des Folliculinidae (Infusoria Heterotricha). *Mém. Mus. Hist. nat. Belg.* (*sér.* 2), 3: 1129–1175.

—— (1943a) Étude biométrique de quelques trichodines. *Bull. Soc. zool. Fr.*, 68: 158–169.

—— (1943b) Commensalisme et adaptation chez un acinétien: *Erastophrya Chattoni*, n. gen., n. sp. *Bull. Soc. zool. Fr.*, 68: 145–147.

—— (1945a) Polymorphisme du *Monodinium vorax* nov. sp. *Bull. Soc. zool. Fr.*, 70: 69–79.

—— (1945b) Symétrie et polarité chez les ciliés bi- ou multicomposites. *Bull. biol. France Belg.*, 79: 106–150.

—— (1948a) Les mécanismes de la morphogenèse chez les ciliés. *Folia biotheor.*, 3: 25–58.

—— (1948b) Le rythme de marée du *Strombidium oculatum* Gruber. *Bull. biol. France Belg.*, 82: 3–23.

—— (1948c) Doublets homopolaires et régulation morphogénétique chez le cilié *Leucophrys patula*. *Arch. Anat. micr. Morph. exp.*, 37: 183–203.

—— (1948d) Croissance et morphogenèse des colonies de *Carchesium limneticum* Svec. *Ann. Acad. bras. Sci.*, 20: 103–115.

—— (1949a) Action du lithium sur la stomatogenèse chez les ciliés. *Belg.-Nederl. Cyto-embryol. Dagen.*, *Gent*, pp. 100–102.

—— (1949b) Morphologie comparée des ciliés holotriches Trichostomata et Hymenostomata. (Abstr.) *C. R. XIII Congr. int. Zool.*, Paris, 1948, pp. 215–216.

—— (1949c) The ecology of some infusorian communities of intertidal pools. *J. Anim. Ecol.*, 17: 127–130.

—— (1950a) Morphologie comparée et systématique des ciliés. *Bull. Soc. zool. Fr.*, 75: 109–122.

—— (1950b) Écologie des ciliés psammophiles littoraux. *Bull. biol. France Belg.*, 84: 35–75.

—— (1950c) Mécanismes de la morphogenèse chez quelques ciliés gymnostomes hypostomiens. *Arch. Anat. micr. Morph. exp.*, 39: 1–14.

—— (1950d) Morphologie comparée des ciliés holotriches trichostomes. *Ann. Acad. bras. Sci.*, 22: 257–261.

—— (1950e) Ecology of ciliate infusoria. *Endeavour*, 9: 183–187.

—— (1950f) Une nouvelle vorticellide libre, *Telotrochidium johanninae* n. sp. *Bull. Soc. zool. Fr.*, 75: 148–150.

—— (1951a) Associations infusoriennes à *Beggiatoa*. *Hydrobiologia*, 3: 65–71.

—— (1951b) Écologie des protistes littoraux. *Année biol.*, 27: 437–447.

——— (1951c) The marine sand-dwelling ciliates of Cape Cod. *Biol. Bull.*, 100: 59–70.

—— (1952a) Symbiontes bactériens des ciliés du genre *Euplotes*. *C. R. Acad. Sci., Paris*, 135: 402–403.

—— (1952b) La diversification structurale des ciliés. *Bull. Soc. zool. Fr.*, 77: 274–281.

—— (1953a) Morphology of protozoa. *Ann. Rev. Microbiol.*, 7: 1–18.

—— (1953b) L'hypothèse de la sénescence et les cycles de réorganisation nucléaire chez les ciliés. *Rev. suisse Zool.*, 60: 426–438.

—— (1953c) La bipartition énantiotrope chez les ciliés oligotriches. *Arch. Anat. micr. Morph. exp.*, 42: 209–225.

—— (1954a) Réorganisation du type endomixique chez les Loxodidae et chez les *Centrophorella*. *J. Protozool.*, 1: 20–27.

—— (1954b) Morphogenèse de bipartition chez *Urocentrum turbo* (cilié holotriche). *J. Embryol. exp. Morph.*, 2: 227–238.

—— (1954c) Les problèmes de la différenciation chez les protistes. *Bull. Soc. zool. Fr.*, 79: 311–329.

—— (1955) La position systématique du genre *Balantidium*. *J. Protozool.*, 2: 54–58.

—— (1956) La réorganisation macronucléaire chez les *Euplotes*. *Exp. Cell Res.*, 12: 135–144.

—— (1957a) Finer morphology of microorganisms. *Ann. Rev. Microbiol.*, 11: 1–6.

—— (1957b) Le macronucleus hétéromère de quelques ciliés. *J. Protozool.*, 4: 7–17.

—— (1957c) *Trichopus lachmanni*, n. sp.; structure et morphogenèse. *J. Protozool.*, 4: 145–150.

—— (1957d) Organismes, cellules, molécules. Le cas des infusoires ciliés. *Biol. Jaarb.*, 24: 47–55.

—— (1958a) Le cilié *Condylostoma tenuis* n. sp. et son algue symbiote. *Hydrobiologia*, 10: 43–48.

—— (1958b) Structure et ultrastructure des protistes. *Rev. Path. gén. Physiol. clin.*, 58: 265–279.

—— (1959a) Ultrastructure et differenciations protoplasmiques chez les Ciliata. *Proc. XV int. Congr. Zool.*, London, 1958, p. 475.

—— (1959b) La famille des Nassulidae (Ciliata gymnostomatida) et le genre *Nassulopsis* n. gen. *C. R. Acad. Sci., Paris*, 249: 1429–1433.

—— (1961?) La différenciation des structures buccales au cours de l'évolution des Ciliata. *K. Vlaam. Acad.* [In press]

FAURÉ-FREMIET, E. and M. GAUCHERY (1957) Concrétions minérales intracytoplasmiques chez les ciliés. *J. Protozool.*, 4: 96–109.

FAURÉ-FREMIET, E., GAUCHERY, M., and M. TUFFRAU (1954) Les processus d'enkystement chez *Euplotes muscicola* Kahl. *Bull. biol. France Belg.*, 88: 154–167.

FAURÉ-FREMIET, E. and Y. GUILCHER (1947) *Trochilioides filans*, n. sp., infusoire holotriche de la famille des Dysteriidae. *Bull. Soc. zool. Fr.*, 72: 106–112.

FAURÉ-FREMIET, E. and M. HAMARD (1944) Composition chimique du tégument chez *Coleps hirtus*. *Bull. biol. France Belg.*, 78: 136–142.

FAURÉ-FREMIET, E. and H. MUGARD (1946) Sur un infusoire holotriche histiophage, *Deltopylum rhabdoides* n. g., n. sp. *Bull. Soc. zool. Fr.*, 71: 161–164.

——— (1949a) Un infusoire apostome parasite d'un polychète; *Cyrtocaryum halosydnae*, n. gen., n. sp. *C. R. Acad. Sci.*, *Paris*, 228: 1753–1755.

——— (1949b) Le dimorphisme de *Espejoia mucicola*. *Hydrobiologia*, 1: 379–389.

FAURÉ-FREMIET, E. and C. ROUILLER (1958a) Réseau canaliculaire dans les myonèmes endoplasmiques de quelques ciliés. *C. R. Acad. Sci.*, *Paris*, 246: 2039–2042.

——— (1958b) Myonèmes et cinétodesmes chez les ciliés du genre *Stentor*. *Bull. Micr. appl.*, 8: 117–119.

——— (1959) Le cortex de la vacuole contractile et son ultrastructure chez les ciliés. *J. Protozool.*, 6: 29–37.

FAURÉ-FREMIET, E., ROUILLER, C., and M. GAUCHERY (1956a) Structure et origine du péduncule chez *Chilodochona*. *J. Protozool.*, 3: 188–193.

——— (1956b) Les structures myoïdes chez les ciliés. Étude au microscope électronique. *Arch. Anat. micr. Morph. exp.*, 45: 139–161.

——— (1956c) L'appareil squelettique et myoïde des urcéolaires; étude au microscope électronique. *Bull. Soc. zool. Fr.*, 81: 77–84.

—— (1957) La réorganisation macronucléaire chez les *Euplotes*. Étude au microscope électronique. *Exp. Cell Res.*, 12: 135–144.

FAURÉ-FREMIET, E., STOLKOWSKI, J., and J. DUCORNET (1948) Étude expérimentale de la calcification tégumentaire chez un infusoire cilié, *Coleps hirtus*. *Biochim. biophys. Acta*, 2: 668–673.

FAURÉ-FREMIET, E. and J. THAUREAUX (1944) Protéines de structure et cytosquelette chez les urcéolaires. *Bull. biol. France Belg.*, 78: 143–156.

FAURÉ-FREMIET, E. and M. TUFFRAU (1955) *Sonderia labiata*, n. sp., cilié trichostome psammobie. *Hydrobiologia*, 7: 210–218.

FAUST, E. C., RUSSELL, P. F., and D. R. LINCICOME (1957) Craig and Faust's Clinical Parasitology. 6th ed. Lea and Febiger, Philadelphia. 1,078 pp.

FERBER, K. E. and T. WINOGRADOWA-FEDOROWA (1929) Zählung und Teilungsquote der Infusorien im Pansen der Wiederkäuer. *Biol. Zbl.*, 49: 321–328.

FERMOR, X. (1913) Die Bedeutung der Encystierung bie *Stylonychia pustulata* Ehrbg. *Zool. Anz.*, 42: 380–384.

FERNÁNDEZ-GALIANO, D. (1949) Sobre el aparato neuromotor y otras estructuras protoplasmaticas de *Ophryoscolex purkinjei* Stein. *Trab. Inst. Ciênc. nat. Acosta (Biol.)*, *Madrid*, 2: 257–302.

——— (1955) El aparato neuromotor de *Eudiplodinium maggii* Fior. *Bol. Soc. esp. Hist. nat.*, 53: 53–70.

────── (1958) La infraciliación en *Polyplastron multivesiculatum* y su génesis durante la división del ciliado. *Bol. Soc. esp. Hist. nat.*, 56: 89–102.

────── (1959) La infraciliacion en *Cycloposthium edentatum* Strelkow. *Bol. Soc. esp. Hist. nat.*, 57: 139–150.

FINLEY, H. E. (1930) Toleration of fresh water protozoa to increased salinity. *Ecology*, 11: 337–347.

────── (1943) The conjugation of *Vorticella microstoma*. *Trans. Amer. micr. Soc.*, 62: 97– 121.

────── (1952) Sexual differentiation in peritrichous ciliates. *J. Morph.*, 91: 569–606.

────── (1955) Electron microscopical observations on *Spirostomum ambiguum*. *Ann. N. Y. Acad. Sci.*, 62: 229–246.

FINLEY, H. E., McLOUGHLIN, D., and D. M. HARRISON (1959) Non-axenic and axenic growth of *Vorticella microstoma*. *J. Protozool.*, 6: 201–205.

FINLEY, H. E. and H. B. WILLIAMS (1955) Chromatographic analysis of the asexual and sexual stages of a ciliate (*Vorticella microstoma*). *J. Protozool.*, 2: 13–18.

FJELD, P. (1955) On some marine psammobiotic ciliates from Drøbak (Norway). *Nytt Mag. Zool.*, 3: 5–65.

FOETTINGER, A. (1881) Recherches sur quelques infusoires nouveaux; parasites des céphalopodes. *Arch. Biol.*, *Paris*, 2: 344–378.

FRAIPONT, J. (1877–1878) Recherches sur les acinétiniens de la côte d'Ostende. *Bull. Acad. Belg. Cl. Sci.* (sér. 2), 44: 770–814; 45: 247–297, 475–516.

FRANKEL, J. (1960a, b) [Please see p. 287]

FRISCH, J. A. (1939) The experimental adaptation of *Paramecium* to sea water. *Arch. Protistenk.*, 93: 38–71.

FROMENTEL, E. DE (1874) Études sur les Microzoaires ou Infusoires Proprement Dits. Paris.

FROUD, J. (1949) Observations on hypotrichous ciliates: the genera *Stichotricha* and *Chaetospira*. *Quart. J. micr. Sci.*, 90: 141–158.

FURGASON, W. H. (1940) The significant cytostomal pattern of the " *Glaucoma-Colpidium* group," and a proposed new genus and species, *Tetrahymena geleii*. *Arch. Protistenk.*, 94: 224–266.

FURSSENKO, A. (1929) Lebenscyclus und Morphologie von *Zoothamnium arbuscula* Ehrenberg. (Infusoria Peritricha.) *Arch. Protistenk.*, 67: 376–500.

GAJEWSKAJA, N. (1933) Zur Oekologie, Morphologie und Systematik der Infusorien des Baikalsees. *Zoologica, Stuttgart*, 32: 1–298.

GALL, J. G. (1959) Macronuclear duplication in the ciliated protozoan *Euplotes*. *J. biophys. biochem. Cytol.*, 5: 295–308.

GANGULY, D. N. and S. K. BANERJEE (1956) A study of pH of the body of some parasitic ciliates and its effect on the host with a comment on the validity of Methyl green Pyronin stain (Brachet). *Arch. Protistenk.*, 101: 203–214.

GARNJOBST, L. (1928) Induced encystment and excystment in *Euplotes taylori*, sp. nov. *Physiol. Zoöl.*, 1: 561–575.

—— (1937) A comparative study of protoplasmic reorganization in two hypotrichous ciliates, *Stylonethes sterkii* and *Euplotes taylori*, with special reference to cystment. *Arch. Protistenk.*, 89: 317–381.

—— (1947) The effect of certain deficient media on resting cyst formation in *Colpoda duodenaria*. *Physiol. Zoöl.*, 20: 5–14.

GASSOVSKY, G. (1919) On the microfauna of the intestine of the horse. *Trav. Soc. Nat. St. Pétersb. (Leningr.)*, 49: 20–37, 65–69. [In Russian with English summary]

GAUSE, G. F. (1934) The Struggle for Existence. Williams and Wilkins, Baltimore. 163 pp.

—— (1941) The effect of natural selection in the acclimatization of *Euplotes* to different salinities of the medium. *J. exp. Zool.*, 87: 85–100.

GEIMAN, Q. M. (1931) Morphological variations in *Coleps octospinus*. *Trans. Amer. micr. Soc.*, 50: 136–143.

GELEI, G. VON (1937) Ein neues Fibrillensystem im Ectoplasma von *Paramecium;* zugleich ein Vergleich zwischen dem neuen und dem alten Gittersystem. *Arch. Protistenk.*, 89: 133–162.

—— (1939) Neuere Beiträge zum Bau und zu Funktion des Exkretionssystems vom *Paramecium*. *Arch Protistenk.*, 92: 384–400.

—— (1940) *Cinetochilum* und sein Neuronemensystem. *Arch. Protistenk.*, 94: 57–79.

GELEI, J. VON (1925) Ein neues Paramaecium aus der Umgebung von Szeged. *Paramaecium nephridiatum* n. sp. *Állatorv. Közl.*, 22: 121–159, 245–248. [In Hungarian with German summary]

—— (1927) Eine neue Osmium-Toluidinmethod für Protistenforschung. *Mikrokosmos*, 20: 97–103.

—— (1929) Ein neuer Typ der hypotrichen Infusorien aus der Umgebung von Szeged. *Spirofilum tisiae* n. sp., n. gen., n. fam. *Arch. Protistenk.*, 65: 165–182.

—— (1932a) Die reizleitenden Elemente der Ciliaten in nass hergestellten Silber- bzw. Goldpräparaten. *Arch. Protistenk.*, 77: 152–174.

—— (1932b) Beiträge zur Ciliatenfauna der Umgebung von Szeged. I. *Nassula tricirrata* nov. sp. *Acta Biol. szeged.*, 2: 162–164.

—— (1934a) Der feinere Bau des Cytopharynx von *Paramecium* und seine systematische Bedeutung. *Arch. Protistenk.*, 82: 331–362.

—— (1934b) Die Differenzierung der Cilienmeridiane der Ciliaten und der Begriff des Richtungsmeridians. *Math. Naturwiss. Anz. ung. Akad. Wiss.* [also: *Mat. Term. Ért.*], 51: 613–644. [In Hungarian with German summary]

——— (1934c) Der Cytopharynx der Paramecien. *Math. Naturwiss. Anz. ung. Akad. Wiss.*, 51: 717–750. [In Hungarian with German summary]

——— (1934d) Eine mikrotechnische Studie über die Färbung der subpelliculären Elemente der Ciliaten. *Z. wiss. Mikr.*, 51: 103–178.

——— (1935a) Das Exkretionsorgan der Protozoen, morphologisch, entwicklungsgeschichtlich und physiologisch betrachtet. *Mat. Term. Közl., Budapest*, 37: 1–128. [In Hungarian with German summary]

——— (1935b) Eine neue Abänderung der Klein'schen trockenen Silvermethode und das Silberliniensystem von *Glaucoma scintillans. Arch. Protistenk.*, 84: 446–455.

——— (1935c) Der Richtungsmeridian und die Neubildung des Mundes während und ausserhalb der Teilung bei den Ziliaten. *Biol. Zbl.*, 55: 436–445.

——— (1938a) Beiträge zur Ciliatenfauna der Umgebung von Szeged. VII. *Paramecium nephridiatum* (Gelei). *Arch. Protistenk.*, 91: 343–356.

——— (1938b) Vollkommene Sinneselemente bei den höheren Ciliaten. I. Studie über die Sinnesorganellen von *Euplotes*-Arten. *Math. Naturwiss. Anz. ung. Akad. Wiss.*, 57: 831–887.

——— (1938c) Über die biologische Bedeutung der Pulsationsblasen (Kontraktile Vacuole der Protisten). *Math. Naturwiss. Anz. ung. Akad. Wis.*, 57: 1037–1069. [In Hungarian with German summary]

——— (1939a) Das äussere Stützgerüstsystem des *Paramecium*körpers. *Arch. Protistenk.*, 92: 245–272.

——— (1939b) Vollkommene Sinneselemente bei den höheren Ciliaten. II. Studie über Sinnesorganellen von *Aspidisca*-Arten. Allgemeines. *Math. Naturwiss. Anz. ung. Akad. Wiss.*, 58: 474–518.

——— (1940) Körperbau und Erregungsleitung bei den Ciliaten. Eine Studie an *Loxocephalus* und einigen anderen Ciliaten. *Arch. Protistenk.*, 93: 273–316.

——— (1944) Sonderbare planktonische Hypotrichen in den temporären Gewässern. XII. Beitrag zur Ciliatenfauna Ungarns. *Muz. Fuz. Kolozsvár* (N. S.), 2: 137–157. [In Hungarian with German summary]

——— (1950a) Die Morphogenese der Einzeller mit Rucksicht auf die morphogenetischen Prinzipien von Sewertzoff. *Acta biol. Acad. sci. hung.*, 1: 69–134.

——— (1950b) Ein besonderer Ciliat: *Ophryoglena monophthalma* n. sp. XVI. Mitteilung über die ungarische Ciliatenwelt. *Ann. Biol. Univ. szeged.*, 1: 237–242. [In Hungarian with German summary]

——— (1950c) Die Marynidae der Sodagewässer in der Nähe von Szeged. XIV. Beitrag zur Ziliatenfauna Ungarns. *Hidrol. Közl.*, 30: 107–119, 157–158.

—— (1952) Einiges über die Systematik der Unterordnung Trichostomata der Ciliaten. *Ann. Biol. Univ. hung.*, 1: 351–360. [In Hungarian with German summary]

—— (1954) Über die Lebensgemeinschaft einiger temporärer Tümpel auf einer Bergwiese im Börzsöygebirge (Oberungarn). III. Ciliaten. *Acta. biol. Acad. sci. hung.*, 5: 259–343.

GELEI, J. VON and P. HORVÁTH (1931a) Eine nasse Silber-bzw. Goldmethode für die Herstellung der reizleitenden Elemente bei den Ciliaten. *Z. wiss. Mikr.*, 48: 9–29.

—— (1931b) Die Bewegungs- und Reizleitende Elemente bei *Glaucoma* und *Colpidium* bearbeitet mit der Sublimat-Silbermethode. *Arb. I. Abt. ung. biol. ForschInst.*, 4: 40–58.

GELEI, J. VON and M. SZABADOS (1950) Massenproduktion in einer städtischen Regenwasserpfütze. *Ann. Biol. Univ. szeged.*, 1: 249–294. [In Hungarian with Russian and German summaries]

GELLÉRT, J. (1955) Die Ciliaten des sich unter der Flechte *Paramelia saxatilis* Mass. gebildeten Humus. *Acta. biol. Acad. sci. hung.*, 6: 77–111.

—— (1956) Ciliaten des sich unter dem Moosrasen auf Felsen gebildeten Humus. *Acta. biol. Acad. sci. hung.*, 6: 337–359.

—— (1957) Ciliatenfauna im Humus einiger ungarischen Laub- und Nadelholzwälder. *Ann. Inst. Biol., Hung. Acad. Sci.*, 24: 11–34. [In Hungarian with German summary]

GELLÉRT, J. and M. MÜLLER (1954) Die wissenschaftlichen Arbeiten von József Gelei. *Acta biol. Acad. sci. hung.*, 5: 221–226.

GELLÉRT, J. and G. TAMÁS (1958) Ökologische Untersuchungen an Diatomeen und Ciliaten der Detritus-Drifte am Ostufer der Halbinsel Tihany. *Ann. Inst. Biol., Hung. Acad. Sci.*, 25: 217–240. [In Hungarian with German summary]

—— (1959) Ökologische Untersuchungen der Kieselalgen und Ciliaten der Detritus-Driften an dem Südufer der Halbinsel Tihany. *Ann. Inst. Biol., Hung. Acad. Sci.*, 26: 223–235. [In Hungarian with German summary]

GEORGÉVITCH, J. (1941a) [I. Study on Infusoria Astomata of the Ochrida Lake Oligochaeta.] *Ghlas Srpsk. kralj. Akad.*, 93: 1–99. [In Serbian].

—— (1941b) [Infusoria Astomata of Ochrida Lake Triclada.] *Ghlas Srpsk. kralj. Akad.*, 94: 149. [In Serbian]

—— (1950) Nouvelles recherches sur les infusoires astomes des oligochètes et des triclades du lac d'Ochrid. *Bull. Acad. serbe Sci. math. nat.* (N. S.), 1: 63–73.

GESNER, K. (1565) De Omne Rerum Fossilium Genere. Tiguri. 169 pp.

GIESE, A. C. (1938) Cannibalism and gigantism in *Blepharisma*. *Trans. Amer. micr. Soc.*, 57: 245–255.

—— (1953) Some properties of a photodynamic pigment from *Blepharisma*. *J. gen. Physiol.*, 37: 259–269.

—————— (1957) Mating types in *Paramecium multimicronucleatum*. *J. Protozool.*, 4: 120–124.

GIESE, A. C. and R. H. ALDEN (1938) Cannibalism and giant formation in *Stylonychia*. *J. exp. Zool.*, 78: 117–134.

GIESE, A. C. and M. LUSIGNAN (1960) Stimulation of postirradiation recovery of cells by cutting. *Science*, 132: 806–807.

GILMAN, L. C. (1941) Mating types in diverse races of *Paramecium caudatum*. *Biol. Bull.*, 80: 384–402.

—————— (1958) European varieties of *Paramecium caudatum*. (Abstr.) *J. Protozool.*, 5 (Suppl.): 17.

—————— (1959) Nuclear reorganization in *Paramecium caudatum*. (Abstr.) *J. Protozool.*, 6 (Suppl.): 19.

GLASER, R. W. and N. A. CORIA (1930) Methods for the pure culture of certain protozoa. *J. exp. Med.*, 51: 787–806.

GOLDSCHMIDT, R. B. (1956) Portraits from Memory: Recollections of a Zoologist. Univ. Washington Press, Seattle. 181 pp.

GOLDSMITH, W. M. (1922) The process of ingestion in the ciliate *Frontonia*. *J. exp. Zool.*, 36: 333–346.

GOLDSTEIN, L. (1958) Localization of nucleus-specific protein as shown by transplantation experiments in *Amoeba proteus*. *Exp. Cell Res.*, 15: 635–637.

GONDER, R. (1905) Beiträge zur Kenntnis der Kernverhältnisse bei den in Cephalopoden schmarotzenden Infusorien. *Arch. Protistenk.*, 5: 240–262.

GÖNNERT, R. (1935) Über Systematik, Morphologie, Entwicklungsgeschichte und Parasiten einiger Dendrosomidae nebst Beschreibung zweier neuer Suktorien. *Arch. Protistenk.*, 86: 113–154.

GOODEY, T. (1913) The excystation of *Colpoda cucullus* from its resting cysts, and the nature and properties of the cyst membrane. *Proc. Roy. Soc. London*, B 86: 427–439.

—————— (1915) Note on the remarkable retention of vitality by protozoa from old stored soils. *Ann. appl. Biol.*, 1: 395–399.

GOODRICH, J. P. and T. L. JAHN (1943) Epizoic suctoria (protozoa) from turtles. *Trans. Amer. micr. Soc.*, 62: 245–253.

GOURRET, P. and P. ROESER (1886) Les protozoaires du vieux-port de Marseille. *Arch. Zool. exp. gén.*, 4: 443–534.

—————— (1888) Contribution à l'étude des protozoaires de la Corse. *Arch. Biol., Paris*, 8: 139–204.

GRAAF, F. DE (1957) The microflora and fauna of a quaking bog in the nature reserve " Het Hol " near Kortenhoef in the Netherlands. *Hydrobiologia*, 9: 210–317.

GRANDORI, R. and L. GRANDORI (1934) Studi sui protozoi del terreno. *Boll. Lab. Zool. agr. Bachicolt. Milano*, 5: 1–339.

—————— (1935) Rettifiche di nomenclatura zoologica. *Boll. Lab. Zool. agr. Bachicolt. Milano*, 6: 3.

GRASSÉ, P. P., editor (1952) *Traité de Zoologie. Anatomie, Systématique, Biologie.* Vol. I, fasc. 1. Phylogénie. Protozoaires: Généralités, Flagellés. Pp. 1–1071. Masson et Cie, Paris.

—— (1953) *Traité de Zoologie. Anatomie, Systématique, Biologie.* Vol. I, fasc. 2. Protozoaires: Rhizopodes, Actinopodes, Sporozoaires, Cnidosporidies. Pp. 1–1160. Masson et Cie, Paris.

GRAY, E. (1952) The ecology of the ciliate fauna of Hobson's Brook, a Cambridgeshire chalk stream. *J. gen. Microbiol.*, 6: 108–122.

GRAY, J. (1928) Ciliary Movement. Macmillan, New York. 162 pp.

GREEFF, R. (1888) Land-Protozoen. *S. B. Ges. ges. Naturwiss. Marburg*, No. 3, pp. 90–158.

GRELL, K. G. (1949) Die Entwicklung der Makronucleusanlage im Exkonjuganten von *Ephelota gemmipara* R. Hertwig. *Biol. Zbl.*, 68: 289–312.

—— (1953a) Der Stand unserer Kenntnisse über den Bau der Protistenkerne. *Verh. dtsch. zool. Ges.*, yr. 1952, 89: 212–251.

—— (1953b) Die Struktur des Makronucleus von *Tokophrya*. *Arch. Protistenk.*, 98: 466–468.

—— (1956) Protozoologie. Springer, Berlin. 284 pp.

GRIEPENBURG, W. (1933) Die Protozoenfauna einiger westfälischer Höhlen. *S. B. Ges. naturforsch. Fr. Berl.*, yr. 1933, 1–3, pp. 78–92.

GRIFFIN, L. E. (1910) *Euplotes Worcesteri* sp. nov.: I. Structure. II. Division. *Philipp. J. Sci.*, D, 5: 291–312, 315–336.

GRIMSTONE, A. V. (1961) [Please see p. 287]

GRUBER, A. (1884) Die Protozoen des Hafens von Genua. *Nova Acta Leop. Carol.*, 46: 1–67.

GRUBY, D. and O. DELAFOND (1843) Recherches sur des animalcules se développant dans l'estomac et dans les intestins pendant la digestion des animaux herbivores et carnivores. *C. R. Acad. Sci., Paris*, 17: 1304–1308.

GRUCHY, D. F. (1955) The breeding system and distribution of *Tetrahymena pyriformis*. *J. Protozool.*, 2: 178–185.

GUILCHER, Y. (1948) Affinités structurales des bourgeons migrateurs d'infusoires acinétiens. *C. R. Acad. Sci., Paris*, 226: 958–960.

—— (1950) Morphogenèse et morphologie comparée chez les ciliés gemmipares: chonotriches et tentaculifères. *Ann. Biol., Paris*, 26: 465–478.

—— (1951) Contribution à l'étude des ciliés gemmipares, chonotriches et tentaculifères. *Ann. Sci. nat., Zool.* (sér. 11), 13: 33–132.

GUTIERREZ, J. (1958) Observations on bacterial feeding by the rumen ciliate *Isotricha prostoma*. *J. Protozool.*, 5: 122–126.

GUTIERREZ, J. and R. E. DAVIS (1959) Bacterial ingestion by the rumen ciliates *Entodinium* and *Diplodinium*. *J. Protozool.*, 6: 222–226.

GUTTES, E. and S. GUTTES (1959) Regulations of mitosis in *Stentor coeruleus*. *Science*, 129: 1483–1484.

—— (1960) [Please see p. 287]

Q

HAAS, G. (1933) Beiträge zur Kenntnis der Cytologie von *Ichthyophthirius multifiliis* Fouq. *Arch. Protistenk.*, 81: 88–137.

HADA, Y. (1932a) The Tintinnoinea from the Sea of Okhotsk and its neighborhood. *J. Fac. Sci. Hokkaido Univ.*, 2: 37–59.

———— (1932b) Report of the biological survey of Matsu Bay. 24: the pelagic Ciliata, suborder Tintinnoinea. *Sci. Rep. Tôhoku Imp. Univ.*, ser. 4, Biol., 7: 553–573.

HADŽI, J. (1940a) The development of suctoria: *Spelaeophrya polypoides* sp. n., *S. lacustris* sp. n. and *Acineta karamani* sp. n. *Ghlas Srpsk. kralj. Akad.*, 91: 81–143.

———— (1940b) [Epizoic ciliate fauna on the wood-louse, *Microlista spinosissima* Rac.] *Razpr. mat.-prir. Akad. Ljubljana*, 1: 121–148. [In Serbo-Croatian]

———— (1951) Studien über Follikuliniden. *Dela Slov. Akad. Znan. Umet. Hist. nat. Med.*, 4:1–390. [In German with Slovenian summary pp. 351–386]

———— (1953) An attempt to reconstruct the system of animal classification. *Syst. Zool.*, 2: 145–154.

HAECKEL, E. (1866) Generelle Morphologie der Organismen. II. Allgemeine Entwicklungsgeschichte der Organismen. G. Reimer, Berlin.

———— (1873) Zur Morphologie der Infusorien. *Z. Naturgesch.*, 7: 516–560.

HAIRSTON, N. G. (1958) Observations on the ecology of *Paramecium*, with comments on the species problem. *Evolution*, 12: 440–450.

HALL, R. P. (1950) Phytoflagellates as a source of food for *Tetrahymena*. (Abstr.) *Proc. Amer. Soc. Protozool.*, 1: 5.

———— (1953) Protozoology. Prentice-Hall, New York. 682 pp.

———— (1954) Effects of certain metal ions on growth of *Tetrahymena pyriformis*. *J. Protozool.*, 1: 74–79.

HALL, R. P. and C. H. ALVEY (1933) The vacuome and so-called canalicular system of *Colpidium*. *Trans. Amer. micr. Soc.*, 52: 26–32.

HAMBURGER, C. and W. VON BUDDENBROCK (1911) Nordische Ciliata mit Ausschluss der Tintinnoidea. *In* Brandt, K. and C. Apstein, *Nordisches Plankton*. Lief. 13, pp. 1–152. Lipsius u. Tischer, Keil u. Leipzig.

———— (1913) Nordische Suctoria. *In* Brandt, K. and C. Apstein, *Nordische Plankton*, Lief. 13, pp. 153–193. Lipsius u. Tischer, Keil u. Leipzig.

HAMILTON, J. M. (1952a) Studies on loricate Ciliophora. I. *Cothurnia variabilis* Kellicott. *Trans. Amer. micr. Soc.*, 71: 382–392.

———— (1952b) Studies on loricate Ciliophora. II. *Folliculina boltoni* Kent. *Proc. Iowa Acad. Sci.*, 58: 469–476.

HAMMOND, D. M. (1937) The neuromotor system of *Euplotes patella* during binary fission and conjugation. *Quart. J. micr. Sci.*, 79: 507–557.

HAMMOND, D. M. and C. A. KOFOID (1937) The continuity of structure and function in the neuromotor system of *Euplotes patella* during its life-cycle. *Proc. Amer. phil. Soc.*, 77: 207–218.

HANCE, R. T. (1917) Studies on a race of *Paramoecium* possessing extra contractile vacuoles. I. An account of the morphology, physiology, genetics and cytology of this new race. *J. exp. Zool.*, 23: 287–333.

HANSON, E. D. (1955) Inheritance and regeneration of cytoplasmic damage in *Paramecium aurelia*. *Proc. nat. Acad. Sci.*, *Wash.*, 41: 783–786.

—— (1957) Some aspects of the quantitative study of cytoplasmic particles: mixed populations of kappa in *Paramecium aurelia*, variety 4. *J. exp. Zool.*, 135: 29–56.

—— (1958) On the origin of the Eumetazoa. *Syst. Zool.*, 7: 16–47.

HARRIS, J. (1696) Some microscopical observations of vast numbers of animalcula seen in water. *Phil. Trans. roy. Soc.*, 19: 254–259.

HARTOG, M. (1906) Protozoa. *In* Harmer, S. F. and A. E. Shipley, *The Cambridge Natural History*, Vol. I, pp. 3–162. Macmillan, London.

HAWES, R. S. J. (1961) The Ciliata. *In* Mackinnon, D. L. and R. S. J. Hawes, An Introduction to the Study of Protozoa. Clarendon Press, Oxford. [In press]

HAYE, A. (1930) Über den Exkretionsapparat bei den Protisten, nebst Bemerkungen über einige andere feinere Strukturverhältnisse der untersuchten Arten. *Arch. Protistenk.*, 70: 1–86.

HAYES, M. L. (1938) Cytological studies on *Dileptus anser*. *Trans. Amer. micr. Soc.*, 57: 11–25.

HEGNER, R. W. (1926a) The interrelations of protozoa and the utricles of Utricularia. *Biol. Bull.*, 50: 239–270.

—— (1926b) The protozoa of the pitcher plant, *Sarracenia purpurea*. *Biol. Bull.*, 50: 271–276.

—— (1934) Specificity in the genus *Balantidium* based on size and shape of body and macronucleus, with descriptions of six new species. *Amer. J. Hyg.*, 19: 38–67.

HEGNER, R. W. and J. ANDREWS, editors (1930) Problems and Methods of Research in Protozoology. Macmillan, New York. 532 pp.

HEIDENREICH, E. (1935a) Untersuchungen an parasitischen Ciliaten aus Anneliden. Teil I: Systematik. *Arch. Protistenk.*, 84: 315–392.

—— (1935b) Untersuchungen an parasitischen Ciliaten aus Würmern. Teil II: Kernveränderungen. *Arch. Protistenk.*, 84: 393–414.

—— (1935c) Ergänzende Untersuchungen an parasitischen Ciliaten aus Oligochäten. *Arch. Protistenk.*, 84: 528–532.

HELSON, L., PECORA, P., and H. I. HIRSHFIELD (1959) Macronuclear changes in a strain of *Blepharisma undulans* during the divisional cycle. *J. Protozool.*, 6: 131–135.

HEMMING, F. (1953) Copenhagen Decisions on Zoological Nomenclature. London. 135 pp.

—— (1956) Opinion 418. Validation under the plenary powers of the generic name *Stentor* Oken, 1815 (Class Ciliophora). *Opin. int. Comm. zool. Nom.*, 14: 43–68.

—— (1958) Official text of the " Règles Internationales de la Nomenclature Zoologique " as it existed up to the opening of the Paris Congress in 1948. *Bull. zool. Nom.*, 14: i–xxviii.

HENNEGUY, L. F. (1890) Sur une infusoire hétérotriche *Fabrea salina*, n. sp. *Ann. Microgr.*, 3: 118–136.

—— (1898) Sur les rapports des cils vibratiles avec les centrosomes. *Arch. Anat. micr.*, 1: 481–496.

HERTWIG, R. (1876) Ueber *Podophrya gemmipara* nebst Bemerkungen zum Bau und zur systematischen Stellung der Acineten. *Morph. Jb.*, 1: 20–82.

—— (1877) Ueber den Bau und die Entwicklung der *Spirochona gemmipara*. *Jen. Z. Naturwiss.*, 11: 149–187.

—— (1889) Über die Konjugation der Infusorien. *Abh. bayr. Akad. Wiss.*, 17: 150–233.

—— (1902) Die Protozoen und die Zelltheorie. *Arch. Protistenk.*, 1: 1–40.

HETHERINGTON, A. (1933) The culture of some holotrichous ciliates. *Arch. Protistenk.*, 80: 255–280.

HICKSON, S. J. (1903) The Infusoria or Corticata Heterokaryota. *In* Lankester, E. R., *A Treatise on Zoology*, Vol. I. Introduction and Protozoa, 2nd fasc., sctn L, pp. 361–426. Black, London.

HICKSON, S. J. and J. T. WADSWORTH (1902) *Dendrocometes paradoxus*. Part I.—Conjugation. *Quart. J. micr. Sci.*, 45: 325–362.

—— (1909) *Dendrosoma radians*, Ehrenberg. *Quart. J. micr. Sci.*, 54: 141–183.

HILL, J. (1752) An History of Animals. *In* Compleat Natural History. Vol. III. Osborne, London.

HIRSCH, E. (1914) Untersuchungen über die biologische Wirkung einiger Salze. *Zool. Jb. (Abt. Allg. Zool. u. Physiol.)*, 34: 559–682.

HIRSHFIELD, H. (1949) The morphology of *Urceolaria karyolobia* sp. nov., *Trichodina tegula*, sp. nov., and *Scyphidia ubiquita*, sp. nov., three new ciliates from Southern California limpets and turbans. *J. Morph.*, 85: 1–33.

HIWATASHI, K. (1958) Inheritance of mating types in variety 12 of *Paramecium caudatum*. *Sci. Rep. Tôhoku Univ., Biol.*, 24: 119–129.

—— (1959) Induction of conjugation by ethylenediamine tetraacetic acid (EDTA) in *Paramecium caudatum*. *Sci. Rep. Tôhoku Univ., Biol.*, 25: 81–90.

HOARE, C. A. (1927a) Schewiakoff's keys for the determination of the holotrichous ciliates. *Proc. zool. Soc. Lond.*, yr. 1927, pp. 399–418.

—— (1927b) Studies on coprozoic ciliates. *Parasitology*, 19: 154–222.

—— (1937) A new cycloposthiid ciliate (*Triplumaria hamertoni* gen. n., sp. n.) parasitic in the Indian rhinoceros. *Parasitology*, 29: 559–569.

—— (1949) Handbook of Medical Protozoology. Baillière, Tindall and Cox, London. 334 pp.

HOFKER, J. (1932) Studien über Tintinnoidea. *Arch. Protistenk.*, 75: 315–402.

HOLZ, G. G., Jr. (1960) Structural and functional changes in a generation in *Tetrahymena. Biol. Bull.*, 118: 84–95.

HOLZ, G. G., Jr. and J. O. CORLISS (1956) *Tetrahymena setifera* n. sp., a member of the genus *Tetrahymena* with a caudal cilium. *J. Protozool.*, 3: 112–118.

HOLZ, G. G., Jr., ERWIN, J. A., and R. J. DAVIS (1959) Some physiological characteristics of the mating types and varieties of *Tetrahymena pyriformis. J. Protozool.*, 6: 149–156.

HOLZ, G. G., Jr., SCHERBAUM, O. H., and N. E. WILLIAMS (1957) The arrest of mitosis and stomatogenesis during temperature-induction of synchronous division in *Tetrahymena pyriformis*, mating type 1, variety 1. *Exp. Cell Res.*, 13: 618–621.

HONIGBERG, B. M. and H. A. DAVENPORT (1954) Staining flagellate protozoa by various silver-protein compounds. *Stain Tech.*, 29: 241–246.

HOOKE, R. (1665) Micrographia. Martyn and Allestry, London. 246 pp.

—— (1678) Lectures and Collections. Martyn, London. 112 pp.

HORVÁTH, J. (1933) Beiträge zur hypotrichen Fauna der Umgebung von Szeged. I. *Arch. Protistenk.*, 80: 281–302.

—— (1936a) Beiträge zur hypotrichen Fauna der Umgebung von Szeged. II. *Arch. Protistenk.*, 86: 482–499.

—— (1936b) Beiträge zur Physiologie von *Kahlia simplex. Arch. Protistenk.*, 86: 482–499.

—— (1951) Contributions to studies on the soil protozoa of the Ciliata group, with special regard to their adaptation to soil conditions. *Arch. Biol. Hung.*, 19: 151–162.

—— (1956) Beiträge zur Kenntnis einiger neuer Bodenciliaten. *Arch. Protistenk.*, 101: 269–276.

HORVÁTH, P. (1935) *Microthorax hungaricus* nov. spec. aus der Umgebung von Szeged. *Acta Biol. szeged.*, 3: 167–189. [In Hungarian with German summary]

HOVASSE, R. (1950) *Spirobütschliella chattoni* nov. gen. nov. sp., cilié astome parasite en Méditerranée du serpulien *Potamoceros triqueter* L., et parasité par la microsporidie *Gurleya nova*, sp. nov. *Bull. Inst. océanogr. Monaco*, No. 962. 10 pp.

HSIUNG, T. (1938) Biometrische Untersuchungen an *Balantidium* des Schweines in der Kultur. *Z. Parasitenk.*, 10: 108–131.

HSIUNG, T. S. (1929) A survey of the protozoan fauna of the large intestine of the horse. (Abstr.) *J. Parasit.*, 16: 99.

—— (1930) A monograph on the protozoa of the large intestine of the horse. *Iowa St. Coll. J. Sci.*, 4: 356–423.

HULL, R. W. (1954) Feeding processes in *Solenophrya micraster* Penard 1914. *J. Protozool.*, 1: 178–182.

—— (1961a) Studies on suctorian protozoa: the mechanism of prey adherence. *J. Protozool.*, 8. [In press]

—— (1961b) Studies on suctorian protozoa: the mechanism of ingestion of prey cytoplasm. *J. Protozool.*, 8. [In press]

HULL, R. W. and J. E. MORRISSEY (1960) Metabolic efficiency of *Tetrahymena pyriformis*, strain W, as related to culture age. *Trans. Amer. micr. Soc.*, 79: 127–135.

HUNGATE, R. E. (1955) Mutualistic intestinal protozoa. *In* Hutner, S. H. and A. Lwoff, editors, Biochemistry and Physiology of Protozoa, Vol. II, pp. 159–199. Academic Press, New York.

HUTNER, S. H., editor (1961?) Biochemistry and Physiology of Protozoa. Vol. III. Academic Press, New York. [In preparation]

HUTNER, S. H., CURY, A., and H. BAKER (1958) Microbiological assays. *Analyt. Chem.*, 30: 849–867.

HUTNER, S. H. and A. LWOFF, editors (1955) Biochemistry and Physiology of Protozoa. Vol. II. Academic Press, New York. 388 pp.

HUXLEY, T. H. (1857) On *Dysteria*, a new genus of infusoria. *Quart. J. micr. Sci.*, 5: 78–82.

—— (1877) A Manual of the Anatomy of Invertebrated Animals. Churchill, London. 698 pp.

HYMAN, L. H. (1940) The Invertebrates: Protozoa through Ctenophora. Vol. I. McGraw-Hill, New York. 726 pp.

—— (1959) The Invertebrates: Smaller Coelomate Groups. Vol. V. McGraw-Hill, New York. 783 pp. [Phylum Protozoa, pp. 698–713, in Chapter 23: " Retrospect "]

ILOWAISKY, S. A. (1926) Material zum Studium der Cysten der Hypotrichen. *Arch. Protistenk.*, 54: 92–136.

INABA, F., NAKAMURA, R., and S. YAMAGUCHI (1958) An electron microscopic study on the pigment granules of *Blepharisma*. *Cytologia*, 23: 72–79.

INOKI, S. and A. MATSUSHIRO (1958) Antigenic variation in *Tetrahymena pyriformis*. *Med. J. Osaka Univ.*, 8: 763–770.

IVANIĆ, M. (1929a) Über die centrosomenähnlichen Gebilde bei der Grosskernteilung und die promitotische Kleinkernteilung, nebst Bemerkungen über die Chromosomenverhältnisse bei einem Infusor (*Euplotes patella* Ehrbg.). *Arch. Protistenk.*, 66: 33–60.

—— (1929b) Zur Auffassung der sog. bandförmigen Grosskerne bei Infusorien; zugleich ein Beitrag zur Kenntnis der sog. parthenogenetischen und ihnen ähnlichen Reorganisationsprozesse des Kernapparates bei Protozoen. *Arch. Protistenk.*, 66: 133–159.

——— (1931) Über die mit der Encystierung verbundene Entstehung der kleinkernlosen Stämme, nebst einem Beitrag zur Entstehung der Grosskernlosen Stämme bei *Stylonychia pustulata* Ehrbg. *Arch. Protistenk.*, 74: 429–448.

——— (1933a) Neue Beiträge zur Kenntnis der mit den Reorganisationsprozessen des Kernapparates verbundenen Vermehrungsruhestadien von *Chilodon uncinatus* Ehrbg., nebst einem neuen Beiträge zur Kenntnis der promitotischen Teilung des Grosskernes bei Infusorien. *Arch. Protistenk.*, 79: 170–199.

——— (1933b) Die Conjugation von *Chilodon cucullulus* Ehrbg. *Arch. Protistenk.*, 79: 313–348.

——— (1938) Ueber die mit der Chromosomenbildung verbundene promitotische Grosskernteilung bei den Vermehrungsruhestadien von *Chilodon uncinatus*. *Arch. Protistenk.*, 91: 61–68.

IVERSON, R. M. (1958) Nuclear transfer studies on ultraviolet-irradiated *Amoeba proteus*. *Exp. Cell Res.*, 15: 268–270.

IVERSON, R. M. and A. C. GIESE (1957) Nucleic acid content and ultraviolet susceptibility of *Tetrahymena pyriformis*. *Exp. Cell Res.*, 13: 213–223.

JACOBS, M. H. (1914) Physiological studies on certain protozoan parasites of *Diadema setosum*. *Pap. Tortugas Lab.*, 6: 147–157.

JACOBSON, I. (1931) Fibrilläre Differenzierungen bei Ciliaten. *Arch. Protistenk.*, 75: 31–100.

JAHN, T. L. and F. F. JAHN (1949) How to Know the Protozoa. Brown, Dubuque, Iowa. 234 pp.

JAKUS, M. A. (1945) The structure and properties of the trichocysts of *Paramecium*. *J. exp. Zool.*, 100: 457–485.

JAKUS, M. A. and C. E. HALL (1946) Electron microscope observations of the trichocysts and cilia of *Paramecium*. *Biol. Bull.*, 91: 141–144.

JAKUS, M. A., HALL, C. E., and F. O. SCHMITT (1942) Electron microscope studies of the structure of *Paramecium* trichocysts. (Abstr.) *Anat. Rec.*, 84: 474–475.

JANDA, V. and O. JÍROVEC (1937) Ueber künstlich hervorgerufenen Parasitismus eines freilebenden Ciliaten *Glaucoma piriformis* und Infektionsversuche mit *Euglena gracilis* und *Spirochaeta biflexa*. *Mém. Soc. zool. tchécosl.*, 5: 34–58.

JAROCKI, J. (1934) Two new hypocomid ciliates, *Heterocineta janickii* sp. n. and *H. lwoffi* sp. n., ectoparasites of *Physa fontinalis* (L.) and *Viviparus fasciatus* Müller. *Mém. Acad. Sci. Cracovie* (B), yr. 1934, pp. 167–187.

——— (1935) Studies on ciliates from fresh-water molluscs. I. General remarks on protozoan parasites of Pulmonata. Transfer experiments with species of *Heterocineta* and *Chaetogaster limnaei*, their additional host. Some new hypocomid ciliates. *Bull. int. Acad. Cracovie (Acad. polon. Sci.)*, (B: II) yr. 1935, pp. 201–230.

JAROCKI, J. and Z. RAABE (1932) Ueber drei neue Infusorien-Genera der Familie Hypocomidae (Ciliata Thigmotricha), Parasiten in Süsswassermuscheln. *Bull. int. Acad. Cracovie (Acad. polon. Sci.)*, (B: II), yr. 1932, pp. 29–45.

JEFFRIES, W. B. (1956) Studies on excystment in the hypotrichous ciliate *Pleurotricha lanceolata. J. Protozool.*, 3: 136–144.

JENNINGS, H. S. (1897) Studies on reactions to stimuli in unicellular organisms. I. Reactions to chemical, osmotic and mechanical stimuli in the ciliate infusoria. *J. Physiol.*, 21: 258–322.

—— (1904) Contributions to the Study of the Behavior of Lower Organisms. *Publ. Carneg. Instn.*, No. 16, pp. 1–256.

—— (1920) Life and Death, Heredity and Evolution in Unicellular Organisms. Badger, Boston. 233 pp.

—— (1929) Genetics of the Protozoa. *Bibliogr. genet.*, 5: 105–330.

—— (1931) Behavior of the Lower Organisms. Rev. ed. Columbia Univ. Press, New York. 366 pp.

—— (1939) Genetics of *Paramecium bursaria*. I. Mating types and groups, their interrelations and distribution; mating behavior and self sterility. *Genetics*, 24: 202–233.

—— (1942) Senescence and death in protozoa and invertebrates. *In* Cowdry, E. V., editor, Problems of Aging, pp. 29–48. 2nd ed. Williams and Wilkins, Baltimore.

—— (1944) *Paramecium bursaria:* Life history. I. Immaturity, maturity and age. *Biol. Bull.*, 86: 131–145.

—— (1945) *Paramecium bursaria:* Life history. V. Some relations of external conditions, past or present, to ageing and to mortality of exconjugants, with summary of conclusions on age and death. *J. exp. Zool.*, 99: 15–31.

JENNINGS, H. S. and P. OPITZ (1944) Genetics of *Paramecium bursaria*. IV. A fourth variety from Russia. Lethal crosses with an American variety. *Genetics*, 29: 576–583.

JENSEN, D. D. (1959) A theory of the behavior of *Paramecium aurelia* and behavioral effects of feeding, fission, and ultra-violet microbeam irradiation. *Behaviour*, 15: 82–122.

JEPPS, M. W. (1937) On the protozoan parasites of *Calanus finmarchicus* in the Clyde Sea area. *Quart. J. micr. Sci.*, 79: 589–658.

JÍROVEC, O. (1950) Das Infusorium *Glaucoma piriformis* als Testobjekt in Pharmakologie und Physiologie. *Path. Bakt.*, 13: 129–138.

JÍROVEC, O., WENIG, K., FOTT, B., BARTOŠ, E., WEISER, J., and R. ŠRÁMEK-HUŠEK (1953) Protozoologie. Prague. 643 pp. [In Czechoslovakian. Section on ciliates by R. Šrámek-Hušek.]

JOBLOT, L. (1718) Descriptions et Usages de Plusieurs Nouveaux Microscopes . . . avec de Nouvelles Observations. Paris.

JOHNSON, H. P. (1893) A contribution to the morphology and biology of the stentors. *J. Morph.*, 8: 467–562.

JOHNSON, W. H. (1956) Nutrition of protozoa. *Ann. Rev. Microbiol.*, 10: 193–212.
JOHNSON, W. H. and F. R. EVANS (1940) Environmental factors affecting cystment in *Woodruffia metabolica*. *Physiol. Zoöl.*, 13: 102–121.
——— (1941) A further study of environmental factors affecting cystment in *Woodruffia metabolica*. *Physiol. Zoöl.*, 14: 227–237.
JOHNSON, W. H. and E. LARSON (1938) Studies on the morphology and life history of *Woodruffia metabolica* nov. sp. *Arch. Protistenk.*, 90: 383–392.
JOHNSON, W. H. and C. A. MILLER (1956) A further analysis of the nutrition of *Paramecium*. *J. Protozool.*, 3: 221–226.
JOLLOS, V. (1921) Experimentelle Protistenstudien. I. Untersuchungen über Variabilität und Vererbung bei Infusorien. *Arch. Protistenk.*, 43: 1–222.
——— (1934) Dauermodifikationen und Mutationen bei Protozoen. *Arch. Protistenk.*, 83: 197–219.
JONES, E. E. (1951) Encystment, excystment, and the nuclear cycle in the ciliate *Dileptus anser*. *J. Elisha Mitchell sci. Soc.*, 67: 205–217.
——— (1956) The ciliate *Dileptus beersi*, n. sp. *J. Elisha Mitchell sci. Soc.*, 72: 67–73.
JONES, E. E. and C. D. BEERS (1953) Some observations on structure and behavior in the ciliate *Dileptus monilatus*. *J. Elisha Mitchell sci. Soc.*, 69: 42–48.
JÖRGENSEN, E. (1924) Mediterranean Tintinnidae. *Rep. Danish oceanogr. Exped.*, 1908–1910, *Medit.*, 2 (Biol.), pp. 1–110.
——— (1927) Ciliata. Tintinnidae. *In* Grimpe, G. and E. Wagler, *Die Tierwelt der Nord- und Ostsee*, Lief. 8 (Teil II, c₁), pp. 1–26. Leipzig.
JÖRGENSEN, E. and A. KAHL (1933) Tintinnidae (Nachträge). *In* Grimpe, G. and E. Wagler, *Die Tierwelt der Nord- und Ostsee*, Lief. 23 (Teil II, c₂), pp. 27–28. Leipzig.

KAHL, A. (1926) Neue und wenig bekannte Formen der holotrichen und heterotrichen Ciliaten. *Arch. Protistenk.*, 55: 197–438.
——— (1927a) Neue und ergänzende Beobachtungen heterotricher Ciliaten. *Arch. Protistenk.*, 57: 121–203.
——— (1927b) Neue und ergänzende Beobachtungen holotricher Ciliaten. I. *Arch. Protistenk.*, 60: 34–129.
——— (1928) Die Infusorien (Ciliata) der Oldesloer Salzwasserstellen. *Arch. Hydrobiol.*, 19: 50–123, 189–246.
——— (1929) Persönliche Erwiderung auf Wetzel's Kritik an meiner Bearbeitung der Gattung *Metopus* (Infusoria heterotricha). *Z. Morph. Ökol. Tiere*, 15: 723–734.
——— (1930) Neue und ergänzende Beobachtungen holotricher Ciliaten. II. *Arch. Protistenk.*, 70: 313–416.
——— (1930/1931) *Metopus*, eine interessante Infusoriengattung (Infusoria heterotricha). *Mikrokosmos*, 24: 7–12.

——— (1930–1935) Urtiere oder Protozoa. I: Wimpertiere oder Ciliata (Infusoria), eine Bearbeitung der freilebenden und ectocommensalen Infusorien der Erde, unter Ausschluss der marinen Tintinnidae. *In* Dahl, F., *Die Tierwelt Deutschlands*, Teil 18 (yr. 1930), 21 (1931), 25 (1932), 30 (1935), pp. 1–886. G. Fischer, Jena.

——— (1931a) Über die verwandtschaftlichen Beziehungen der Suctorien zu den prostomen Infusorien. *Arch. Protistenk.*, 73: 423–481.

——— (1931b) Familie Plagiopylidae (Plagiopylina) Schew. 1896, Infusoria, Trichostomata. *Ann. Protist.*, *Paris*, 3: 111–135.

——— (1932) Ctenostomata (Lauterborn) n. subordo. Vierte Unterordnung der Heterotricha. *Arch. Protistenk.*, 77: 231–304.

——— (1933a) Ciliata libera et ectocommensalia. *In* Grimpe, G. and E. Wagler, *Die Tierwelt der Nord- und Ostsee*, Lief. 23 (Teil II, c₃), pp. 29–146. Leipzig.

——— (1933b) Die Infusorien des marinen Sandgrundes. [Unpublished MS, cited in Kahl (1930–1935)]

——— (1933c) Anmerkungen zu der Arbeit von Bruno Pestel: Beiträge zur Morphologie und Biologie des *Dendrocometes paradoxus* Stein. *Arch. Protistenk.*, 80: 65–71.

——— (1934a) Ciliata entocommensalia et parasitica. *In* Grimpe, G. and E. Wagler, *Die Tierwelt der Nord- und Ostsee*, Lief. 26 (Teil II, c₄), pp. 147–183. Leipzig.

——— (1934b) Suctoria. *In* Grimpe, G. and E. Wagler, *Die Tierwelt der Nord- und Ostsee*, Lief. 26 (Teil II, c₅), pp. 184–226. Leipzig.

KALMUS, H. (1929) Beobachtungen und Versuche über die Tätigkeit Kontraktilen Vakuole eines marinen Infusors: *Amphileptus gutta* Cohn, nebst morphologischen und systematischen Vorbemerkungen. *Arch. Protistenk.*, 66: 409–420.

——— (1931) *Paramecium* das Pantoffeltierchen. Eine Monographische Zusammenfassung der Wichtigsten Kenntnisse. G. Fischer, Jena. 188 pp.

KAMIYA, T. (1959) Carbohydrate changes in the acid-soluble fractions of the ciliate protozoon *Tetrahymena geleii* W during the course of synchronous culture. *J. Biochem.*, *Tokyo*, 46: 1187–1192.

——— (1960) Acid-soluble phosphate compounds of the ciliate protozoon *Tetrahymena geleii* W. *J. Biochem.*, *Tokyo*, 47: 69–76.

KANEDA, M. (1959) The morphology and morphogenesis of the cortical structures during binary fission of *Chlamydodon pedarius*. *J. Sci. Hiroshima Univ.* (B, 1), 18: 265–277. [Appeared in 1960]

——— (1960a) Phase contrast microscopy of cytoplasmic organelles in the gymnostome ciliate *Chlamydodon pedarius*. *J. Protozool.*, 7: 306–313.

——— (1960b) The structure and reorganization of the macronucleus during the binary fission of *Chlamydodon pedarius*. *Jap. J. Zool.*, 12: 477–491.

KANTOR, S. (1956) The infraciliature in the Ophryoscolecidae and its morphogenetic and phylogenetic significance. (Abstr.) *J. Protozool.*, 3 (Suppl.): 2–3.

KATASHIMA, R. (1952) Studies on *Euplotes*. I. Conjugation and cytogamy induced by split pair method in *Euplotes harpa*. *J. Sci. Hiroshima Univ.* (B, 1), 13: 111–120.

—— (1953) Studies on *Euplotes*. II. Macronuclear reorganization process, double and giant animals from two-united ex-conjugants. *J. Sci. Hiroshima Univ.* (B, 1), 14: 57–71.

—— (1959a) Mating types in *Euplotes eurystomus*. *J. Protozool.*, 6: 75–83.

—— (1959b) The intimacy of union between the two members of the conjugating pairs in *Euplotes eurystomus*. *Jap. J. Zool.*, 12: 329–343.

KATE, C. G. B. TEN (1927) Uber das Fibrillensystem der Ciliaten. *Arch. Protistenk.*, 57: 362–426.

—— (1928) Über das Fibrillensystem der Ciliaten. 2. Das Fibrillensystem der Isotrichen (*Isotricha* und *Dasytricha*). *Arch. Protistenk.*, 62: 328–354.

KAUDEWITZ, F. (1958) Versuche mit radioaktivem Phosphor an einzelnen Zellen verschiedener Protozoenarten. *Arch. Protistenk.*, 102: 321–448.

KAY, M. W. (1945a) Studies on *Oxytricha bifaria* Stokes. I. Analysis of the cytological structure. *Trans. Amer. micr. Soc.*, 64: 91–108.

—— (1945b) Studies on *Oxytricha bifaria* Stokes. II. Cystic reorganization. *Trans. Amer. micr. Soc.*, 64: 267–281.

—— (1946) Studies on *Oxytricha bifaria*. III. Conjugation. *Trans. Amer. micr. Soc.*, 65: 132–148.

KAZUBSKI, S. L. (1958a) *Thigmocoma acuminata* gen. nov., sp. nov. (Thigmotricha–Thigmocomidae fam. nov.) a parasite of the renal organ of *Schistophallus orientalis* Cless. (Pulmonata–Zonitidae). *Bull. Acad. polon. Sci.*, 6: 167–172.

—— (1958b) *Trichia lubomirskii* Slós. (Helicidae), a new host of *Tetrahymena limacis* (Warren, 1932) Kozloff, 1946 (Ciliata) and *Zonitoides nitidus* Müll. (Zonitidae), a new host of *T. rostrata* (Kahl, 1926) Corliss, 1952 in Poland. *Bull. Acad. polon. Sci.*, 6: 247–252.

KEILIN, D. (1921) On a new ciliate, *Lambornella stegomyiae*, n. g., n. sp., parasitic in the body cavity of the larvae of *Stegomyia scutellaris* Walker (Diptera, Nematocera, Culicidae). *Parasitology*, 13: 216–224.

KEISER, A. (1921) Die sessilen peritrichen Infusorien und Suctorien von Basel und Umgebung. *Rev. suisse Zool.*, 28: 221–341.

KENT, W. S. (1880–1882) A Manual of the Infusoria. Vols. I–III. David Bogue, London. 913 pp.

KEPPEN, N. (1888) [Observations on the tentaculiferous Infusoria] *Mém. Soc. Nat. nouv-russ. Est.*, 13: 1–79. [In Russian]

KERKUT, G. A. (1958) Borradaile and Potts' The Invertebrata. 3rd ed. Cambridge Univ. Press. 795 pp.

KHAINSKY, A. (1910) Zur Morphologie und Physiologie einiger Infusorien (*Paramaecium caudatum*) auf Grund einer neuen histologischen Methode. *Arch. Protistenk.*, 21: 1–60.

KIDDER, G. W. (1933a) Studies on *Conchophthirius mytili* DeMorgan. I. Morphology and division. *Arch. Protistenk.*, 79: 1–24.

———— (1933b) Studies on *Conchophthirius mytili* DeMorgan. II. Conjugation and nuclear reorganization. *Arch. Protistenk.*, 79: 25–49.

———— (1933c) On the genus *Ancistruma* Strand (*Ancistrum* Maupas). I. The structure and division of *A. mytili* Quenn. and *A. isseli* Kahl. *Biol. Bull.*, 64: 1–20.

———— (1933d) On the genus *Ancistruma* Strand (=*Ancistrum* Maupas). II. The conjugation and nuclear reorganization. *Arch. Protistenk.*, 81: 1–18.

———— (1933e) *Conchophthirius caryoclada*, sp. nov. (Protozoa, Ciliata). *Biol. Bull.*, 65: 175–178.

———— (1934a) Studies on the ciliates from fresh water mussels. I. The structure and neuromotor system of *Conchophthirius anodontae* Stein, *C. curtus* Engl. and *C. magna* sp. nov. *Biol. Bull.*, 66: 69–90.

———— (1934b) Studies on the ciliates from fresh water mussels. II. The nuclei of *Conchophthirius anodontae* Stein, *C. curtus* Engl. and *C. magna* Kidder, during binary fission. *Biol. Bull.*, 66: 286–303.

———— (1937) The intestinal protozoa of the wood-feeding roach *Panesthia*. *Parasitology*, 29: 163–205.

———— (1938) Nuclear reorganization without cell division in *Paraclevelandia* simplex (family Clevelandellidae), an endocommensal ciliate of the wood-feeding roach, *Panesthia*. *Arch. Protistenk.*, 81: 69–77.

———— (1951) Nutrition and metabolism of protozoa. *Ann. Rev. Microbiol.*, 5: 139–156.

KIDDER, G. W. and C. L. CLAFF (1938) Cytological investigations of *Colpoda cucullus*. *Biol. Bull.*, 74: 178–197.

KIDDER, G. W. and V. C. DEWEY (1945) Studies on the biochemistry of *Tetrahymena*. III. Strain differences. *Physiol. Zoöl.*, 18: 136–157.

———— (1951) The biochemistry of ciliates in pure culture. *In* Lwoff, A., editor, Biochemistry and Physiology of Protozoa, Vol. I, pp. 323–400. Academic Press, New York.

———— (1957) Deazapurines as growth inhibitors. *Arch. Biochem. Biophys.*, 66: 486–492.

KIDDER, G. W. and W. F. DILLER (1934) Observations on the binary fission of four species of common free-living ciliates, with special reference to the macronuclear chromatin. *Biol. Bull.*, 67: 201–219.

KIDDER, G. W., LILLY, D. M., and C. L. CLAFF (1940) Growth studies on ciliates. IV. The influence of food on the structure and growth of *Glaucoma vorax* sp. nov. *Biol. Bull.*, 78: 9–23.

KIDDER, G. W. and C. A. STUART (1939a) Growth studies on ciliates. I. The role of bacteria in the growth and reproduction of *Colpoda*. *Physiol. Zoöl.*, 12: 329–340.

—— (1939b) Growth studies on ciliates. II. The food factor in the growth, reproduction, and encystment of *Colpoda*. *Physiol. Zoöl.*, 12: 341–347.

KIDDER, G. W., STUART, C. A., McGANN, V. G., and V. C. DEWEY (1945) Antigenic relationships in the genus *Tetrahymena*. *Physiol. Zoöl.*, 18: 415–425.

KIDDER, G. W. and F. M. SUMMERS (1935) Taxonomic and cytological studies on the ciliates associated with the amphipod family Orchestiidae from the Woods Hole district. I. The stomatous holotrichous ectocommensals. *Biol. Bull.*, 68: 51–68.

KIESSELBACH, A. (1936) Zur Ciliatenfauna der nördlichen Adria. *Thalassia*, 2: 1–53.

KIJENSKY, G. (1926) Ciliates in the intestinal cavity of the Oligochaeta from the surroundings of Prague. *Sbornik Zool. Praci*, yr. 1925, 75 (VI): 1–35. [In Czechoslovakian with English summary]

KIMBALL, R. F. (1941) Double animals and amicronucleate animals in *Euplotes patella* with particular reference to their conjugation. *J. exp. Zool.*, 86: 1–33.

—— (1942) The nature and inheritance of mating types in *Euplotes patella*. *Genetics*, 27: 269–285.

—— (1943) Mating types in the ciliate protozoa. *Quart. Rev. Biol.*, 18: 30–45.

—— (1953) The structure of the macronucleus of *Paramecium aurelia*. *Proc. nat. Acad. Sci., Wash.*, 39: 345–347.

—— (1958) Experiments with *Stentor coeruleus* on the nature of the radiation-induced delay in fission in the ciliates. *J. Protozool.*, 5: 151–155.

KIMBALL, R. F. and T. BARKA (1959) Quantitative cytochemical studies on *Paramecium aurelia*. II. Feulgen microspectrophotometry of the macronucleus during exponential growth. *Exp. Cell Res.*, 17: 173–182.

KIMBALL, R. F., CASPERSSON, T. O., SVENSSON, G., and L. CARSON (1959) Quantitative cytochemical studies on *Paramecium aurelia*. I. Growth in total dry weight measured by the scanning interference microscope and X-ray absorption methods. *Exp. Cell Res.*, 17: 160–172.

KIMBALL, R. F., GAITHER, N., and S. M. WILSON (1959) Reduction of mutation by postirradiation treatment after ultraviolet and various kinds of ionizing radiations. *Radiation Res.*, 10: 490–497.

KING, E. (1693) Several observations and experiments on the Animalcula, in pepper-water, &c. *Phil. Trans. roy. Soc.*, 17: 861–865.

KING, R. L. (1935) The contractile vacuole of *Paramecium multimicronucleata*. *J. Morph.*, 58: 555–565.

—— (1954) Origin and morphogenetic movements of the pores of the contractile vacuoles in *Paramecium aurelia*. *J. Protozool.*, 1: 121–130, 143.

KING, R. L. and H. W. BEAMS (1937) The effect of ultracentrifuging on *Paramecium*, with special reference to recovery and macronuclear reorganization. *J. Morph.*, 61: 27–49.

———— (1941) Some effects of mechanical agitation on *Paramecium caudatum*. *J. Morph.*, 68: 149–159.

KIRBY, H. (1934) Some ciliates from salt marshes in California. *Arch. Protistenk.*, 82: 114–133.

———— (1941a) Relationships between certain protozoa and other animals. *In* Calkins, G. N. and F. M. Summers, editors, Protozoa in Biological Research, pp. 890–1008. Columbia Univ. Press, New York.

———— (1941b) Organisms living on and in protozoa. *In* Calkins, G. N. and F. M. Summers, editors, Protozoa in Biological Research, pp. 1009–1113. Columbia Univ. Press, New York.

———— (1945) The structure of the common intestinal trichomonad of man. *J. Parasit.*, 31: 163–175.

———— (1950) Materials and Methods in the Study of Protozoa. Univ. Calif. Press, Berkeley. 72 pp.

———— (1954) On the need for validating the name " *Stentor* " Oken, 1815 (class Ciliophora) for use in its accustomed sense. *Bull. zool. Nom.*, 9: 208–214.

KITCHING, J. A. (1954) On suction in suctoria. *Colston Papers* (Proc. 7th Symp. Colston Res. Soc.), 7: 197–203.

———— (1956a) Contractile vacuoles of protozoa. *Protoplasmatologia*, III, D, 3a: 1–45.

———— (1956b) Food vacuoles of protozoa. *Protoplasmatologia*, III, D, 3b: 1–54.

———— (1957a) Some factors in the life of free-living protozoa. *In* Microbial Ecology (7th Symp. Soc. Gen. Microbiol., London), pp. 259–286. Cambridge Univ. Press, Cambridge.

———— (1957b) Effects of high hydrostatic pressures on the activity of flagellates and ciliates. *J. exp. Biol.*, 34: 494–510.

KLEE, E. E. (1926) Der Formwechsel im Lebenskreis reiner Linien von *Euplotes longipes*. *Zool. Jb.* (*Abt. allg. Zool. u. Physiol.*), 42: 307–366.

KLEIN, B. M. (1926a) Über eine neue Eigentümlichkeit der Pellicula von *Chilodon uncinatus* Ehrbg. *Zool. Anz.*, 67: 160–162.

———— (1926b) Ergebnisse mit einer Silbermethode bei Ciliaten. *Arch. Protistenk.*, 56: 243–279.

———— (1927) Die Silberliniensysteme der Ciliaten. Ihr Verhalten während Teilung und Konjugation, neue Silberbilder, Nachträge. *Arch. Protistenk.*, 58: 55–142.

———— (1928) Die Silberliniensysteme der Ciliaten. Weitere Resultate. *Arch. Protistenk.*, 62: 177–260.

———— (1929) Weitere Beiträge zur Kenntnis des Silberliniensystems der Ciliaten. *Arch. Protistenk.*, 65: 183–257.

—— (1930) Das Silberliniensystem der Ciliaten. Weitere Ergebnisse. IV. *Arch. Protistenk.*, 69: 235–326.

—— (1932) Das Ciliensystem in seiner Bedeutung für Lokomotion, Koordination und Formbildung mit besonderer Berücksichtigung der Ciliaten. *Ergebn. Biol.*, 8: 75–179.

—— (1933) Silberliniensystem und Infraciliatur. Eine kritische Gegenüberstellung. *Arch. Protistenk.*, 79: 146–169.

—— (1943) Das Silberlinien- oder neuroformative System der Ciliaten. *Ann. natur-hist. Mus. Wien*, 53: 156–336.

—— (1958) The " dry " silver method and its proper use. *J. Protozool.*, 5: 99–103.

KNIGHT, D. R. and H. C. McDOUGLE (1944) A protozoon of the genus *Tetrahymena* found in domestic fowl. *Amer. J. vet. Res.*, 5: 113–116.

KOEHLER, O. (1922) Über die Geotaxis von *Paramecium*. *Arch. Protistenk.*, 45: 1–94.

—— (1930) Über die Geotaxis von *Paramecium*. II. *Arch. Protistenk.*, 70: 279–306.

KOFOID, C. A. (1930) Factors in the evolution of the pelagic Ciliata, the Tintinnoinea. *In* Contributions to Marine Biology, pp. 1–39. Stanford Univ. Press, California.

—— (1935) On two remarkable ciliate protozoa from the caecum of the Indian elephant. *Proc. nat. Acad. Sci., Wash.*, 21: 501–506.

KOFOID, C. A. and A. S. CAMPBELL (1929) A conspectus of the marine and fresh-water Ciliata belonging to the suborder Tintinnoinea, with descriptions of new species principally from the Agassiz expedition to the eastern tropical Pacific, 1904–1905. *Univ. Calif. Publ. Zool.*, 34: 1–403.

—— (1939) The Ciliata: The Tintinnoinea. Reports on the scientific results of the expedition to the eastern tropical Pacific . . . 1904–1905. *Bull. Mus. comp. Zool. Harv.*, 84: 1–473.

KOFOID, C. A. and J. F. CHRISTENSON (1934) Ciliates from *Bos gaurus* H. Smith. *Univ. Calif. Publ. Zool.*, 39: 341–392.

KOFOID, C. A. and R. F. MacLENNAN (1930) Ciliates from *Bos indicus* Linn. I. The genus *Entodinium* Stein. *Univ. Calif. Publ. Zool.*, 33: 471–544.

—— (1932) Ciliates from *Bos indicus* Linn. II. A revision of *Diplodinium* Schuberg. *Univ. Calif. Publ. Zool.*, 37: 53–152.

—— (1933) Ciliates from *Bos indicus* Linn. III. *Epidinium* Crawley, *Epiplastron* gen. nov., and *Ophryoscolex* Stein. *Univ. Calif. Publ. Zool.*, 39: 1–34.

KOFOID, C. A. and L. E. ROSENBERG (1940) The neuromotor system of *Opisthonecta henneguyi* (Fauré-Fremiet). *Proc. Amer. phil. Soc.*, 82: 421–436.

KOLTZOFF, N. K. (1912) Untersuchungen über die Kontraktilität des Vorticellenstiels. *Arch. Zellforsch.*, 7: 344–423.

KOPPERI, A. J. (1937) Über die nicht-pathogene Protozoenfauna des Blinddarms einiger Nagetiere. *Ann. (bot.-zool.) Zool. Soc. zool.-bot. fenn. Vanamo*, yr. 1935, 3: 1–92.

KORMOS, J. (1935a) Geschlechtsdimorphismus und Conjugation bei *Prodiscophrya collini* (Root). *Állatorv. Közl.*, 32: 152–167. [In Hungarian with German summary]

—— (1935b) Beiträge zur Kenntnis der Entwicklung der Suctorien. *Math. Naturwiss. Anz. ung. Akad. Wiss.*, 53: 522–541.

KORMOS, J. and K. KORMOS (1957a) Die Entwicklungsgeschichtlichen Grundlagen des Systems der Suctorien. *Acta zool. Acad. sci. hung.*, 3: 147–162.

—— (1957b) Die Ontogenese der Protozoen. *Acta biol. Acad. sci. hung.*, 7: 385–402.

—— (1958a) Äussere und innere Konjugation. *Acta biol. Acad. sci. hung.*, 8: 103–126.

—— (1958b) Die Zellteilungstypen der Protozoen. *Acta. biol. Acad. sci. hung.*, 8: 127–148.

—— (1960a) Direkte Beobachtung der Kernveränderungen der Konjugation von *Cyclophrya katharinae* (Ciliata, Protozoa). *Acta biol. Acad. sci. hung.*, 10: 373–394.

—— (1960b) Experimentelle Untersuchung der Kernveränderungen der Konjugation von *Cyclophrya katharinae* (Ciliata, Protozoa). *Acta biol. Acad. sci. hung.*, 10: 395–419.

KOWALEWSKI, M. (1882) Beiträge zur Naturgeschichte der Oxytrichinen. *Physiogr. Denkschr. Warschaw*, 2: 395–413. [In Polish]

KOZLOFF, E. N. (1945) *Cochliophilus depressus* gen. nov., sp. nov. and *Cochliophilus minor* sp. nov., holotrichous ciliates from the mantle cavity of *Phytia setifer* (Cooper). *Biol. Bull.*, 89: 95–102.

—— (1946a) The morphology and systematic position of a holotrichous ciliate parasitizing *Deroceras agreste* (L). *J. Morph.*, 79: 445–465.

—— (1946b) Studies on ciliates of the family Ancistrocomidae Chatton and Lwoff (order Holotricha, suborder Thigmotricha). I. *Hypocomina tegularum* sp. nov. and *Crebricoma* gen. nov. *Biol. Bull.*, 90: 1–7.

—— (1946c) Studies on ciliates of the family Ancistrocomidae Chatton and Lwoff (order Holotricha, suborder Thigmotricha). II. *Hypocomides mytili* Chatton and Lwoff, *Hypocomides botulae* sp. nov., *Hypocomides parva* sp. nov., *Hypocomides kelliae* sp. nov., and *Insignicoma venusta* gen. nov., sp. nov. *Biol. Bull.*, 90: 200–212.

—— (1946d) Studies on ciliates of the family Ancistrocomidae Chatton and Lwoff (order Holotricha, suborder Thigmotricha). III. *Ancistrocoma pelseneeri* Chatton & Lwoff, *Ancistrocoma dissimilis* sp. nov., and *Hypocomagalma pholadidis* sp. nov. *Biol. Bull.*, 91: 189–199.

——— (1946e) Studies on ciliates of the family Ancistrocomidae Chatton and Lwoff (order Holotricha, suborder Thigmotricha). IV. *Heterocineta janickii* Jarocki, *Heterocineta goniobasidis* sp. nov., *Heterocineta fluminicolae* sp. nov., and *Enerthecoma properans* Jarocki. *Biol. Bull.*, 91: 200–209.

——— (1954) Studies on an astomatous ciliate from a fresh-water limpet, *Ferrissia peninsulae*. *J. Protozool.*, 1: 200–206.

——— (1955) *Lwoffia cilifera* gen. nov., sp. nov., a ciliated member of the family Sphenophryidae (Holotricha: Thigmotricha). *Biol. Bull.*, 108: 283–289.

——— (1956a) Experimental infection of the gray garden slug, *Deroceras reticulatum* (Müller), by the holotrichous ciliate *Tetrahymena pyriformis* (Ehrenberg). *J. Protozool.*, 3: 17–19.

——— (1956b) *Tetrahymena limacis* from the terrestrial pulmonate gastropods *Monadenia fidelis* and *Prophysaon andersoni*. *J. Protozool.*, 3: 204–208.

——— (1957) A species of *Tetrahymena* parasitic in the renal organ of the slug *Deroceras reticulatum*. *J. Protozool.*, 4: 75–79.

——— (1960) Morphological studies on holotrichous ciliates of the family Hysterocinetidae. I. *Hysterocineta eiseniae* Beers and *Ptychostomum campelomae* sp. nov. *J. Protozool.*, 7: 41–50.

KRASCHENINNIKOW, S. (1953) The silver-line system of *Chilodonella cyprini* (Moroff). *J. Morph.*, 92: 79–113.

——— (1955) Observations on the morphology and division of *Eudiplodinium neglectum* Dogiel (Ciliata Entodiniomorpha) from the stomach of a moose (*Alces americana*). *J. Protozool.*, 2: 124–134.

KRASCHENINNIKOW, S. and D. H. WENRICH (1958) Some observations on the morphology and division of *Balantidium coli* and *Balantidium caviae*(?). *J. Protozool.*, 5: 196–202.

KRÜGER, F. (1930) Untersuchungen über den Bau und die Funktion der Trichocysten von *Paramaecium caudatum*. *Arch. Protistenk.*, 72: 91–134.

——— (1931) Dunkelfelduntersuchungen über den Bau der Trichocysten von *Frontonia leucas*. *Arch. Protistenk.*, 74: 207–235.

——— (1934) Untersuchungen über die Trichocysten einiger *Prorodon*-Arten. *Arch. Protistenk.*, 83: 275–320.

——— (1936) Die Trichocysten der Ciliaten im Dunkelfeldbild. *Zoologica, Stuttgart*, 34: 1–83.

KUDO, R. R. (1931) Handbook of Protozoology. Thomas, Springfield, Illinois. 451 pp.

——— (1936) Studies on *Nyctotherus ovalis* Leidy, with special reference to its nuclear structure. *Arch. Protistenk.*, 87: 10–42.

——— (1939) Protozoology. 2nd ed. Thomas, Springfield, Illinois. 689 pp.

——— (1946) Protozoology. 3rd ed. Thomas, Springfield, Illinois. 778 pp.

R

—————— (1954) Protozoology. 4th ed. Thomas, Springfield, Illinois. 966 pp.

KUDO, R. R. and P. A. MEGLITSCH (1938) On *Balantidium praenucleatum* n. sp., inhabiting the colon of *Blatta orientalis*. *Arch. Protistenk.*, 91: 111–124.

KUFFERATH, H. (1953) *Gonzeella coloniaris* n. gen., n. spec., cilié coloniare péritriche du Congo Belge. *Rev. Zool. Bot. afr.*, 48: 30–34.

KUNZ, H. (1936) Eine neue Suctorie, *Cucumophrya leptomesochrae* n. g., n. sp. von Helgoland. *Zool. Anz.*, 114: 173–174.

KURIHARA, Y. (1958) Analysis of the structure of microcosm, with special reference to the succession of protozoa in the bamboo container. *Jap. J. Ecol.*, 8: 163–171. [In Japanese with English summary]

KUTORGA, S. (1839) Naturgeschichte der Infusionsthiere vorzüglich nach Ehrenbergs Beobachtungen. St. Petersburg. [In Russian; a compilation directly from Ehrenberg (1838)]

—————— (1841) Naturgeschichte der Infusionsthiere vorzüglich nach Ehrenbergs Beobachtungen. Karlsruhe. 143 pp. [A German translation of Kutorga (1839)]

LACHMANN, J. (1856) Ueber die Organisation der Infusorien, besonders der Vorticellen. *Arch. Anat. Physiol., Lpz.* [" *Müller's Archiv* "], pp. 340–398.

LACKEY, J. B. (1925) Studies on the biology of sewage disposal. The fauna of Imhoff tanks. *Bull. N. J. agric. Exp. Sta.*, No. 417, pp. 1–39.

—————— (1936) Occurrence and distribution of the marine protozoan species in the Woods Hole area. *Biol. Bull.*, 70: 264–278.

—————— (1938) A study of some ecological factors affecting the distribution of protozoa. *Ecol. Monogr.*, 8: 501–527.

LAIRD, M. (1953) The protozoa of New Zealand intertidal zone fishes. *Trans. roy. Soc. N. Z.*, 81: 79–143.

—————— (1959) *Caliperia brevipes* n. sp. (Ciliata: Peritricha) epizoic on *Raja erinacea* Mitchill at Saint Andres, New Brunswick. *Canad. J. Zool.*, 37: 283–288.

LAMY, L. and H. ROUX (1950) Remarques morphologiques, biologiques et spécifiques sur les *Balantidium* de culture. *Bull. Soc. Path. exot.*, 43: 422–427.

LANDIS, E. M. (1925) Conjugation of *Paramecium multimicronucleata* Powers and Mitchell. *J. Morph.*, 40: 111–167.

LANESSAN, J. L. (1882) Traité de Zoologie. Protozoaires. Octave Doin, Paris. 336 pp.

LANKESTER, E. R. (1873) Blue stentorin.—The colouring matter of *Stentor coeruleus*. *Quart. J. micr. Soc.*, 13: 139–142.

—————— (1885) Protozoa. *In* Encyclopaedia Britannica, 9th ed., Vol. XIX, pp. 830–866.

LAPAGE, G. (1956) Veterinary Parasitology. Oliver and Boyd, London and Edinburgh. 964 pp.

LATTEUR, B. (1958) Les ciliates Polydiniinae. *Thoracodinium vorax* n. g.; n. sp. *Cellule*, 59: 269–296.

LAUTERBORN, R. (1908) Protozoen-Studien. V. Teil. Zur Kenntnis einiger Rhizopoden und Infusorien aus dem Gebiete des Oberrheins. *Z. wiss. Zool.*, 90: 645–669.

—— (1916) Die sapropelische Lebewelt. Ein Beitrag zur Biologie des Faulschlammes natürlicher Gewässer. *Verh. naturh.-med. Ver. Heidelb.* (N.S.), 13: 396–480.

LEBEDEW, W. (1908) Über *Trachelocerca phoenicopterus* Cohn. Ein marines Infusor. *Arch. Protistenk.*, 13: 70–114.

LE DANTEC, F. (1892) Recherches sur la symbiose des algues et des protozoaires. *Ann. Inst. Pasteur*, 6: 190–198.

LEEGAARD, C. (1915) Untersuchungen über einige Planktonciliaten des Meeres. *Nytt Mag. Naturv.*, 53: 1–37.

LEEUWENHOEK, A. VAN (1674) More observations from Mr. Leewenhook, in a letter of September 7, 1674, sent to the publisher. *Phil. Trans. roy. Soc.*, 9: 178–182.

LEPSI, J. (1926a) Die Infusorien des Süsswassers und Meeres. Bermühler, Berlin. 100 pp.

—— (1926b) Über die Protozoen fauna einiger Quellen der Dobrudscha. *Arch. Hydrobiol.*, 17: 751–770.

—— (1926c) Zur Kenntnis einiger Holotrichen. *Arch. Protistenk.*, 53: 378–406.

—— (1929) Zur Phylogenie der Ciliaten. *Bul. fac. Ştiinţe Cernăuţi*, 3: 258–303.

—— (1932) Recherches préliminaires sur les protozoaires des torrents de Sinaïa. *Publ. Soc. nat. Rom.*, No. 10, pp. 1–53.

—— (1957a) Protozoen aus dem anmoorigen Gebirgssee St. Anna in Rumänien. *Trav. Mus. Hist. nat.*, " Gr. Antipa," 1: 73–104.

—— (1957b) [Holotrich ciliates from the East Carpathian highlands of Poiano Stampei (Vatre Dornei).] *Bul. Ştiinţ. Acad. rômane*, ser. Zool., 9: 5–13. [In Roumanian with Russian and German summaries]

—— (1959) Über einige neue holotriche Süsswasser-Ciliaten. *Arch. Protistenk.*, 104: 254–260.

LEVANDER, K. M. (1893) Beiträge zur Kenntniss einiger Ciliaten. *Acta Soc. Fauna Flora fenn.*, 9: 1–87. [Reprinted as a separate in 1894]

—— (1894) Materialen zur Kenntniss der Wasserfauna in der Umgebung von Helsingfors, mit besonderer Berücksichtigung der Meeresfauna. I. Protozoa. *Acta Soc. Fauna Flora fenn.*, 12: 1–116.

LEVINE, M. (1953) The interaction of nucleus and cytoplasm in the isolation and evolution of species of *Paramecium*. *Evolution*, 7: 366–385.

LEVINE, N. D. (1940) The effect of food intake upon the dimensions of *Balantidium* from swine in culture. *Amer. J. Hyg.*, 32C: 81–87.

—— (1961) Protozoan Parasites of Domestic Animals and of Man. Burgess, Minneapolis. [In press]

LICHTENBERG, E. (1955a) Untersuchungen über die Auslösung der Konjugation und das Überleben der Exkonjuganten bei *Stylonychia mytilus*. *Arch. Protistenk.*, 100: 378–394.

———— (1955b) Die Beeinflussung der Lebensfähigkeit und Teilungsrate von *Stylonychia mytilus* durch Aussenfactoren und Wirkstoffe. *Arch. Protistenk.*, 100: 395–430.

LILLIE, F. (1896) On the smallest part of *Stentor* capable of regeneration; a contribution on the limits of divisibility of living matter. *J. Morph.*, 12: 239–249.

LILLY, D. M. (1942) Nutritional and supplementary factors in the growth of carnivorous ciliates. *Physiol. Zoöl.*, 15: 146–167.

———— (1953) The nutrition of carnivorous protozoa. *Ann. N. Y. Acad. Sci.*, 56: 910–920.

LILLY, D. M. and W. H. CEVALLOS (1956) Chemical supplements promoting growth in carnivorous ciliates. *Trans. N. Y. Acad. Sci.*, 18: 531–539.

LILLY, D. M. and S. M. HENRY (1956) Supplementary factors in the nutrition of *Euplotes*. *J. Protozool.*, 3: 200–203.

LINNAEUS, C. (1758) Systema Naturae. Vol. I. 10th ed. Salvii, Holmiae. 823 pp.

———— (1766) Systema Naturae. Vol. I. 12th ed. Salvii, Holmiae. 1,327 pp.

LOEFER, J. B. (1952) Some observations on the size of *Tetrahymena*. *J. Morph.*, 90: 407–414.

———— (1959) Ciliary antigens of Tetrahymenidae. *Proc. XV int. Congr. Zool.*, London, 1958, pp. 126–127.

LOEFER, J. B., OWEN, R. D., and E. CHRISTENSEN (1958) Serological types among thirty-one strains of the ciliated protozoan *Tetrahymena pyriformis*. *J. Protozool.*, 5: 209–217.

LOM, J. (1956) Beiträge zur Kenntnis der parasitischen Ciliaten aus Evertebraten I. *Arch. Protistenk.*, 101: 277–288.

———— (1957) Beiträge zur Kenntnis der parasitischen Ciliaten aus Evertebraten II. *Jirovecella hegemonis* n. g. n. sp. *Arch. Protistenk.*, 102: 229–240.

———— (1958) A contribution to the systematics and morphology of endoparasitic trichodinids from amphibians, with a proposal of uniform specific characteristics. *J. Protozool.*, 5: 251–263.

———— (1959a) Beiträge zur Kenntnis der parasitischen Ciliaten aus Evertebraten III. Neue Arten der Gattung *Bütschliellopsis* de Puytorac 1954 und der Gattung *Akidodes* n. g. *Arch. Protistenk.*, 103: 457–488.

———— (1959b) Beiträge zur Kenntnis der parasitischen Ciliaten aus Evertebraten IV. Neue Ciliaten aus der Familie Haptophryidae Cépède 1923, nebst einigen Bemerkungen zum heutigen Stand dieser Gruppe. *Arch. Protistenk.*, 104: 133–154.

———— (1959c) On the systematics of the genus *Trichodinella* Šrámek-Hušek (= *Brachyspira* Raabe). *Acta Parasit. polon.*, 7: 573–590.

────── (1959d) A contribution to the knowledge of astomatous ciliates. *Mém. Soc. zool. tchécosl.*, 23: 200–210.

────── (1960) Polysaccharidenreserven bei den Ciliaten aus der Ordnung Astomata. *Zool. Anz.*, 164: 111–114.

Losina-Losinsky, L. K. (1931) Zur Ernährungsphysiologie der Infusorien: Untersuchungen über die Nahrungsauswahl und Vermehrung bei *Paramaecium caudatum*. *Arch. Protistenk.*, 74: 18 120.

Lubinsky, G. (1957a) Studies on the evolution of the Ophryoscolecidae (Ciliata: Oligotricha). I. A new species of *Entodinium* with " caudatum," " loboso-spinosum," and " dubardi " forms, and some evolutionary trends in the genus *Entodinium*. *Canad. J. Zool.*, 35: 111–133.

────── (1957b) Studies on the evolution of the Ophryoscolecidae (Ciliata: Oligotricha). II. On the origin of the higher Ophryoscolecidae. *Canad. J. Zool.*, 35: 135–140.

────── (1957c) Studies on the evolution of the Ophryoscolecidae (Ciliata: Oligotricha) III. Phylogeny of the Ophryoscolecidae based on their comparative morphology. *Canad. J. Zool.*, 35: 141–159.

────── (1958a) Ophryoscolecidae (Ciliata: Entodiniomorphida) of reindeer (*Rangifer tarandus* L.) from the Canadian Arctic. I. Entodiniinae. *Canad. J. Zool.*, 36: 819–835.

────── (1958b) Ophryoscolecidae (Ciliata: Entodiniomorphida) of the reindeer (*Rangifer tarandus* L) from the Canadian Arctic. II. Diplodiniinae. *Canad. J. Zool.*, 36: 937–959.

Lucas, M. S. (1932a) A study of *Cyathodinium piriforme*. An endozoic protozoan from the intestinal tract of the guinea-pig. *Arch. Protistenk.*, 77: 64–72.

────── (1932b) The cytoplasmic phases of rejuvenescence and fission in *Cyathodinium piriforme*. II. A type of fission heretofore undescribed for ciliates. *Arch. Protistenk.*, 77: 406–423.

────── (1934) Ciliates from Bermuda sea urchins. I. *Metopus*. *J. roy. micr. Soc.*, 54: 79–93.

────── (1940) *Cryptochilidium* (*Cryptochilum*) *bermudense*, a ciliate from Bermuda sea urchins. *J. Morph.*, 66: 369–390.

Ludwig, W. (1930) Zur Theorie der Flimmerbewegung (Dynamik, Nutzeffekt, Energiebilanz). *Z. vergl. Physiol.*, 13: 397–504.

Lund, E. E. (1933) A correlation of the silverline and neuromotor systems of *Paramecium*. *Univ. Calif. Publ. Zool.*, 39: 35–76.

────── (1935) The neuromotor system of *Oxytricha*. *J. Morph.*, 58: 257–273.

Lust, S. (1950) Symphorionte Peritrichen auf Käfern und Wanzen. *Zool. Jb. (Abt. Syst., Ökol. u. Geog. Tiere)*, 79: 353–436.

Luyet, B. J. and P. M. Gehenio (1935) Comparative ultra-violet absorption by the constituent parts of protozoan cells (*Paramaecium*). *Biodynamica*, 1 (7): 1–14.

LWOFF, A. (1923) Sur la nutrition des infusoires. *C. R. Acad. Sci., Paris*, 176: 928–930.

————— (1924) Infection expérimentale à *Glaucoma piriformis* chez *Galleria mellonella* (Lepidoptère). *C. R. Acad. Sci., Paris*, 178: 1106–1108.

————— (1932) Recherches Biochimiques sur la Nutrition des Protozoaires. Le Pouvoir Synthèse. Monogr. Inst. Pasteur. Masson et Cie, Paris. 158 pp.

————— (1936) Le cycle nucléaire de *Stephanopogon Mesnili* Lw. (cilié homocaryote). *Arch. Zool. exp. gén.*, 78 (*Notes et Rev.*): 117–132.

————— (1943) L'Évolution Physiologique: Étude des Pertes de Fonctions chez les Microorganismes. Hermann et Cie, Paris. 308 pp.

————— (1948) La vie et l'oeuvre d'Édouard Chatton. *Arch. Zool. exp. gén.*, 85: 121–137.

————— (1950) Problems of Morphogenesis in Ciliates. Wiley and Sons, New York. 103 pp.

—————, editor (1951) Biochemistry and Physiology of Protozoa. Vol. I. Academic Press, New York. 434 pp.

LYNCH, J. E. (1929) Studies on the ciliates from the intestine of *Strongylocentrotus*. I. *Entorhipidium* gen. nov. *Univ. Calif. Publ. Zool.*, 33: 27–56.

————— (1930) Studies on the ciliates from the intestine of *Strongylocentrotus*. II. *Lechriopyla mystax*, gen. nov., sp. nov. *Univ. Calif. Publ. Zool.*, 33: 307–350.

LYNCH, J. E. and A. E. NOBLE (1931) Notes on the genus *Endosphaera* Engelmann and on its occasional host *Opisthonecta henneguyi* Fauré-Fremiet. *Univ. Calif. Publ. Zool.*, 36: 97–114.

MACDOUGALL, M. S. (1925) Cytological observations on gymnostomatous ciliates, with a description of the maturation phenomena in diploid and tetraploid forms of *Chilodon uncinatus*. *Quart. J. micr. Sci.*, 69: 361–384.

————— (1928) The neuromotor apparatus of *Chlamydodon* sp. *Biol. Bull.*, 54: 471–484.

————— (1929a) Modifications of *Chilodon uncinatus* produced by use of ultraviolet radiation. *J. exp. Zool.*, 54: 95–109.

————— (1929b) The conjugation of a triploid *Chilodon*. *Quart. J. micr. Sci.*, 73: 215–223.

————— (1931) Another mutation of *Chilodon uncinatus* produced by use of ultraviolet radiation, with a description of its maturation processes. *J. exp. Zool.*, 58: 229–236.

————— (1935) Cytological studies of the genus *Chilodonella* Strand, 1926 (*Chilodon* Ehrbg., 1838). I. The conjugation of *Chilodonella* sp. *Arch. Protistenk.*, 84: 199–206.

——— (1936) Étude cytologique de trois espèces du genre *Chilodonella* Strand. Morphologie, conjugaison, réorganisation. *Bull. biol. France Belg.*, 70:308–331.

MacLennan, R. F. (1935a) Ciliates from the stomach of mule-deer. *Trans. Amer. micr. Soc.*, 54: 181–188.

——— (1935b) Dedifferentiation and redifferentiation in *Ichthyophthirius*. I. Neuromotor system. *Arch. Protistenk.*, 86: 191–210.

——— (1939) The morphology and locomotor activities of *Cyclochaeta domerguei* Wallengren (Protozoa). *J. Morph.*, 65: 241–255.

——— (1943) Centrifugal stratification of granules in the ciliate *Ichthyophthiris*. *J. Morph.*, 72: 1–25.

——— (1944) The pulsatory cycle of the contractile canal in the ciliate *Haptophrya*. *Trans. Amer. micr. Soc.*, 63: 187–198.

MacLennan, R. F. and F. H. Connell (1931) The morphology of *Eupoterion pernix* gen. nov., sp. nov., a holotrichous ciliate from the intestine of *Acmaea persona* Eschscholtz. *Univ. Calif. Publ. Zool.*, 36: 141–156.

Madsen, H. (1931) Bemerkungen über einige entozoische und freilebende marine Infusorien der Gattungen *Uronema, Cyclidium, Cristigera, Aspidisca* und *Entodiscus* gen. n. *Zool. Anz.*, 96: 99–112.

Maier, H. N. (1903) Über den feineren Bau der Wimperapparate der Infusorien. *Arch. Protistenk.*, 2: 73–179.

Mandl, L. (1839) Recherches sur l'Organisation dex Animaux Infusoires, par D. Chr. G. Ehrenberg. Paris. 486 pp. [French " extraction " of Ehrenberg (1838)].

Mansfeld, K. (1923) 16 neue oder wenig bekannte marine Infusorien. *Arch. Protistenk.*, 46: 97–140.

Manwell, R. D. (1928) Conjugation, division and encystment in *Pleurotricha lanceolata*. *Biol. Bull.*, 54: 417–463.

——— (1961) Protozoology. St. Martin's Press, New York. [In press]

Margolin, P. (1954) A method for obtaining amacronucleated animals in *Paramecium aurelia*. *J. Protozool.*, 1: 174–177.

Margolin, P., Loefer, J. B., and R. D. Owen (1959) Immobilizing antigens of *Tetrahymena pyriformis*. *J. Protozool.*, 6: 207–215.

Markees, D. G., Dewey, V. C., and G. W. Kidder (1960) The inhibition of certain protozoa by diaminoalkoxypyridines. *Arch. Biochem. Biophys.*, 86: 179–184.

Marshall, S. M. (1934) The Silicoflagellata and Tintinnoinea. *Sci. Rep. Gr. Barrier Reef Exped., London*, 4, 15: 623–664.

Maskell, W. M. (1886–1887) On the freshwater infusoria of the Wellington district. *Trans. Proc. N. Z. Inst.*, 19: 44–61; 20: 3–19.

Mast, S. O. (1909) The reactions of *Didinium nasutum* with special reference to the feeding-habits and the function of trichocysts. *Biol. Bull.*, 16: 91–118.

—— (1911) Habits and reactions of the ciliate, *Lacrymaria*. *J. Anim. Behav.*, 1: 229–243.

—— (1947) The food vacuole in *Paramecium*. *Biol. Bull.*, 92: 31–72.

MAST, S. O. and W. J. BOWEN (1944) The food-vacuole in the Peritricha, with special reference to the hydrogen-ion concentration of its content and of the cytoplasm. *Biol. Bull.*, 87: 188–222.

MATTHES, D. (1950) Beitrag zur Peritrichenfauna der Umgebung Erlangens. *Zool. Jb.* (*Abt. Syst., Ökol. u. Geog. Tiere*), 79: 437–448.

—— (1954) Beitrag zur Kenntnis der Gattung *Discophrya* Lachmann. *Arch. Protistenk.*, 99: 187–226.

—— (1956) Suktorienstudien VIII. *Thecacineta calix* (Schröder 1907) (Thecacinetidae nov. fam.) und ihre Fortpflanzung durch Vermoid-Schwärmer. *Arch. Protistenk.*, 101: 477–528.

—— (1958) Das peritriche Ciliat *Cyclodonta bipartita* (Stokes) nov. gen. *Arch. Protistenk.*, 102: 481–500.

MAUPAS, É. (1876) Sur l'organisation et le passage à l'état mobile de la *Podophrya fixa*. *Arch. Zool. exp. gén.*, 5: 401–428.

—— (1881) Contribution à l'étude des acinétiens. *Arch. Zool. exp. gén.*, 9: 299–368.

—— (1883) Contribution à l'étude morphologique et anatomique des infusoires ciliés. *Arch. Zool. exp. gén.* (sér. 2), 1: 427–664.

—— (1885) Sur *Coleps hirtus* (Ehrenberg). *Arch. Zool. exp. gén.* (sér. 2), 3: 337–367.

—— (1888) Recherches expérimentales sur la multiplication des infusoires ciliés. *Arch. Zool. exp. gén.* (sér. 2), 6: 165–277.

—— (1889) La rajeunissement karyogamique chez les ciliés. *Arch. Zool. exp. gén.* (sér. 2), 7: 149–517.

MAYER, M. (1956) Kultur und Präparation der Protozoen. Keller, Stuttgart. 83 pp.

MAYR, E., LINSLEY, E. G., and R. L. USINGER (1953) Methods and Principles of Systematic Zoology. McGraw-Hill, New York. 328 pp.

MAZIA, D., BREWER, P. A., and M. ALFERT (1953) The cytochemical staining and measurement of protein with mercuric bromphenol blue. *Biol. Bull.*, 104: 57–67.

MCARDLE, E. W. (1959) The preparation of ciliates for nuclear staining by embedding in albumin. (Abstr.). *J. Protozool.*, 6 (Suppl.): 12–13.

—— (1960a) A comparative investigation of free-living strains of *Tetrahymena rostrata*. (Abstr.). *J. Protozool.*, 7 (Suppl.): 17.

—— (1960b) The occurrence of " small " strains from normal clones of *Tetrahymena rostrata*. (Abstr.). *J. Protozool.*, 7 (Suppl.): 23.

MCDONALD, B. B. (1958) Quantitative aspects of deoxyribose nucleic acid (DNA) metabolism in an amicronucleate strain of *Tetrahymena*. *Biol. Bull.*, 114: 71–94.

MCDONALD, J. D. (1922) On *Balantidium coli* Malmsten and *Balantidium suis* (sp. nov.). *Univ. Calif. Publ. Zool.*, 20: 243–300.

McLaughlin, R. E. (1959) Experimental infection of larval and pupal stages of *Galleria mellonella* (L.) (Pyralidae, Lepidoptera) by the ciliate *Tetrahymena pyriformis* (Ehrbg.). (Abstr.) *J. Protozool.*, 6 (Suppl.): 27.

McLoughlin, D. K. (1957) Macronuclear morphogenesis during division of *Blepharisma undulans. J. Protozool.*, 4: 150–153.

Mereschkowsky, C. von (1877) [Studies on the protozoa of northern Russia.] *Trud. Sank. Petersb. obs. estestvoispytat.*, 7: 203–385. [In Russian]

—— (1879) Studien über Protozoen des nördlichen Russlands. *Arch. mikr. Anat.*, 16: 153–248.

Mermod, G. (1914) Recherches sur la faune infusoriennes des tourbières et des eaux voisines de Sainte-Croix (Jura vaudois). *Rev. suisse Zool.*, 22: 31–114.

Merton, H. (1935) Versuche zur Geotaxis von *Paramaecium. Arch. Protistenk.*, 85: 33–60.

Metcalf, M. M. (1909) *Opalina.* Its anatomy and reproduction, with a description of infection experiments and a chronological review of the literature. *Arch. Protistenk.*, 13: 195–375.

—— (1923) The opalinid ciliate infusorians. *Bull. U. S. nat. Mus.*, No. 120, pp. 1–484.

—— (1940) Further studies on the opalinid ciliate infusorians and their hosts. *Proc. U. S. nat. Mus.*, 87: 465–635.

Métalnikow, S. (1912) Contributions à l'étude de la digestion intracellulaire chez les protozoaires. *Arch. Zool. exp. gén.* (sér. 5), 9: 373–499.

Metz, C. B. (1954) Mating substances and the physiology of fertilization in ciliates. *In* Wenrich, D. H., editor, Sex in Microorganisms, pp. 284–334. AAAS Pub., Washington, D.C.

Metz, C. B., Pitelka, D. R., and J. A. Westfall (1953) The fibrillar systems of ciliates as revealed by the electron microscope. I. *Paramecium. Biol. Bull.*, 104: 408–425.

Metz, C. B. and J. A. Westfall (1954) The fibrillar systems of ciliates as revealed by the electron microscope. II. *Tetrahymena. Biol. Bull.*, 107: 106–122.

Meunier, A. (1910) Microplankton des Mers de Barents et de Kara. Duc d'Orleans, Campagne Arctique de 1907. Bulen, Bruxelles. 355 pp.

Michelson, E. (1928) Existenzbedingungen und Cystenbildung bei *Paramaecium caudatum* Ehrbg. *Arch. Protistenk.*, 61: 167–184.

Miller, C. A. and W. H. Johnson (1957) A purine and pyrimidine requirement for *Paramecium multimicronucleatum. J. Protozool.*, 4: 200–204.

Miller, C. A. and W. J. van Wagtendonk (1956) The essential metabolites of a strain of *Paramecium aurelia* (stock 47.8) and a comparison of the growth rate of different strains of *Paramecium aurelia* in axenic culture. *J. gen. Microbiol.*, 15: 280–291.

MINCHIN, E. A. (1912) An Introduction to the Study of the Protozoa, with Special Reference to the Parasitic Forms. Arnold, London. 517 pp.

—— (1915) The evolution of the cell. *Rep. Brit. Ass. Adv. Sci.*, *London*, yr. 1915, No. 85, pp. 437–464. [Reprinted in 1916 in *Amer. Nat.*, 50: 5–38, 106–118, 271–283.]

MINKIEWICZ, R. (1912) *Ciliata chromatophora*, nouvel ordre d'infusoires à morphologie et reproduction bizarres. *C. R. Acad. Sci., Paris*, 155: 513–515.

—— (1914) Études sur les infusoires syndesmogames, à gamontes et gamètes. *Bull. int. Acad. Cracovie (Acad. polon. Sci.)*, (B), yr. 1913, pp. 742–749.

MIYAKE, A. (1956) Artificially induced micronuclear variation in *Paramecium caudatum*. *J. Inst. Polytech., Osaka*, 7 D: 147–161.

—— (1957) Physiological analysis of the life cycle of the protozoa. IV. Artificial induction of excystment in *Bursaria truncatella*. *Physiol. Ecol.*, 7: 123–126.

—— (1958) Induction of conjugation by chemical agents in *Paramecium caudatum*. *J. Inst. Polytech., Osaka*, 9 D: 251–296.

MIYASHITA, Y. (1929) Ueber eine primitive Form von Infusoria-Astomata, *Protoanoplophrya stomata* gen. n., sp. n. *Annot. zool. jap.*, 12: 289–293.

—— (1933) Studies on a freshwater foettingeriid ciliate, *Hyalospira caridinae* n. g., n. sp. *Jap. J. Zool.*, 4: 439.

MÖBIÜS, K. (1888) Bruchstücke einer Infusorienfauna der Kieler Bucht. *Arch. Naturgesch.*, 54: 81–116.

MOHR, J. L. (1948) *Trichochona lecythoides*, a new genus and species of marine chonotrichous ciliate from California, with a consideration of the composition of the order Chonotricha Wallengren, 1895. *Occ. Pap. Allan Hancock Fdn.*, 5: 1–21.

—— (1959) Ciliates on crustaceans: the evolution of the order Chonotrichida. *Proc. XV int. Congr. Zool.*, London, 1958, pp. 651–653.

MOHR, J. L. and J. A. LEVEQUE (1948) Occurrence of *Conidophrys pilisuctor* on *Corophium acherusicum* in Californian waters. (Abstr.) *J. Parasit.*, 34: 253.

MØLLER, K. M. (1958) On the nature of stentorin. *IV int. Congr. Biochem.*, Vienna, 1958, *Abstrs. of Communications*, p. 162.

MOODY, J. E. (1912) Observations on the life history of two rare ciliates, *Spathidium spathula* and *Actinobolus radians*. *J. Morph.*, 23: 349–407.

MOORE, E. L. (1924a) Regeneration at various phases in the life-history of *Spathidium spathula* and *Blepharisma undulans*. *J. exp. Zool.*, 39: 249–316.

—— (1924b) Endomixis and encystment in *Spathidium spathula*. *J. exp. Zool.*, 39: 317–337.

MOORE, J. (1934) Morphology of the contractile vacuole and cloacal region in *Blepharisma undulans*. *J. exp. Zool.*, 69: 59–104.

MORGAN, B. B. and P. A. HAWKINS (1948) Veterinary Protozoology. Burgess, Minneapolis. 195 pp.

MORGAN, T. H. (1901) Regeneration of proportionate structure in *Stentor*. *Biol. Bull.*, 2: 311–328.

MOSES, M. J. (1950) Nucleic acids and proteins of the nuclei of *Paramecium*. *J. Morph.*, 87: 493–536.

MOXON, W. (1869) On some points in the anatomy of *Stentor*, and on its mode of division. *J. Anat.*, *Lond.*, yr. 1869, pp. 279–293.

MUČIBABIĆ, S. (1957a) The growth of mixed populations of *Chilomonas paramecium* and *Tetrahymena pyriformis*. *J. gen. Microbiol.*, 16: 561–571.

——— (1957b) The growth of mixed populations of *Chilomonas paramecium* and *Tetrahymena patula*. *Quart. J. micr. Sci.*, 98: 251–263.

MUDREZOWA-WYSS, F. K. (1929) Eine neue Form der *Infusoria aspirotricha*. " *Triloba paradoxa* " nov. gen. nov. sp. *Arch. Protistenk.*, 68: 422–426.

MUGARD, H. (1948) Régulation du nombre des cinéties au cours du cycle de croissance et de division chez un cilié: *Ichthyophthirius multifiliis* Fouquet. *Arch. Anat. micr. Morph. exp.*, 37: 204–213.

——— (1949) Contribution à l'étude des infusoires hyménostomes histiophages. *Ann. Sci. nat.*, *Zool.* (sér. 11), 10: 171–268.

——— (1957) Nouvelle technique de coloration pour les noyaux et la ciliature des infusoires. *Bull. Micr. appl.*, 7: 36–39.

MUGARD, H. and L. LORSIGNOL (1957) Étude de la division et de la régénération chez deux Ophryoglenidae d'eau douce: *Ophryoglena pectans* et *Deltopylum rhabdoides*. *Bull. biol. France Belg.*, 90: 446–464.

MUGARD, H. and P. RENAUD (1960) Étude de l'effet des ultrasons sur un infusoire cilié *Paramecium caudatum*. *Arch. Biol.*, 71: 73–91.

MÜGGE, E. (1957) Die Konjugation von *Vorticella campanula* (Ehrbg.). *Arch. Protistenk.*, 102: 165–208.

MÜLLER, M. and É. TÓTH (1959) Effect of acethylcholine and serine on the ciliary reversal in *Paramecium multimicronucleatum*. (Abstr.) *J. Protozool.*, 6 (Suppl.): 28.

MÜLLER, O. F. (1773) Vermium Terrestrium et Fluviatilium, seu Animalium Infusorium, Helminthicorum et Testaceorum, non Marinorum, Succincta Historia. Havniae et Lipsiae. 135 pp.

——— (1776) Zoologiae Danicae Prodromus, seu Animalium Daniae et Norvegiae Indigenarum Characteres, Nomina, et Synonyma Imprimis Popularium. Havniae. 282 pp.

——— (1786) Animalcula Infusoria Fluviatilia et Marina. Havniae et Lipsiae. 367 pp.

MÜLLER, R. (1936) Die osmoregulatorische Bedeutung der Kontraktilen Vakuolen von *Amoeba proteus*, *Zoothamnium hiketes* und *Frontonia marina*. *Arch. Protistenk.*, 87: 345–382.

MÜLLER, W. (1932) Cytologische und vergleichend-physiologische Unter-suchungen über *Paramaecium multimicronucleatum* und *Paramaecium caudatum*, zugleich ein Versuch zur Kreuzung beider Arten. *Arch. Protistenk.*, 78: 361–462.

NADLER, J. E. (1929) Notes on the loss and regeneration of the pellicle in *Blepharisma undulans*. *Biol. Bull.*, 56: 327–330.

NANNEY, D. L. (1953) Nucleo-cytoplasmic interaction during conjugation in *Tetrahymena*. *Biol. Bull.*, 105: 133–148.

—— (1956) Caryonidal inheritance and nuclear differentiation. *Amer. Nat.*, 90: 291–307.

—— (1957) Inbreeding degeneration in *Tetrahymena*. *Genetics*, 42: 137–146.

—— (1958) Epigenetic control systems. *Proc. nat. Acad. Sci., Wash.*, 44: 712–717.

—— (1959a) Vegetative mutants and clonal senility in *Tetrahymena*. *J. Protozool.*, 6: 171–177.

—— (1959b) Genetic factors affecting mating type frequencies in variety 1 of *Tetrahymena pyriformis*. *Genetics*, 44: 1173–1184.

—— (1960) Temperature effects on nuclear differentiation in variety 1 of *Tetrahymena pyriformis*. *Physiol. Zoöl.*, 33: 146–151.

NANNEY, D. L. and S. L. ALLEN (1959) Intranuclear co-ordination in *Tetrahymena*. *Physiol. Zoöl.*, 32: 221–229.

NANNEY, D. L. and P. A. CAUGHEY (1953) Mating type determination in *Tetrahymena pyriformis*. *Proc. nat. Acad. Sci., Wash.*, 39: 1057–1063.

—— (1955) An unstable nuclear condition in *Tetrahymena pyriformis*. *Genetics*, 40: 388–398.

NANNEY, D. L., CAUGHEY, P. A., and A. TEFANKJIAN (1955) The genetic control of mating type potentialities in *Tetrahymena pyriformis*. *Genetics*, 40: 668–680.

NANNEY, D. L. and M. A. RUDZINSKA (1960) The Protozoa. Chapt. 3 (pp. 109–150) in Vol. IV, Specialized Cells, *in* Brachet, J. and A. E. Mirsky, editors, The Cell. Academic Press, New York.

NASSONOV, D. (1924) Der Exkretionsapparat (kontraktile Vakuole) der Protozoa als Homologon des Golgischen Apparats der Metazoazellen. *Arch. mikr. Anat.*, 103: 437–482.

NEAVE, S. A. (1939–1950) Nomenclator Zoologicus. Vols. I–V. Zoo-logical Society of London. 4,113 pp.

NEEDHAM, J. G., GALTSOFF, P. S., LUTZ, F. E., and P. S. WELCH, editors (1937) Culture Methods for Invertebrate Animals. Comstock, Ithaca, New York. 590 pp. [Reprinted in 1959 by Dover Publications, Inc.]

NEMETSCHEK, T., HOFMANN, U., and K. E. WOHLFARTH-BOTTERMANN (1953) Die Querstreifung der *Paramecium*-Trichocysten. *Z. Natur-forsch.*, 8b: 383–384.

NENNINGER, U. (1948) Die Peritrichen der Umgebung von Erlangen mit besonderer Berücksichtigung ihrer Wirtsspezifität. *Zool. Jb. (Abt. Syst., Ökol. u. Geog. Tiere)*, 77: 169–266.

NERESHEIMER, E. R. (1903) Ueber die Höhe histologischer Differenzierung bei heterotrichen Ciliaten. *Arch. Protistenk.*, 2: 305–324.

NEVEU-LEMAIRE, M. (1943) Traité de Protozoologie Médicale et Vétérinaire. Vigot Frères, Paris. 844 pp.

NIE, D. (1950) Morphology and taxonomy of the intestinal protozoa ot the guinea pig, *Cavia porcella. J. Morph.*, 86: 381–493.

NIE, D. and P. CH'ENG (1947) Tintinnoinea of the Hainan region. *Contrib. biol. Lab. Sci. Soc. China, Zool.*, 16: 41–86.

NIE, D. and K. S. Y. LU (1945) Studies on *Spathocyathus caridina* gen. et sp. nov., a suctoria attached to the antennae of a fresh-water shrimp, *Caridina* sp. *Sinensia*, 16: 57–64.

NIRENSTEIN, E. (1905) Beiträge zur Ernährungsphysiologie der Protisten. *Z. allg. Physiol.*, 5: 435–510.

NISSENBAUM, G. (1953) A combined method for the rapid fixation and adhesion of ciliates and flagellates. *Science*, 118: 31–32.

NOBLE, A. E. (1929) Two new species of the protozoan genus *Ephelota* from Monterey Bay, California. *Univ. Calif. Publ. Zool.*, 33: 13–26.

NOBLE, G. A. (1940) *Trichodina urechi* n. sp., an entozoic ciliate from the echiuroid worm, *Urechis caupo. J. Parasit.*, 26: 387–405.

NOIROT, C. and C. NOIROT-TIMOTHÉ (1959) *Termitophrya* gen. nov., nouveau type d'infusoire cilié commensal de certain termites. *C. R. Acad. Sci., Paris*, 249: 775–777.

NOIROT-TIMOTHÉE, C. (1956a) Les structures infraciliaires des Ophryocolecidae (infusoires oligotriches). Étude du genre *Ophryoscolex* Stein. *C. R. Acad. Sci., Paris*, 242: 2865–2867.

———— (1956b) La limite ectoplasme-endoplasme chez *Eudiplodinium medium* (infusoires Ophryoscolecidae). *Bull. Soc. zool. Fr.*, 81: 47–52.

———— (1957) L'ultrastructure de l'appareil de Golgi des infusoires Ophryoscolecidae. *C. R. Acad. Sci., Paris*, 244: 2847–2849.

———— (1958a) Étude au microscope électronique des fibres rétrociliaires des Ophryoscolecidae: leur ultrastructure, leur insertion, leur rôle possible. *C. R. Acad. Sci., Paris*, 246: 1286–1289.

———— (1958b) L'ultrastructure du blépharoplaste des infusoires ciliés. *C. R. Acad. Sci., Paris*, 246: 2293–2295.

———— (1959) [Please see p. 287]

———— (1960) [Published form of doctoral thesis, University of Paris, just now available. Please see p. 287 for full reference.]

NOLAND, L. E. (1925a) Factors influencing the distribution of fresh-water ciliates. *Ecology*, 6: 437–452.

———— (1925b) A review of the genus *Coleps* with descriptions of two new species. *Trans. Amer. micr. Soc.*, 44: 3–13.

—— (1927) Conjugation in the ciliate *Metopus sigmoides* C. and L. *J. Morph.*, 44: 341–361.

—— (1937) Observations on marine ciliates of the Gulf coast of Florida. *Trans. Amer. micr. Soc.*, 56: 160–171.

—— (1959) Ciliophora. *In* Edmondson, W. T., editor, Ward and Whipple's Fresh-Water Biology, 2nd ed., pp. 265–297. Wiley and Sons, New York.

NOLAND, L. E. and H. E. FINLEY (1931) Studies on the taxonomy of the genus *Vorticella*. *Trans. Amer. micr. Soc.*, 50: 81–123.

NOZAWA, K. (1938) Some new fresh-water suctoria. *Annot. zool. jap.*, 17: 247–259.

—— (1939) Two new species of the freshwater suctorians, *Pottsia* and *Metacineta*. *Annot. zool. jap.*, 18: 58–64.

—— (1941) A new primitive hypotrichous ciliate, *Kiitricha marina* n. g., n. sp. *Annot. zool. jap.*, 20: 24–26.

OBERTHÜR, K. (1937) Untersuchungen an *Frontonia marina* Fabre-Dom. aus einer Binnenland-Salzquelle unter besonderer Berücksichtigung der pulsierenden Vakuole. *Arch. Protistenk.*, 88: 387–420.

OKADA, T. A. (1956) Cytological study of *Frontonia leucas*, with a note on the variation of the number of micronuclei. *Annot. zool. jap.*, 29: 213–218.

OKAJIMA, A. (1957) Protoplasmic contraction observed on the tentacles of the Suctorian. I. Effects of electrolytes in the medium. *Annot. zool. jap.*, 30: 51–62.

ÖRDÖGH, F. (1959) Kernteilung in *Kahlia simplex* (Ciliata, Protozoa). *Acta biol. Acad. sci. hung.*, 10: 127–139.

ORIAS, E. (1958) The breeding system of variety 8, *Tetrahymena pyriformis*. (Abstr.) *J. Protozool.*, 5 (Suppl.): 17.

—— (1959) Mating interaction between varieties 6 and 8, *Tetrahymena pyriformis*. (Abstr.) *J. Protozool.*, 6 (Suppl.): 19.

—— (1960) The genetic control of two lethal traits in variety 1, *Tetrahymena pyriformis*. *J. Protozool.*, 7: 64–69.

OSTROUMOW, W. (1929) Ueber den Bau und Biologie von *Nyctotherus ovalis* Leidy. *Arch. russes Protist.*, 8: 24–50. [In Russian with German summary]

OXFORD, A. E. (1955) The rumen ciliate protozoa: their chemical composition, metabolism, requirements for maintenance and culture, and physiological significance for the host. *Exp. Parasit.*, 4: 569–605.

PADMAVATHI, P. B. (1959) Studies on the cytology of an Indian species of *Blepharisma* (Protozoa: Ciliata). *Mém. Soc. zool. tchécosl.*, 23: 230–246.

PADNOS, M., JAKOWSKA, S., and R. F. NIGRELLI (1954) Morphology and life history of *Colpoda maupasi*, Bensonhurst strain. *J. Protozool.*, 1: 131–139.

PAI, K.-T. (1948) The fibrillar system of *Frontonia leucas* (Ehrbg.). *Sinensia*, 19: 99–108.

PAI, K.-T. and C. C. WANG (1948) The variation of *Nyctotherus ovalis* Leidy, and its fibrillar system. *Sinensia*, 18: 43–58.

PALINCSAR, E. E. (1959) Nutritional effects of nucleic acids and nucleic acid components on cultures of the suctorian *Podophrya collini*. *J. Protozool.*, 6: 195–201.

PÁRDUCZ, B. (1936) Beiträge zur phylogenetischen Ableitung der hymenostomen Infusorien. *Arb. I. Abt. ung. biol. ForschInst.*, 8: 120–141. [In Hungarian with German summary]

——— (1939) Festsitzende Ciliaten in der Gruppe der Holotricha. *Acta. Biol. szeged.*, 5: 57–78. [In Hungarian with German summary]

——— (1940) Verwandtschaftliche Beziehungen zwischen den Gattungen *Uronema* und *Cyclidium*. Bau und Lebensweise von *Cyclidium glaucoma* Müll. *Arch. Protistenk.*, 93: 185–214.

——— (1952) Eine neue Schnellfärbemethode im Dienste der Protistenforschung und des Unterrichtes. *Ann. hist-nat. Mus. hung.* (N.S.), 2: 5–12. [In Hungarian with German and Russian summaries]

——— (1954) Reizphysiologische Untersuchungen an Ziliaten. I. Über das aktionssystem von *Paramecium*. *Acta microbiol. Acad. sci. hung.*, 1: 175–221.

——— (1957) Über den feineren Bau des Neuronemensystems der Ziliaten. *Ann. hist.-nat. Mus. hung.* (N.S.), 8: 231–246.

——— (1958a) Reizphysiologische Untersuchungen an Ziliaten. VII. Das Problem der vorbestimmten Leitungsbahnen. *Acta biol. Acad. sci. hung.*, 8: 219–251.

——— (1958b) Das interziliare Fasernsystem in seiner Beziehung zu gewissen Fibrillenkomplexen der Infusorien. *Acta biol. Acad. sci. hung.*, 8: 191–218.

——— (1959) Reizphysiologische Untersuchungen an Ziliaten. VIII. Ablauf der Fluchtreaktion bei allseitiger und anhaltender Reizung. *Ann. hist-nat. Mus. hung.*, 51: 227–246.

PEARL, R. (1907) A biometrical study of conjugation in *Paramecium*. *Biometrika*, 5: 213–297.

PEASE, D. C. (1947) The structure of trichocysts revealed by the electron microscope. *J. cell. comp. Physiol.*, 29: 91–94.

PEEBLES, F. (1912) Regeneration and regulation in *Paramecium caudatum*. *Biol. Bull.*, 23: 154–170.

PENARD, E. (1914a) Un curieux infusoire *Legendrea bellerophon*. *Rev. suisse Zool.*, 22: 407–433.

——— (1914b) Les cothurnidés muscicoles. *Mém. Soc. Phys., Genève*, 38: 19–73.

——— (1917) Le genre *Loxodes*. *Rev. suisse Zool.*, 25: 453–489.

——— (1920) Études sur les infusoires tentaculifères. *Mém Soc. Phys. Genève*, 39: 131–229.

258   THE CILIATED PROTOZOA

—— (1922) Études sur les Infusoires d'Eau Douce. Georg et Cie. Genève. 331 pp.

—— (1938) Les Infiniment Petits dans Leurs Manifestations Vitales. Georg et Cie, Genève. 212 pp.

PENN, A. B. K. (1935) Factors which control encystment in *Pleurotricha lanceolata*. *Arch. Protistenk.*, 84: 101–132.

PENNAK, R. W. (1953) Fresh-Water Invertebrates of the United States. Ronald Press, New York. 769 pp.

PERCY, M. (1929) *Physophaga sappheira*, n. g., n. sp. *Quart. J. micr. Sci.*, 73: 107–120.

PEREJASLAWZEWA, S. (1886) [Protozoa of the Black Sea.] *Schr. Naturforsch. Ges. Odessa*, 10: 79–114. [In Russian]

PERTY, M. (1852) Zur Kenntniss Kleinster Lebensformen nach Bau, Funktionen, Systematik, mit Specialverzeichniss der in der Schweiz beobachteten. Jent u. Reinert, Bern. 228 pp.

PERTZEWA, T. A. (1929) Zur Morphologie von *Plagiotoma lumbrici* Duj. *Arch. Protistenk.*, 65: 330–363.

PESCHKOFF, M. (1929) Beiträge zur Kenntniss der Biologie und Morphologie der *Bursaria truncatella* O. F. Müll., sowie ihres Kernapparates während der Teilung. *Arch. russes Protist.*, 8: 1–16. [In Russian with German summary]

PESCHKOWSKY, L. (1927) Skelettgebilde bei Infusorien. *Arch. Protistenk.*, 57: 31–57.

—— (1929) On the biology and morphology of *Climacostomum virens*. *Arch. russes Protist.*, 7: 205–234.

—— (1931) Zur Morphologie von *Dileptus gigas* und *Loxophyllum meleagris*. *Arch. Protistenk.*, 73: 179–202.

PESTEL, B. (1932) Beiträge zur Morphologie und Biologie des *Dendrocometes paradoxus* Stein. *Arch. Protistenk.*, 75: 403–471.

PHELPS, A. (1959) Effect of visible light on the growth of *Tetrahymena pyriformis*. *Ecology*, 40: 512–513.

PHILPOTT, C. H. (1930) Effect of toxins and venoms on protozoa. *J. exp. Zool.*, 56: 167–183.

—— (1932) Natural and acquired resistance in protozoa to the action of antigenic poisons. *J. exp. Zool.*, 63: 553–571.

PICKARD, E. A. (1927) The neuromotor apparatus of *Boveria teredinidi* Nelson, a ciliate from the gills of *Teredo navalis*. *Univ. Calif. Publ. Zool.*, 29: 405–428.

PICKEN, L. E. R. (1937) The structure of some protozoan communities. *J. Ecol.*, 25: 368–384.

—— (1960) The Organization of Cells and Other Organisms. Clarendon Press, Oxford. 629 pp.

PICK-LEVONTIN, E. M. and E. M. CHEISSIN (1940) [The variability of infusoria *Balantidium coli* from man and pig.] *Zool. Zh.*, 19: 99–118. [In Russian]

PIEKARSKI, G. (1939) Cytologische Untersuchungen an einem normalen und einem mikronucleus-losen Stamm von *Colpoda steini* Maupas. *Arch. Protistenk.*, 92: 117–130.
—— (1941) Endomitose beim Grosskern der Ziliaten? Versuch einer Synthese. *Biol. Zbl.*, 61: 416–426.
—— (1954) Lehrbuch der Parasitologie unter besonderer Berücksichtigung der Parasiten des Menschen. Springer, Berlin. 760 pp.
PIERSON, B. F. (1943) A comparative morphological study of several species of *Euplotes* closely related to *Euplotes patella*. *J. Morph.*, 72: 125–157.
PIGOŃ, A. (1950) The structure of the pellicle of *Paramecium caudatum* Ehrb. as revealed by micro-dissection. *Bull. int. Acad. Cracovie* (*Acad. polon. Sci.*), yr. 1949, pp. 215–229.
—— (1959) Respiration of *Colpoda cucullus* during life and encystment. *J. Protozool.*, 6: 303–308.
PITELKA, D. R. (1959a) Comparative morphology of the ciliary apparatus. *Proc. XV int. Congr. Zool.*, London, 1958, pp. 473–475.
—— (1959b) Ultrastructure of the silver-line system in three tetrahymenid ciliates. (Abstr.) *J. Protozool.*, 6 (Suppl.): 22.
PLATE, L. (1886) Untersuchungen einiger an den Kiemenblättern des *Gammarus pulex* lebenden Ektoparasiten. *Z. wiss. Zool.*, 43: 175–241.
—— (1889) Studien über Protozoen. *Zool. Jb.* (*Abt. Anat. u. Ontog. Thiere*), 3: 135–198.
PLOUGH, H. (1916) The genus *Aspidisca*, Ehrenberg. *Trans. Amer. micr. Soc.*, 35: 233–244.
POCHE, F. (1913) Das System der Protozoa. *Arch. Protistenk.*, 30: 125–321.
POLJANSKY, G. I. (1934) Geschlechtprozesse bie *Bursaria truncatella*. *Arch. Protistenk.*, 81: 420–546.
—— (1951a) [On some parasitic infusoria of marine molluscs and holothurians.] *Mag. Parasit.*, *Moscow*, 13: 355–370. [In Russian]
—— (1951b) [Intestinal infusoria of sea urchins.] *Mag. Parasit.*, *Moscow*, 13: 371–393. [In Russian]
—— (1959) Experimental investigation of temperature adaptations of infusoria. *Proc. XV int. Congr. Zool.*, London, 1958, pp. 716–718.
POLJANSKY, G. I. and M. N. GOLIKOWA (1957) Über Infusorien aus dem Darme der Seeigel. Mitteilung II. Eine neue Gattung der Infusorien aus *Strongylocentrotus droebachiensis* der Murmauküste. *Trav. Soc. Nat. St. Pétersb.* (*Leningr.*) 73: 138–142. [In Russian with German summary]
—— (1959) On the infusoria dwelling in the intestine of sea urchins. Part III. Infusoria of sea urchins of the Barrents Sea. *Zool. Zh.*, 38: 1138–1145. [In Russian with English summary]
POLJANSKY, G. I. and A. STRELKOW (1938) Étude expérimentale sur la variabilité de quelques ophryoscolécidés. *Arch. Zool. exp. gén.*, 80: 1–123.

S

POPOFF, M. (1908) Experimentelle Zellstudien. I. Teilung der Zelle und eng damit verknupfte Fragen. *Arch. Zellforsch.*, 1: 245–379.

——— (1909a) Experimentelle Zellstudien. II. Über die Zellgrösse, ihre Fixierung und Vererbung. *Arch. Zellforsch.*, 3: 124–180.

——— (1909b) Experimentelle Zellstudien. III. Über einige Ursachen der physiologischen Depression der Zelle. *Arch. Zellforsch.*, 4: 1–43.

PORTER, E. D. (1960) The buccal organelles in *Paramecium aurelia* during fission and conjugation, with special reference to the kinetosomes. *J. Protozool.*, 7: 211–217.

POTTAGE, R. H. (1959) Electron microscopy of the adults and migrants of the suctorian ciliate *Discophrya piriformis*. *Proc. XV int. Congr. Zool.*, London, 1958, pp. 472–473.

POTTS, B. P. (1955) Electron microscope observations on trichocysts. *Biochim. biophys. Acta*, 16: 464–470.

POTTS, B. P. and S. G. TOMLIN (1955) The structure of cilia. *Biochim. biophys. Acta*, 16: 66–74.

POWERS, E. L. (1943) The mating types of double animals in *Euplotes patella*. *Amer. Midl. Nat.*, 30: 175–195.

——— (1955) Radiation effects in *Paramecium*. *Ann. N. Y. Acad. Sci.*, 59: 619–636.

POWERS, E. L., EHRET, C. F., and L. E. ROTH (1955) Mitochondrial structure in *Paramecium* as revealed by electron microscopy. *Biol. Bull.*, 108: 182–195.

POWERS, E. L., EHRET, C. F., ROTH, L. E., and O. T. MINICK (1956) The internal organization of mitochondria. *J. biophys. biochem. Cytol.*, 2 (Suppl.): 341–346.

POWERS, J. H. and C. MITCHELL (1910) A new species of *Paramecium* (*P. multimicronucleata*) experimentally determined. *Biol. Bull.*, 19: 324–332.

POWERS, P. B. A. (1932) *Cyclotrichium meunieri* sp. n.: cause of red water in the Gulf of Maine. *Biol. Bull.*, 63: 74–80.

——— (1933a) Studies on the ciliates from sea urchins. I. General taxonomy. *Biol. Bull.*, 65: 106–121.

——— (1933b) Studies on the ciliates from sea urchins. II. *Entodiscus borealis* (Hentschel), (Protozoa, Ciliata), behavior and morphology. *Biol. Bull.*, 65: 122–136.

——— (1935) Studies on the ciliates of sea urchins. A general survey of the infestations occurring in Tortugas echinoids. *Pap. Tortugas Lab.*, 29: 293–326.

PRANDTL, H. (1906) Die Konjugation von *Didinium nasutum* O. F. M. *Arch. Protistenk.*, 7: 229–258.

PRATT, H. S. (1935) A Manual of the Common Invertebrate Animals Exclusive of Insects. Rev. ed. Blakiston, Philadelphia. 854 pp.

PRECHT, H. (1935) Epizoen der Kieler Bucht. *Nova Acta Leop. Carol.* (N.F.), 3: 405–474.

PREER, J. R., Jr. (1950) Microscopically visible bodies in the cytoplasm of the " killer " strains of *Paramecium aurelia*. *Genetics*, 35: 344–362.

——— (1957) Genetics of the protozoa. *Ann. Rev. Microbiol.*, 11: 419–438.

——— (1959) Nuclear and cytoplasmic differentiation in the protozoa. *In* Rudnick, D., editor, Developmental Cytology, pp. 3–20. Ronald Press, New York.

PREER, J. R., Jr. and L. B. PREER (1959) Gel diffusion studies on the antigens of isolated cellular components of *Paramecium*. *J. Protozool.*, 6: 88–100.

PREER, J. R., Jr. and P. STARK (1953) Cytological observations on the cytoplasmic factor " kappa " in *Paramecium aurelia*. *Exp. Cell Res.*, 5: 478–491.

PRENANT, A. (1913–1914) Les appareils ciliés et leurs dérivés. *J. Anat. Physiol.*, 49–50. [364 pages (total), appearing in various sections of the journal.]

PRENANT, M. (1935) Protozoaires. Infusoires Ciliés. Paris. 77 pp.

PRESCOTT, D. M. (1957) Change in the physiological state of a cell population as a function of culture growth and age (*Tetrahymena geleii*). *Exp. Cell Res.*, 12: 126–134.

——— (1959) Variations in the individual generation times of *Tetrahymena geleii* HS. *Exp. Cell Res.*, 16: 279–284.

PRESCOTT, D. M. and T. W. JAMES (1955) Culturing of *Amoeba proteus* on *Tetrahymena*. *Exp. Cell Res.*, 8: 256–258.

PRINGSHEIM, E. G. (1928) Physiologische Untersuchungen an *Paramaecium bursaria*. Ein Beitrag zur Symbioseforschung. I, II. *Arch. Protistenk.*, 64: 289–360, 361–418.

PRITZE, F. (1928) Beiträge zur kenntnis des *Balantidium coli*. Das Balantidium des Schweines in seiner Beziehung zum menschlichen Balantidium und sein Verhalten unter natürlichen und künstlichen Bedingungen. *Z. Parasitenk.*, 1: 345–415.

PROWAZEK, S. VON (1898–1903) Protozoenstudien. I, II, III. *Arb. zool. Inst. Univ. Wien*, 11: 195–268; 12: 243–300; 14: 81–88.

PUYTORAC, P. DE (1954a) Contribution à l'étude cytologique et taxonomique des infusoires astomes. *Ann. Sci. nat., Zool.* (sér. 11), 16: 85–270.

——— (1954b) Hématophagie chez *Nyctotherus scinci*, sp. nov., cilié hétérotriche parasite de *Scincus scincus* L. Remarques sur les nyctothères. *Bull. Soc. zool. Fr.*, 79: 121–127.

——— (1955) Sur *Hovasseiella polydorae* nov. gen., n. sp., cilié astome endoparasite de *Polydora giardi* Mesn. *Arch. Zool. exp. gén.*, 93 (*Notes et Rev.*): 20–34.

——— (1957a) L'infraciliature de quelques ciliés Haptophryidae. Comparaison avec celle de certains thigmotriches. *C. R. Acad. Sci., Paris*, 244: 1962–1965.

————— (1957b) Nouvelles données sur les ciliés Hoplitophryidae. *Arch. Zool. exp. gén.*, 94 (*Notes et Rev.*): 89–120.

————— (1959a) Quelques observations sur l'évolution et les origines des ciliés Astomatida. *Proc. XV int. Congr. Zool.*, London, 1958, pp. 649–651.

————— (1959b) Le cytosquelette et les systèmes fibrillaires du cilié *Metaradiophrya gigas* de Puytorac, d'après étude au microscope électronique. *Arch. Anat. micr. Morph. exp.*, 48: 49–62.

————— (1959c) Les *Lubetiella* nov. gen., ciliés endoparasites des vers Megascolecidae sont la preuve de l'origine trichostomienne de certains infusoires astomes. *C. R. Acad. Sci.*, Paris, 248: 1579–1582.

————— (1960) Observations sur quelques ciliés astomes des oligochètes de lac d'Ochrid (Yougoslavie). II. Familles des Hoplitophryidae (Hoplitophryinae et Maupasellinae), des Intoshellinidae et des Anoplophryidae. *J. Protozool.*, 7: 278–289.

QUENNERSTEDT, A. (1865–1869) Bidrag til sweriges Infusorienfauna. *Acta Univ. lund.*, 1: 64 pp.; 4: 47 pp.; 6: 35 pp. [In Swedish]

RAABE, H. (1946) L'appareil nucléaire d'*Urostyla grandis* Ehrbg. I. Appareil micronucléaire. *Ann. Univ. M. Curie-Skłodowska*, Sect. C, 1: 1–34. [In Polish with French translation]

————— (1947) L'appareil nucléaire d'*Urostyla grandis* Ehrbg. II. Appareil macronucléaire. *Ann. Univ. M. Curie-Skłodowska*, Sect. C, 1: 133–170. [In Polish with French translation]

RAABE, J. and Z. RAABE (1959) Urceolariidae of molluscs of the Baltic Sea. *Acta Parasit. polon.*, 7: 453–465.

RAABE, Z. (1933) Untersuchungen an einigen Arten des Genus *Conchophthirus* Stein. *Bull. int. Acad. Cracovie* (*Acad. polon. Sci.*), (B: II), yr. 1932, pp. 295–310.

————— (1936) Weitere Untersuchungen an parasitischen Ciliaten aus dem polonischen Teil der Ostsee. I. Ciliata Thigmotricha aus den Familien: Thigmophryidae, Conchophthiridae und Ancistrumidae. *Ann. Mus. zool. polon.*, 11: 419–442.

————— (1938) Weitere Untersuchungen an parasitischen Ciliaten aus dem polonischen Teil der Ostssee. II. Ciliata Thigmotricha aus den Familien: Hypocomidae Bütschli und Sphaerophryidae Ch. und Lw. *Ann. Mus. zool. polon.*, 13: 41–75.

————— (1947a) Les voies des adaptations morphologiques à la vie parasitique chez les ciliés. *Ann. Univ. M. Curie-Skłodowska*, Sect. C, 2: 299–411. [In Polish with French summary]

————— (1947b) Recherches sur les ciliés thigmotriches (Thigmotricha Ch. & Lw.). I. Sur un genre nouveau de la famille Conchophthiridae Kahl. *Ann. Univ. M. Curie-Skłodowska*, Sect. C, 1: 61–70.

—— (1948) An attempt of a revision of the system of Protozoa. *Ann. Univ. M. Curie-Skłodowska*, Sect. C, 3: 259–276. [In Polish with English summary]

—— (1949a) Studies on the family Hysterocinetidae Diesing. *Ann. Mus. zool. polon.*, 14: 21–68.

—— (1949b) Remarks on protozoan parasitocenose of some representatives of genus *Mytilus*. *Ann. Univ. M. Curie-Skłodowska*, Sect. C, 4: 1–16.

—— (1950a) Recherches sur les ciliés thigmotriches (Thigmotricha Ch. Lw.). V. Ciliés thigmotriches du lac Balaton (Hongrie). *Ann. Univ. M. Curie-Skłodowska*, Sect. C, 5: 197–215.

—— (1950b) Remarques sur les Urceolariidés (Ciliata — Peritricha), des branchies des poissons. *Ann. Univ. M. Curie-Skłodowska*, Sect. DD, 5: 291–310.

—— (1952) *Ambiphrya miri* g. n., sp. n. — eine Übergangsform zwischen Peritricha-Mobilia und Peritricha-Sessilia. *Ann. Univ. M. Curie-Skłodowska*, Sect. C, 6: 339–358. [In Polish with Russian and German summaries]

—— (1956) Investigations on the parasitofauna of freshwater molluscs in the brackish waters. *Acta Parasit. polon*, 4: 375–406.

—— (1959a) Recherches sur les ciliés thigmotriches (Thigmotricha Ch. Lw.). VI. Sur les genres " *Ancistruma*," " *Ancistrina* " et les genres voisins. *Acta Parasit. polon.*, 7: 215–247.

—— (1959b) *Trichodina pediculus* (O. F. Müller, 1786) Ehrenberg, 1838 et *Trichodina domerguei* (Wallengren, 1897). *Acta Parasit. polon.*, 7: 189–202.

—— (1959c) Urceolariidae of gills of Gobiidae and Cottidae from Baltic Sea. *Acta Parasit. polon.*, 7: 441–452.

Rafalko, M. and T. M. Sonneborn (1959) A new syngen (13) of *Paramecium aurelia* consisting of stocks from Mexico, France and Madagascar. (Abstr.) *J. Protozool.*, 6 (Suppl.): 30.

Raikov, I. B. (1958) Der Formwechsel des Kernapparates einiger niederer Ciliaten. I. Die Gattung *Trachelocerca*. *Arch. Protistenk.*, 103: 129–192.

—— (1959a) Der Formwechsel des Kernapparates einiger niederer Ciliaten. II. Die Gattung *Loxodes*. *Arch. Protistenk.*, 104: 1–42.

—— (1959b) [Cytological and cytochemical peculiarities of the nuclear apparatus and division in the holotrichous ciliate *Geleia nigriceps* Kahl.] *Cytology*, 1: 566–579. [In Russian]

Rammelmeyer, H. (1931) Zur Biologie einiger Raubinfusorien. *Arch. Protistenk.*, 73: 251–273.

Randall, J. T. (1956) The fine structure of some ciliate protozoa. *Nature*, 178: 9–14.

—— (1957) The fine structure of the protozoan *Spirostomum ambiguum*. *In* Mitochondria and Other Cytoplasmic Inclusions, Symp. 10, Soc. Exp. Biol., pp. 185–198. Academic Press, New York.

—————— (1959a) Comparative studies of fine structure and function ın ciliates. *Proc. XV int. Congr. Zool.*, London, 1958, pp. 468–470.

—————— (1959b) The nature and significance of kinetosomes. (Abstr.) *J. Protozool.*, 6 (Suppl.): 30.

—————— (1959c) Contractility in the stalks of Vorticellidae. (Abstr.) *J. Protozool.*, 6 (Suppl.): 30.

—————— (1959d) The stalks of Epistylidae. (Abstr.) *J. Protozool.*, 6 (Suppl.): 30–31.

RANDALL, J. T. and S. F. JACKSON (1958) Fine structure and function in *Stentor polymorphus*. *J. biophys. biochem. Cytol.*, 4: 807–830.

RAO, M. V. N. (1958) Mating types in *Stylonychia pustulata*. *Curr. Sci.*, 27: 395.

RAY, C., Jr. (1956a) Meiosis and nuclear behavior in *Tetrahymena pyriformis*. *J. Protozool.*, 3: 88–96.

—————— (1956b) Preparation of chromosomes of *Tetrahymena pyriformis* for photomicrography. *Stain. Tech.*, 31: 271–274.

RAY, C., Jr. and A. M. ELLIOTT (1954) Chromosome number of four varieties of *Tetrahymena*. (Abstr.) *Anat. Rec.*, 120: 812.

REES, C. W. (1922) The neuromotor apparatus of *Paramecium*. *Univ. Calif. Publ. Zool.*, 20: 333–364.

—————— (1931) The anatomy of *Diplodinium medium*. *J. Morph.*, 52: 195–215.

REES, E. VAN (1884) Protozoaires de l'escault de l'Est. *Tijdschr. ned. dierk. Ver.*, Suppl. D, 1 (2): 592–673.

REICHENOW, E. (1920) Den Wiederkäuer-Infusorien verwandte Formen aus Gorilla und Schimpanse. *Arch. Protistenk.*, 41: 1–33.

—————— (1928) Ergebnisse mit der Nuclealfärbung bei Protozoen. *Arch. Protistenk.*, 61: 144–166.

REYNOLDS, B. D. (1936) *Colpoda steini*, a facultative parasite of the land slug, *Agriolimax agrestis*. *J. Parasit.*, 22: 48–53.

REYNOLDS, M. E. C. (1932) Regeneration in an amicronucleate infusorian. *J. exp. Zool.*, 62: 327–361.

REYNOLDSON, T. B. (1955) Factors influencing population fluctuations of *Urceolaria mitra* (Peritricha) epizoic on freshwater triclads. *J. Anim. Ecol.*, 24: 57–83.

RHUMBLER, L. (1888) Die verschiedenen Cystenbildung und die Entwicklungsgeschichte der holotrichen Infusoriengattung *Colpoda*. *Z. wiss. Zool.*, 46: 549–601.

—————— (1925) Ciliophora. *In* Kükenthal, W. and T. Krumbach, *Handbuch der Zoologie*, Vol. 1, pp. 256–292. Berlin u. Leipzig.

RICHARDSON, U. F. and S. B. KENDALL (1957) Veterinary Protozoology. 2nd ed., rev. Oliver and Boyd, Edinburgh and London. 260 pp.

RIEDER, J. (1936a) Biologische und ökologische Untersuchungen an Süsswasser-Suktorien. *Arch. Naturgesch.* (N.F.), 5: 137–214.

—————— (1936b) Beitrag zur Kenntnis der Süsswasser-Suktorien und Revision der Schweizer Suktorien-Fauna. *Rev. suisse Zool.*, 43: 359–395.

RINGUELET, R. A. (1955) Protozoos folliculinidos y esponjas perforantes en consorcios con la ostra comestible Argentina (*Ostrea puelchana* d'Orb.). *Notas Mus. E. Peron*, 18: 175–190.

ROBERTSON, M. (1939a) A study of the reactions *in vitro* of certain ciliates belonging to the *Glaucoma–Colpidium* group to antibodies in the sera of rabbits immunised therewith. *J. Path. Bact.*, 48: 305–322.

—————— (1939b) An analysis of some of the antigenic properties of certain ciliates belonging to the *Glaucoma–Colpidium* group as shown in their response to immune serum. *J. Path. Bact.*, 48: 323–338.

—————— (1958) Some modern trends in protozoology. *Sci. Progress*, No. 181, pp. 1–14.

ROBERTSON, T. B. (1927) On some conditions affecting the viability of infusoria and the occurrence of allelocatalysis therein. *Aust. J. exp. Biol. med. Sci.*, 4: 1–23.

ROOT, F. M. (1914) Reproduction and reactions to food in the suctorian, *Podophrya collini* n. sp. *Arch. Protistenk.*, 35: 164–196.

ROQUE, M. (1956a) L'évolution de la ciliature buccale pendant l'autogamie et la conjugaison chez *Paramecium aurelia*. *C. R. Acad. Sci., Paris*, 242: 2592–2595.

—————— (1956b) La stomatogenèse pendant l'autogamie, la conjugaison et la division chez *Paramecium aurelia*. *C. R. Acad. Sci., Paris*, 243: 1564–1565.

—————— (1957a) Ciliature somatique et ciliature buccale chez *Disematostoma tetraedrica* (cilié holotriche). *C. R. Acad. Sci., Paris*, 244: 2657–2660.

—————— (1957b) Stomatogenèse chez *Disematostoma tetraedrica* (cilié holotriche). *C. R. Acad. Sci., Paris*, 244: 2849–2851.

—————— (1961) Recherches sur les hyménostomes péniculiens. *Bull. biol. France Belg.* [In press]

ROSE, M. (1937) Documents pour servir à l'étude des infusoires ciliés apostomes parasites des siphonophores et des organismes pélagiques. *Arch. Zool. exp. gén.*, 78 (*Notes et Rev.*): 184–198.

RÖSEL VON ROSENHOF, A. J. (1755) Der Monatlich-Herausgegebenen Insecten-Belustigung. Vol. III (Suppl.). 1st ed. Nürnberg. 624 pp.

ROSENBERG, L. E. (1937) The neuromotor system of *Nyctotherus hylae*. *Univ. Calif. Publ. Zool.*, 41: 249–276.

—————— (1938) Cyst stages of *Opisthonecta henneguyi*. *Trans. Amer. micr. Soc.*, 57: 147–152.

—————— (1940) Conjugation in *Opisthonecta henneguyi*, a free swimming vorticellid. *Proc. Amer. phil. Soc.*, 82: 437–448.

ROSSOLIMO, L. L. (1926a) Parasitische Infusorien aus dem Baikal-See. *Arch. Protistenk.*, 54: 468–509.

———— (1926b) Ueber einige neue und wenig bekannte Infusoria– Astomata aus den Anneliden des Russischen Nordens. *Zool. Anz.*, 68: 52–57.

ROSSOLIMO, L. L. and T. A. PERZEWA (1929) Zur Kenntnis einiger astomen Infusorien: Studien an Skelettbildung. *Arch. Protistenk.*, 67: 237–252.

ROTH, L. E. (1957) An electron microscope study of the cytology of the protozoan *Euplotes patella*. *J. biophys. biochem. Cytol.*, 3: 985–1000.

———— (1958) Ciliary coordination in the protozoa. *Exp. Cell Res.*, Suppl. 5: 573–585.

———— (1960) Observations on division stages in the protozoan hypotrich *Stylonychia*. *Proc. IV int. Conf. Elect. Micr.*, Berlin, 1958, pp. 241–244.

ROUILLER, C. and E. FAURÉ-FREMIET (1957a) L'ultrastructure des trichocystes fusiformes de *Frontonia atra*. *Bull. Micr. appl.*, 7: 135–139.

———— (1957b) Ultrastructure réticulée d'une fibre squelettique chez un cilié. *J. Ultrastr. Res.*, 1: 1–13.

———— (1958) Ultrastructure des cinétosomes à l'état de repos et à l'état cilifère chez un cilié péritriche. *J. Ultrastr. Res.*, 1: 289–294.

ROUILLER, C., FAURÉ-FREMIET, E., and M. GAUCHERY (1956a) Les tentacules d'*Ephelota*: étude au microscope électronique. *J. Protozool.*, 3: 194–200.

———— (1956b) Origine ciliaire des fibrilles scléroprotéiques pédonculaires chez les ciliés péritriches. Étude au microscope électronique. *Exp. Cell Res.*, 11: 527–541.

———— (1957) The pharyngeal protein fibres of the ciliates. *In* Sjöstrand, F. S. and J. Rhodin, editors, Electron Microscopy (Proc. Stockholm Conf., Sept. 1956), pp. 216–218. Academic Press, New York.

ROUSSEAU, E. (1912) Revision des acinétiens d'eau douce. *Ann. Biol. lacust.*, 5: 296–330.

ROUX, J. (1899) Observations sur quelques infusoires ciliés des environs de Genève avec la description de nouvelles espèces. *Rev. suisse Zool.*, 6: 557–636.

———— (1901) Faune Infusorienne des Eaux Stagnantes des Environs de Genève. Kündig, Genève. 148 pp.

RUDZINSKA, M. A. (1951) The influence of amount of food on the reproduction rate and longevity of a suctorian (*Tokophrya infusionum*). *Science*, 113: 10–11.

———— (1952) *Pachystomos olisthus* nov. gen., n. sp. *Trans. Amer. micr. Soc.*, 71: 157–158.

RUDZINSKA, M. A. and K. R. PORTER (1954a) The fine structure of *Tokophrya infusionum* with emphasis on the feeding mechanism. *Trans. N. Y. Acad. Sci.*, 16: 408–411.

———— (1954b) Electron microscope study of intact tentacles and disc in *Tokophrya infusionum*. *Experientia*, 10: 460–462.

REFERENCES   267

——— (1956) Further observations on the fine structure of the macronucleus in *Tokophrya infusionum*. *J. biophys. biochem. Cytol.*, 2
(Suppl.): 425–430.

——— (1958) An electron microscope study of the contractile vacuole
in *Tokophrya infusionum*. *J. biophys. biochem. Cytol.*, 4: 195–202.

Rühmekorf, T. (1935) Morphologie, Teilung und Hungerformen von
Keronopsis. *Arch. Protistenk.*, 85: 255–288.

Ruiz, A. (1959) Algunas consideraciones sobre el aparato bucal del
Cyclidium glaucoma O. F. Müller, 1786. *Rev. Biol. trop.*, 7: 107–108.
[In Spanish with English summary]

Russo, A. (1914) Specie di ciliati viventi nell intestino dello *Strongylocentrotus lividus*. *Boll. Accad. Gioen. Sci. nat. Catania*, fasc. 32,
ser. 2a, pp. 1–10.

——— (1930) Ciclo evolutivo di "*Cryptochilum echini*" Maupas
(Ciliata parassita del *Paracentrotus lividus* (Mrtsn.)). *Mem. Accad.
Lincei*, 4: 167–249.

Sand, R. (1895) Les acinétiens. *Ann. Soc. belge micr.*, 19: 121–187.

——— (1899–1901) Étude monographique sur le groupe des infusoires
tentaculifères. *Ann. Soc. belge micr.*, 24: 57–189; 25: 7–205; 26:
14–119.

Sandon, H. (1927) The Composition and Distribution of the Protozoan
Fauna of the Soil. Oliver and Boyd, Edinburgh. 237 pp.

——— (1932) The Food of Protozoa. Misr-Sokkar Press, Cairo. 187 pp.

——— (1941) Studies on South African endozoic ciliates. II. *Meiostoma
georhychi* gen. nov., sp. nov., from the caecum of the *Georhychus
capensis*. *S. Afr. J. med. Sci.*, 6: 128–135.

Sato, H. and Y. Sato (1956) Studies on the sterile culture of *Paramecium
caudatum*. *Zool. Mag.*, Tokyo, 65: 445–452. [In Japanese with
English summary]

Sauerbrey, E. (1928) Beobachtungen über einige neue oder wenig
bekannte marine Ciliaten. *Arch. Protistenk.*, 62: 355–407.

Savi, L. (1915) I Ciliati Aspirotrichi del lago-stagno craterico Astroni.
Napoli Ann. Mus. Zool. (N.S.), Suppl. 1 (Fauna degli Astroni),
No. 6, pp. 1–35.

Savoie, A. (1957) Le cilié *Trichopelma agilis* n. sp. *J. Protozool.*, 4:
276–280.

Sawaya, M. P. (1940) Sobre um ciliado novo de S. Paulo: *Blepharisma
sinuosum* sp. n. (Ciliata, Heterotricha) e sobre a sub-ordem Odonto-
stomata, nom. nov. *Bol. Fac. Filos. Ciênc. S. Paulo* (Zool., No. 4), 19:
303–308. [In Portuguese with English summary]

Scherbaum, O. H. (1957a) Studies on the mechanism of synchronous
cell division in *Tetrahymena pyriformis*. *Exp. Cell Res.*, 13: 11–23.

——— (1957b) The content and composition of nucleic acids in normal
and synchronously dividing mass cultures of *Tetrahymena pyriformis*.
Exp. Cell Res., 13: 24–30.

——— (1960) [Please see p. 287]

SCHERBAUM, O. H., LOUDERBACK, A. L., and T. L. JAHN (1958) The formation of subnuclear aggregates in normal and synchronized protozoan cells. *Biol. Bull.*, 115: 269–275.

—— (1959) DNA synthesis, phosphate content and growth in mass and volume in synchronously dividing cells. *Exp. Cell Res.*, 18: 150–166.

SCHERBAUM, O. H. and G. RASCH (1957) Cell size distribution and single cell growth in *Tetrahymena pyriformis* GL. *Acta path. microbiol. scand.*, 41: 161–182.

SCHERBAUM, O. H. and E. ZEUTHEN (1954) Induction of synchronous cell division in mass cultures of *Tetrahymena piriformis*. *Exp. Cell Res.*, 6: 221–227.

—— (1955) Temperature-induced synchronous divisions in the ciliate protozoon *Tetrahymena pyriformis* growing in synthetic and proteose-peptone media. *Exp. Cell Res.*, Suppl. 3: 312–325.

SCHEWIAKOFF, W. (1889) Beiträge zur Kenntniss der holotrichen Ciliaten. *Bibl. zool.*, 5: 1–77.

—— (1893a) Ueber die geographische Verbreitung der Süsswasser-Protozoen. *Mém. Acad. impér. Sci. St. Pétersb.* (sér. 7), 41: 1–201. [In Russian]

—— (1893b) Über die Natur der sogenannten Exkretkörner der Infusorien. *Z. wiss. Zool.*, 57: 32–56.

—— (1896) [The Organization and Systematics of the Infusoria Aspirotricha (Holotricha *auctorum*).] *Mém. Acad. impér. Sci. St. Pétersb.* (sér. 8), 4: 1–395. [In Russian]

SCHMÄHL, O. (1926) Die Neubildung des Peristoms bei der Teilung von *Bursaria truncatella*. *Arch. Protistenk.*, 54: 359–430.

SCHMIDT, W. J. (1921) Untersuchungen über Bau und Lebenserscheinungen von *Bursella spumosa*, einem neuen Ciliaten. *Arch. mikr. Anat.*, 95: 1–36.

SCHNEIDER, L. (1959) Neue Befunde über den Feinbau des Cytoplasmas von *Paramecium* nach Einbettung in Vestopal W. *Z. Zellforsch.*, 50: 61–77.

SCHOENICHEN, W. (1927) II Klasse: Infusoria. *In* Einfachste Lebensformen des Tier- und Pflanzenreiches, 5th ed., vol. II, pp. 170–293. Bermühler, Berlin.

SCHÖNFELD, C. (1959) Über das parasitische Verhalten einer *Astasia*-Art in *Stentor coeruleus*. *Arch. Protistenk.*, 104: 261–264.

SCHOUTEDEN, H. (1906) Les infusoires aspirotriches d'eau douce. *Ann. Biol. lacust.*, 1: 383–468; 2: 171–180. [A French adaptation of Schewiakoff's (1896) Russian work]

SCHRÖDER, O. (1906) Beiträge zur Kenntnis von *Vorticella monilata* Tatem. *Arch. Protistenk.*, 7: 395–410.

SCHUBERG, A. (1887) Über den Bau der *Bursaria truncatella*; mit besonderer Berüchsichtigung der protoplasmatischen Strukturen. *Morph. Jb.*, 12: 333–365.

—— (1888) Die Protozoen des Wiederkäuermagens. I. (*Bütschlia, Isotricha, Dasytricha, Entodinium.*) *Zool. Jb.* (*Abt. Syst., Geog. u. Biol. Thiere*), 3: 365–418.

—— (1890) Zur Kenntniss des *Stentor coeruleus. Zool. Jb.* (*Abt. Anat. u. Ontog. Thiere*), 4: 197–238.

—— (1905) Über Cilien und Trichocysten einiger Infusorien. *Arch. Protistenk.*, 6: 61–110.

SCHULTZ, E. (1938) Beiträge zur Kenntnis mariner Suctorien. VIII. *Kieler Meeresforsch.*, 2: 354–355.

SCHULZE, E. (1958) Morphologische, cytologische und ökologisch-physiologische Untersuchungen an Faulschlammciliaten (*Metopus sigmoides* Clap. et. Lachm. und *Metopus contortus* Lev.). *Arch. Protistenk.*, 103: 371–426.

SCHULZE, F. E. *et al.* (1926–1954) Nomenclator Animalium Generum et Subgenerum. Vols. I–V. Preuss. Akad. Wiss., Berlin. 3,716 pp.

SCHULZE, K. L. (1951) Experimentelle Untersuchungen über die Chlorellen-Symbiose bei Ciliaten. *Biol. gen.*, Wien., 19: 281–298.

SCHWARTZ, V. (1935) Versuche über Regeneration und Kerndimorphismus bei *Stentor coeruleus* Ehrbg. *Arch. Protistenk.*, 85: 100–139.

—— (1946) Der Formwechsel des Makronucleus in der Konjugation mikronucleusloser Paramecien. *Biol. Zbl.*, 65: 89–94.

—— (1947) Über die Physiologie des Kerndimorphismus bei *Paramecium bursaria. Z. Naturforsch.*, 2b: 369–381.

—— (1956) Nucleolenformwechsel und Zyklen der Ribosenuclein-säure in der vegetativen Entwicklung von *Paramecium bursaria. Biol. Zbl.*, 75: 1–16.

—— (1957) Über den Formwechsel achromatischer Substanz in der Teilung des Makronucleus von *Paramecium bursaria. Biol. Zbl.*, 76: 1–23.

—— (1958) Chromosomen im Makronucleus von *Paramecium bursaria. Biol. Zbl.*, 77: 347–364.

SCOTT, M. J. (1927) Studies on the *Balantidium* from the guinea pig. *J. Morph.*, 44: 417–453.

SEAMAN, G. R. (1952) Replacement of protogen by lipoic acid in the growth of *Tetrahymena. Proc. Soc. exp. Biol. Med.*, 79: 158–159.

—— (1955) Metabolism of free-living ciliates. *In* Hutner, S. H. and A. Lwoff, editors, Biochemistry and Physiology of Protozoa, Vol. II, pp. 91–158. Academic Press, New York.

—— (1959, 1960) [Please see p. 287]

SEDAR, A. W. and K. R. PORTER (1955) The fine structure of cortical components of *Paramecium multimicronucleatum. J. biophys. biochem. Cytol.*, 1: 583–604.

SEDAR, A. W. and M. A. RUDZINSKA (1956) Mitochondria of protozoa. *J. biophys. biochem. Cytol.*, 2 (Suppl.): 331–336.

SESHACHAR, B. R. (1950) The nucleus and nucleic acids of *Chilodonella uncinatus* Ehrbg. *J. exp. Zool.*, 114: 517–543.

SESHACHAR, B. R. and C. M. S. DASS (1953) Evidence for the conversion of desoxyribonucleic acid (DNA) to ribonucleic acid (RNA) in *Epistylis articulata* From. (Ciliata: Peritricha). *Exp. Cell Res.*, 5: 248–250.

———— (1954) The macronucleus of *Epistylis articulata* From. during conjugation: a photometric study. *Physiol. Zoöl.*, 27: 280–286.

SESHACHAR, B. R. and P. B. PADMAVATHI (1959a) Conjugation in *Spirostomum*. *Nature*, 184: 1510–1511.

———— (1959b) A study of the volume changes in *Spirostomum ambiguum* Ehrbg., during various phases of life history. *Arch. Protistenk.*, 104: 492–502.

SEWELL, R. B. S. (1951) The epibionts and parasites of the planktonic Copepoda of the Arabian Sea. *Sci. Rep. Murray Exped.*, 9: 255–394.

SHAPIRO, N. N. (1927) The cycle of hydrogen-ion concentration in the food vacuoles of *Paramecium*, *Vorticella*, and *Stylonychia*. *Trans. Amer. micr. Soc.*, 46: 45–53.

SHARP, R. G. (1914) *Diplodinium ecaudatum* with an account of its neuromotor apparatus. *Univ. Calif. Publ. Zool.*, 13: 42–122.

SHAWHAN, F. M., JOHNSON, L. P., and T. L. JAHN (1947) Protozoa of Iowa. *Proc. Iowa Acad. Sci.*, 54: 353–367.

SHOMAY, D. (1953) The occurrence of the genus *Lagenophrys* Stein 1852 (Ciliata; Peritricha) in North America. (Abstr.) *Proc. Soc. Protozool.*, 4: 19–20.

———— (1954a) The structure and life history of *Lagenophrys labiata* Stokes (Ciliata, Peritricha). (Abstr.) *J. Protozool.*, 1 (Suppl.): 2.

———— (1954b) The natural history of *Lagenophrys labiata* Stokes (Ciliata, Peritricha). (Abstr.) *J. Protozool.*, 1 (Suppl.): 9.

SHUMWAY, W. (1940) A ciliate protozoon parasitic in the central nervous system of larval *Amblystoma*. *Biol. Bull.*, 78: 283–288.

SIEBOLD, C. T. VON (1848) Lehrbuch der Vergleichenden Anatomie der Wirbellosen Thiere. Heft 1 *in* Siebold, C. T. von and H. Stannuis, *Lehrbuch der Vergleichenden Anatomie*, Vol. I. Pp. 1–679. Berlin.

SIEGEL, R. W. (1956) Mating types in *Oxytricha* and the significance of mating type systems in ciliates. *Biol. Bull.*, 110: 352–357.

———— (1958) Hybrid vigor, heterosis and evolution in *Paramecium aurelia*. *Evolution*, 12: 402–416.

———— (1960) Hereditary endosymbiosis in *Paramecium bursaria*. *Exp. Cell Res.*, 19: 239–252.

SIEGEL, R. W. and L. L. LARISON (1960) The genic control of mating types in *Paramecium bursaria*. *Proc. nat. Acad. Sci.*, *Wash.*, 46: 344–349.

SIEGEL, R. W. and J. R. PREER, Jr. (1957) Antigenic relationships among Feulgen positive cytoplasmic particles in *Paramecium*. *Amer. Nat.*, 91: 253–257.

SILÉN, L. (1947) On Folliculinidae (Ciliophora Heterotricha) from the West Coast of Sweden. *Ark. Zool., Stockholm*, 39: 1–68.

—— (1948) On a new stentor from the west coast of Sweden. *Ark. Zool., Stockholm*, 40A: 1–10.

SIMPSON, G. G. (1945) The principles of classification and a classification of mammals. *Bull. Amer. Mus. nat. Hist.*, 85: 1–350.

—— (1961) [Please see p. 287]

SIMPSON, J. Y. (1901) Observations on binary fission in the life-history of ciliata. *Proc. roy. Soc. Edinb.*, 23: 401–421.

SINGH, B. N. (1955) Culturing soil protozoa and estimating their numbers in soil. *In* Kevan, D. K. McE., editor, Soil Zoology, pp. 403–411. Butterworths Scientific Publications, London.

SINGH, M. (1953) Studies on the protozoa of Indian fishes. I. The morphology and the systematic position of the ciliates inhabiting the intestine of fish *Mystus cavasius* (Hamilton). *Res. Bull. E. Panjab Univ.*, No. 35 (Zool.), pp. 117–138.

SLÁDEČEK, F. (1946) Ophryoscolecidae from the stomach of *Cervus elaphus* L., *Dama dama* L., and *Capreolus capreolus* L. *Mém. Soc. zool. tchécosl.*, 10: 201–231. [In Czechoslovakian with English summary]

SLATER, J. V. (1952) Comparative biological activity of α-lipoic acid in the growth of *Tetrahymena*. *Science*, 115: 376–377.

SLEIGH, M. A. (1956) Metachronism and frequency of beat in the peristomial cilia of *Stentor*. *J. exp. Biol.*, 33: 15–28.

—— (1957, 1960) [Please see p. 287]

SMALL, E. B. and R. J. PROFANT (1960a, b) [Please see p. 287]

SMITH, I. F. (1914) A preliminary report on the infusoria of Kansas. *Kans. Univ. Sci. Bull.*, 9: 147–174.

SOKOLOFF, B. (1924) Das Regenerationsproblem bei Protozoen. *Arch. Protistenk.*, 47: 143–252.

SOKOLOFF, D. (1931) La flora y fauna microscopicas de aguas dulces del Valle de Mexico. *Monog. Inst. Biol. Mexico*, 1: 1–38.

—— (1945) Algunas observaciones sobre quistes de *Gastrostyla steini* Eng. *An. Esc. nac. Ciênc. biol. Méx.*, 4: 41–51.

SOMMER, G. (1951) Die peritrichen Ciliaten des Grossen Plöner Sees. *Arch. Hydrobiol.*, 44: 349–440.

SONNEBORN, T. M. (1937) Sex, sex inheritance and sex determination in *Paramecium aurelia*. *Proc. nat. Acad. Sci., Wash.*, 23: 378–385.

—— (1939) *Paramecium aurelia:* mating types and groups; lethal interactions; determination and inheritance. *Amer. Nat.*, 73: 390–413.

—— (1947) Recent advances in the genetics of *Paramecium* and *Euplotes*. *Adv. Genet.*, 1: 263–358.

—— (1949) Ciliated protozoa: cytogenetics, genetics, and evolution. *Ann. Rev. Microbiol.*, 3: 55–80.

—————— (1950) Methods in the general biology and genetics of *Paramecium aurelia*. *J. exp. Zool.*, 113: 87–147.

—————— (1954a) The relation of autogamy to senescence and rejuvenescence in *Paramecium aurelia*. *J. Protozool.*, 1: 38–53.

—————— (1954b) Patterns of nucleocytoplasmic integration in *Paramecium. Proc. IX int. Congr. Genetics*, Ballagio, Italy, 1953, published in *Caryologia*, 6 (Suppl.): 307–325.

————— (1957) Breeding systems, reproductive methods, and species problems in Protozoa. *In* Mayr, E., editor, The Species Problem, pp. 155–324. AAAS Pub., Washington, D. C.

————— (1958) Classification of syngens of the *Paramecium aurelia-multimicronucleatum* complex. (Abstr.) *J. Protozool.*, 5 (Suppl.): 17–18.

————— (1959) Kappa and related particles in *Paramecium. Adv. Virus Res.*, 6: 229–356.

—————— (1960) [Please see p. 287]

SONNEBORN, T. M. and R. V. DIPPELL (1960) [Please see p. 287]

SONNEBORN, T. M., SCHNELLER, M. V., MUELLER, J. A., and H. E. HOLZMAN (1959) Extensions of the ranges of certain syngens of *Paramecium aurelia*. (Abstr.) *J. Protozool.*, 6 (Suppl.): 31–32.

SONNEBORN, T. M. and D. R. SONNEBORN (1958) Some effects of light on the rhythm of mating type changes in stock 232–6 of syngen 2 of *P. multimicronucleatum*. (Abstr.) *Anat. Rec.*, 133: 601.

SPRUGEL, G., Jr. (1951) Vertical distribution of *Stentor coeruleus* in relation to dissolved oxygen levels in an Iowa pond. *Ecology*, 32: 147–149.

ŠRÁMEK-HUŠEK, R. (1952) Über einige Bemerkenswerte Ciliaten aus böhmischen Moosen. *Česk. Biol., Praha*, 1: 367–376. [In Russian with German summary]

—————— (1953) Zur Frage der Taxonomie und der Pathogenität unserer ektoparasitischen Urceolariiden. *Folia Zool. Ent.*, 2 (16): 167–180. [In Czechoslovakian with Russian and German summaries]

—————— (1954) Neue und wenig bekannte Ciliaten aus der Tschechoslowakei und ihre Stellung in Saprobiensystem. *Arch. Protistenk.*, 100: 246–267.

—————— (1957) Zur Kenntnis der Ciliaten des Ostrauer-Gebietes (Tschechoslovakei). *Mém. Soc. zool. tchécosl.*, 21: 1–24. [In Czechoslovakian with German summary]

STAMMER, H. J. (1935) Zwei neue troglobionte Protozoen: *Spelaeophrya troglocaridis* n. g., n. sp., von den Antennen der Höhlengarnele *Troglocaris schmidti* Dorm. und *Lagenophrys monolistrae* n. sp. von den Kiemen (Pleopoden) der Höhlenasselgattung *Monolistra. Arch. Protistenk.*, 84: 518–527.

—————— (1948) Eine neue eigenartige entoparasitische Peritriche, *Operculariella parasitica* n. g., n. sp. *Zool. Jb. (Abt. Syst., Ökol. u. Geog. Tiere)*, 77: 163–168.

—— (1955) Ökologische Wechselbeziehungen zwischen Insekten und anderen Tiergruppen. *WanderVersamml. dtsch. Ent.*, 7: 12–61.

STATKEWITSCH, P. (1904–1906) Galvanotropismus und Galvanotaxis der Ciliata. [Parts 1–5.] *Z. allg. Physiol.*, 4: 296–332; 5: 511–534; 6: 13–43.

STEIN, F. (1849) Untersuchungen über die Entwicklung der Infusorien. *Arch. Naturgesch.* [" *Wiegmann's Archiv.*," 15th yr.], 1: 92–148.

—— (1851) Neue Beiträge zur Kenntniss der Entwicklungsgeschichte und des feineren Baues der Infusionsthiere. *Z. wiss. Zool.*, 3: 475–509.

—— (1854) Die Infusionsthiere auf ihre Entwicklungsgeschichte untersucht. Leipzig. 265 pp.

—— (1859) Der Organismus der Infusionsthiere nach eigenen Forschungen in systematischer Reihenfolge bearbeitet. I. Leipzig. 206 pp.

—— (1861) Über ein neues parasitisches Infusionsthier (*Ptychostomum Paludinarum*) aus dem Darmkanal von Paludinen und über die mit demselben zunächst verwandten Infusorienformen. *S. B. böhn. Ges. Wiss.*, 1861, pp. 85–90.

—— (1867) Der Organismus der Infusionsthiere nach eigenen Forschungen in systematischer Reihenfolge bearbeitet. II. Leipzig. 355 pp.

STEINHAUS, E. A. (1947) Insect Microbiology. Comstock, Ithaca, New York. 763 pp.

STEPHANIDES, T. (1948) A survey of the freshwater biology of Corfu and of certain other regions of Greece. *Prak. Hellen. hydrobiol. Inst.*, 2: 1–263. [Ciliates treated on pp. 143–149.]

STERBENZ, F. J. and D. M. LILLY (1956) Factors influencing abnormal growth in suctorian protozoa. *Trans. N. Y. Acad. Sci.*, 18: 522–530.

STERKI, V. (1878) Beiträge zur Morphologie der Oxytrichinen. *Z. wiss. Zool.*, 31: 29–58.

STEVENS, N. M. (1901) Studies on ciliate infusoria. *Proc. Calif. Acad. Sci.*, 3rd ser. Zool., 3: 1–42.

—— (1903a) Further studies on the ciliate infusoria, *Licnophora* and *Boveria*. *Arch. Protistenk.*, 3: 1–43.

—— (1903b) Notes on regeneration in *Stentor coeruleus*. *Arch. EntwMech. Organ.*, 16: 461–475.

STILLER, J. (1939) Die Peritrichenfauna der Nordsee bei Helgoland. *Arch. Protistenk.*, 92: 415–452.

—— (1940) Beitrag zur Peritrichenfauna des Grossen Plöner Sees in Holstein. *Arch. Hydrobiol.*, 36: 263–285.

—— (1941) Epizoische Peritrichen aus dem Balaton. *Arb. I. Abt. ung. Biol. ForschInst.*, 13: 211–223.

—— (1946a) Beitrag zur Kenntnis der Peritrichenfauna der Schwefelthermen von Split. *Ann. hist.-nat. Mus. hung.*, 39: 19–57.

—————— (1946b) Beitrag zur Kenntnis der Peritrichenfauna der Adria bei Split (Spalato). *Ann. hist.-nat. Mus. hung.*, 39: 59–74.

—————— (1951) Epizoische Peritrichen aus dem Balaton II. *Arch. Biol. hung.*, 19: 15–37.

—————— (1953) Epizoische Peritrichen aus dem Balaton III. *Hydrobiologia*, 5: 189–221.

—————— (1960) Die limnologisches Verhältnisse des Naturschutzgebietes von Bátorliget in Ungarn nebst Beschreibung einiger neuer Peritrichen-Arten (Ciliata, Protozoa). *Arch. Hydrobiol.*, 56: 186–260.

STOKES, A. C. (1888) A preliminary contribution towards a history of the fresh-water infusoria of the United States. *J. Trenton nat. Hist. Soc.*, 1: 71–344.

—————— (1893) Notices of some undescribed infusoria from the brackish waters of the eastern United States. *J. roy. micr. Soc.*, yr. 1893, pp. 298–302.

—————— (1894) Notices of presumably undescribed infusoria. *Proc. Amer. phil. Soc.*, 33: 338–345.

STOLK, A. (1959a) *Glaucoma* species in the central nervous system of the carp. *Nature*, 184 (Suppl. No. 22): 1737.

—————— (1959b) A parasitic ciliate in the central nervous system of a larval newt. *Naturwissenschaften*, 46: 631.

—————— (1960a) A parasitic ciliate in the central nervous system of a larval newt *Triturus taeniatus*. *Proc. Acad. Sci. Amst.* (ser. C), 63: 71–78.

—————— (1960b) *Glaucoma* sp. in the central nervous system of the carp *Cyprinus carpio* L. *Proc. Acad. Sci. Amst.* (ser. C), 63: 79–86.

STOLTE, H. A. (1922) Der Einfluss der Umwelt auf Macronucleus und Plasma von *Stentor coeruleus* Ehrbg. Ein experimenteller Beitrag. zur Frage der Kernplasmabeziehungen. *Arch. Protistenk.*, 45: 344–389.

—————— (1924) Morphologische und physiologische Untersuchungen an *Blepharisma undulans* Stein. (Studien über den Formwechsel der Infusorien.) *Arch. Protistenk.*, 48: 245–301.

STOUT, J. D. (1954) The ecology, life history and parasitism of *Tetrahymena [Paraglaucoma] rostrata* (Kahl) Corliss. *J. Protozool.*, 1: 211–215.

—————— (1955) Environmental factors affecting the life history of three soil species of *Colpoda* (Ciliata). *Trans. roy. Soc. N. Z.*, 82: 1165–1188.

—————— (1956a) Reaction of ciliates to environmental factors. *Ecology*, 37: 178–191.

—————— (1956b) Excystment of *Frontonia depressa* (Stokes) Penard. *J. Protozool.*, 3: 31–32.

—————— (1958) Biological studies of some tussock-grassland soils. VII. Protozoa. *N. Z. J. agric. Res.*, 1: 974–984.

———— (1960) Morphogenesis in the ciliate *Bresslaua vorax* Kahl and the phylogeny of the Colpodidae. *J. Protozool.*, 7: 26–35.

STRAND, E. (1928) Miscellanea nomenclatorica zoologica et palaeontologica. I–II. *Arch. Naturgesch.*, yr. 1926, 92 (A8): 30–75.

———— (1942) Miscellanea nomenclatorica zoologica et palaeontologica. X. *Folia zool. hydrobiol., Riga*, 11: 386–402.

STRANGHÖNER, E. (1932) Teilungsrate und Kernreorganisationsprozess bei *Paramaecium multimicronucleatum*, Powers und Mitchell. *Arch. Protistenk.*, 78: 302–360.

STRELKOW, A. (1929) Morphologische Studien über oligotriche Infusorien aus dem Darme des Pferdes. I. Äussere Morphologie und Skelett der Gattung *Cycloposthium* Bundle. *Arch. Protistenk.*, 68: 503–554.

———— (1931) Morphologische Studien über oligotriche Infusorien aus dem Darme des Pferdes. II. Cytologische Untersuchungen der Gattung *Cycloposthium* Bundle. III. Körperbau von *Tripalmaria dogieli* Gassovsky. *Arch. Protistenk.*, 75: 191–220, 221–254.

———— (1939) Parasitic Infusoria from the intestine of Ungulata belonging to the family Equidae. A monograph. *Sci. Trans. Leningr. pedagog. Inst.*, 17: 1–262. [In Russian with English summary]

———— (1953) [New species of pelagic Tintinnoinea of Far East waters.] *Trav. Inst. zool. Acad. Sci. U.R.S.S.*, 13: 57–69. [In Russian]

———— (1959a) Parasitic infusoria of sea urchins from the sea shores of southern Kuril Isles. *Zool. Zh.*, 38: 23–30. [In Russian with English summary]

———— (1959b) [Infusoria from sea urchins of the Tsingtao region and the geographical distribution of infusoria of Pacific sea urchins.] *Oceanogr. Limnolog. Sinica*, 2: 61–67. [In Chinese with Russian translation]

STRELKOW, A. and M. A. VIRKETIS (1950) [New planctonic infusorium (suborder Tintinnoinea) from Peter the Great Bay.] *C. R. Acad. Sci.* (N.S.), *Moscow* [*Doklady*], 74: 389–391. [In Russian]

STRICKLAND, A. G. R. and A. J. HAAGEN-SMIT (1948) The excystment of *Colpoda duodenaria*. *Science*, 107: 204–205.

STUART, C. A., KIDDER, G. W., and A. M. GRIFFIN (1939) Growth studies on ciliates. III. Experimental alteration of the method of reproduction in *Colpoda*. *Physiol. Zoöl.*, 12: 348–362.

STUDITSKY, A. N. (1930) Materialien zur Morphologie von *Dileptus gigas* Stein. *Arch. Protistenk.*, 70: 155–184.

SULLIVAN, W. D. (1959) The effect of ultraviolet radiation and the interaction with sulfur compounds on growth and division of *Tetrahymena*. *Trans. Amer. micr. Soc.*, 78: 181–193.

SUMMERS, F. M. (1935) The division and reorganization of the macronuclei of *Aspidisca lynceus* Müller, *Diophrys appendiculata* Stein and *Stylonychia pustulata* Ehrbg. *Arch. Protistenk.*, 85: 173–210.

T

——— (1941) The protozoa in connection with morphogenetic problems. *In* Calkins, G. N. and F. M. Summers, editors, Protozoa in Biological Research, pp. 772–817. Columbia Univ. Press, New York.

SUMMERS, F. M. and H. K. HUGHES (1940) Experiments with *Colpidium campylum* in high-frequency electric and magnetic fields. *Physiol. Zoöl.*, 13: 227–242.

SUMMERS, F. M. and G. W. KIDDER (1936) Taxonomic and cytological studies on the ciliates associated with the amphipod family Orchestiidae from the Woods Hole district. II. The coelozoic astomatous parasites. *Arch. Protistenk.*, 86: 379–403.

SUZUKI, S. (1954) Taxonomic studies on *Blepharisma undulans* Stein, with special reference to the macronuclear variation. *J. Sci. Hiroshima Univ.* (B, 1), 15: 204–220.

——— (1957) Morphogenesis in the regeneration of *Blepharisma undulans japonicus* Suzuki. *Bull. Yamagata Univ., Nat. Sci.*, 4: 85–192.

SVENSSON, R. (1955) On the resistance to heating and cooling of *Balantidium coli* in culture and some observations regarding conjugation. *Exp. Parasit.*, 4: 502–525.

SWARCZEWSKY, B. (1928a) Beobachtungen über *Spirochona elegans* n. sp. *Arch. Protistenk.*, 61: 185–222.

——— (1928b) Zur Kenntnis der Baikalprotistenfauna. Die an den Baikalgammariden lebenden Infusorien. I. Dendrosomidae. *Arch. Protistenk.*, 61: 349–378.

——— (1928c) Zur Kenntnis der Baikalprotistenfauna. Die an den Baikalgammariden lebenden Infusorien. II. Dendrocometidae. *Arch. Protistenk.*, 62: 41–79.

——— (1928d) Zur Kenntnis der Baikalprotistenfauna. Die an den Baikalgammariden lebenden Infusorien. III. Discophryidae. *Arch. Protistenk.*, 63: 1–17.

——— (1928e) Zur Kenntnis der Baikalprotistenfauna. Die an den Baikalgammariden lebenden Infusorien. IV. Acinetidae. *Arch. Protistenk.*, 63: 362–409.

——— (1928f) Zur Kenntnis der Baikalprotistenfauna. Die an den Baikalgammariden lebenden Infusorien. V. Spirochonina. *Arch. Protistenk.*, 64: 44–60.

——— (1930) Zur Kenntnis der Baikalprotistenfauna. Die an den Baikalgammariden lebenden Infusorien. VII. *Lagenophrys, Vaginicola* and *Cothurnia*. *Arch. Protistenk.*, 69: 455–532.

SWEZEY, W. W. (1934) Cytology of *Troglodytella abrassarti*, an intestinal ciliate of the chimpanzee. *J. Morph.*, 56: 621–634.

SZABÓ, M. (1934) Beiträge zur Kenntnis der Gattung *Halteria* (Protozoa, Ciliata). *Arb. I. Abt. ung. Biol. ForschInst.*, 7: 95–101.

——— (1935) Neuere Beiträge zur Kenntnis der Gattung *Halteria* (Protozoa, Ciliata). *Arch. Protistenk.*, 86: 307–317.

Tamás, G. and J. Gellért (1959) Kieselalgen und Ciliaten im Aufwuchs von Ufersteinen an dem Südufer der Halbinsel Tihany. *Ann. Inst. Biol., Hung. Acad. Sci.*, 26: 237–245. [In Hungarian with German summary]

Tannreuther, G. W. (1926) Life history of *Prorodon teres. Biol. Bull.*, 51: 303–320.

Tanzer, C. (1941) Serological studies with free-living protista. *J. Immunol.*, 42: 291–312.

Tarantola, V. A. and W. J. van Wagtendonk (1959) Further nutritional requirements of *Paramecium aurelia. J. Protozool.*, 6: 189–195.

Tartar, V. (1939) The so-called racial variation in the power of regeneration in *Paramecium. J. exp. Zool.*, 81: 181–208.

―――― (1941) Intracellular patterns: facts and principles concerning patterns exhibited in the morphogenesis and regeneration of ciliate protozoa. *Growth*, 3rd Symp., Suppl., 5: 21–40.

―――― (1953) Chimeras and nuclear transplantations in ciliates, *Stentor coeruleus* X *S. polymorphus. J. exp. Zool.*, 124: 63–104.

―――― (1954a) Anomalies in regeneration of *Paramecium. J. Protozool.*, 1: 11–17, 19.

―――― (1954b) Reactions of *Stentor coeruleus* to homoplastic grafting. *J. exp. Zool.*, 127: 511–576.

―――― (1956) Pattern and substance in *Stentor. In* Rudnick, D., editor, Cellular Mechanisms in Differentiation and Growth, pp. 73–100. Princeton Univ. Press, Princeton.

―――― (1957a) Equivalence of macronuclear nodes. *J. exp. Zool.*, 135: 387–401.

―――― (1957b) Deletion experiments on the oral primordium of *Stentor coeruleus. J. exp. Zool.*, 136: 53–74.

―――― (1958a) Induced resorption of oral primordia in regenerating *Stentor coeruleus. J. exp. Zool.*, 139: 1–32.

―――― (1958b) *Stentor introversus*, n. sp. *J. Protozool.*, 5: 93–95.

―――― (1959) Specific inhibition of the oral primordium by formed oral structures in *Stentor coeruleus. J. exp. Zool.*, 139: 479–505.

―――― (1961) The Biology of *Stentor*. Pergamon Press, New York and London. 413 pp.

Taylor, C. V. (1920) Demonstration of the function of the neuromotor apparatus in *Euplotes* by the method of microdissection. *Univ. Calif. Publ. Zool.*, 19: 403–470.

―――― (1923) The contractile vacuole in *Euplotes:* an example of the sol-gel reversibility of cytoplasm. *J. exp. Zool.*, 37: 259–289.

―――― (1928) Protoplasmic reorganization in *Uronychia uncinata* n. sp., during binary fission and regeneration. *Physiol. Zoöl.*, 1: 1–25.

―――― (1941) Fibrillar systems in ciliates. *In* Calkins, G. N. and F. M. Summers, editors, Protozoa in Biological Research, pp. 191–270. Columbia Univ. Press, New York.

TAYLOR, C. V. and W. P. FARBER (1924) Fatal effects of the removal of the micronucleus in *Euplotes*. *Univ. Calif. Publ. Zool.*, 26: 131–144.

TAYLOR, C. V. and W. H. FURGASON (1938) Structural analysis of *Colpoda duodenaria* sp. nov. *Arch. Protistenk.*, 90: 320–339.

TAYLOR, C. V. and L. GARNJOBST (1939) Reorganization of the " silverline system " in the reproductive cysts of *Colpoda duodenaria*. *Arch. Protistenk.*, 92: 73–90.

TAYLOR, C. V. and A. G. R. STRICKLAND (1938) Reactions of *Colpoda duodenaria* to environmental factors. I. Some factors influencing growth and encystment. *Arch. Protistenk.*, 90: 396–409.

—————— (1939) Reactions of *Colpoda duodenaria* to environmental factors. II. Factors influencing the formation of resting cysts. *Physiol. Zoöl.*, 12: 219–230.

TAYLOR, C. V., THOMAS, J. O., and M. G. BROWN (1933) Studies on the protozoa. IV. Lethal effects of the x-radiation of a sterile culture medium for *Colpidium campylum*. *Physiol. Zoöl.*, 6: 467–492.

TCHANG-TSO-RUN, N. (1931) Contribution à l'étude de la division chez les hypotriches. *Ann. Soc. zool. Belg.*, 62: 71–77.

TCHANG-TSO-RUN, N. and C. T. TANG (1957) La mouvement de l'infraciliature pendant la division de *Paramecium aurelia* et la considération sur la formation de cytostome, de suture et de cytopyge. *Acta Zool. Sinica*, 9: 183–194. [In Chinese with French summary]

THOMAS, R. (1952) Sur une nouvelle méthode de coloration des cils et flagelles. *Bull. Micr. appl.*, 2: 70–74.

THOMPSON, J. C., Jr. (1955) Morphology of a new species of *Tetrahymena*. (Abstr.) *J. Protozool.*, 2 (Suppl.): 12.

—————— (1958a) Experimental infections of various animals with strains of the genus *Tetrahymena*. *J. Protozool.*, 5: 203–205.

—————— (1958b) Tetrahymenal ciliary organelles in the buccal cavity of *Cyclidium glaucoma*. (Abstr.) *J. Protozool.*, 5 (Suppl.): 10.

—————— (1959) Buccal infraciliature of *Frontonia*. (Abstr.) *J. Protozool.*, 6 (Suppl.): 13.

THOMPSON, J. C., Jr. and J. O. CORLISS (1958) A redescription of the holotrichous ciliate *Pseudomicrothorax dubius* with particular attention to its morphogenesis. *J. Protozool.*, 15: 175–184.

THOMPSON, J. C., Jr. and C. C. SPEIDEL (1955) The occurrence in amphibians of ciliated protozoan parasites of the genus *Tetrahymena*. (Abstr.) *Anat. Rec.*, 121: 420.

THOMSON, J. G. and A. ROBERTSON (1929) Protozoology: A Manual for Medical Men. Baillière, Tindall and Cox, London. 376 pp.

THON, K. (1905) Über den feineren Bau von *Didinium nasutum* O. F. M. *Arch. Protistenk.*, 5: 281–321.

THORMAR, H. (1959) Delayed division in *Tetrahymena pyriformis* induced by temperature changes. *C. R. Lab. Carlsberg*, 31: 207–226.

TITTLER, I. A. (1938) Regeneration and reorganization in *Uroleptus mobilis* following injury by induced electric currents. *Biol. Bull.*, 75: 533–541.

TÖNNIGES, G. (1914) Die Trichocysten von *Frontonia leucas* und ihr chromidialer Ursprung. *Arch. Protistenk.*, 32: 298–378.

TRAGER, W. (1957) Excystation of apostome ciliates in relation to molting of their crustacean hosts. *Biol. Bull.*, 112: 132–136.

TREMBLEY, A. (1744) Translation of a letter from A. Trembley to the President with observations upon several newly discover'd species of fresh-water Polypi. *Phil. Trans. roy. Soc.*, 43: 169–183.

TRIPATHI, Y. R. (1956) Studies on parasites of Indian fishes. III. Protozoa 2 (Mastigophora and Ciliophora). *Rec. Indian Mus.*, 52: 221–230.

TSUJITA, M., WATANABE, K., and S. TSUDA (1954) Electron-microscopical studies on the inner structure of *Paramecium caudatum* by means of ultra-thin sections. *Cytologia*, 19: 306–316.

TUFFRAU, M. (1952) La morphogenèse de division chez les Colpodidae. *Bull. biol. France Belg.*, 86: 309–320.

——— (1953) Les processus cytologiques de la conjugaison chez *Spirochona gemmipara* Stein. *Bull. biol. France Belg.*, 87: 314–322.

——— (1954a) Les caractères spécifiques dans le genre *Euplotes*. *Bull. Soc. zool. Fr.*, 79: 463–465.

——— (1954b) *Discotricha papillifera*, n. g., n. sp. Cilié psammobie de la famille des Trichopelmidae. *J. Protozool.*, 1: 183–186.

——— (1956) Note sur *Legendrea pes pelicani*, Penard, 1922. *Bull. Soc. zool. Fr.*, 81: 72–74.

——— (1957) Les facteurs essentiels du phototropisme chez le cilié hétérotriche *Stentor niger*. *Bull. Soc. zool. Fr.*, 82: 354–356.

——— (1960) Révision du genre *Euplotes*, fondée sur la comparaison des structures superficielles. *Hydrobiologia*, 15: 1–77.

TUFFRAU, M. and A. SAVOIE (1961) Étude morphologique du cilié hyménostome *Disematostoma colpidioides* von Gelei, 1954. *J. Protozool.*, 8. [In press]

TURNER, H. J., Jr. (1954) An improved method of staining the external organelles of hypotrichs. *J. Protozool.*, 1: 18–19.

TURNER, J. P. (1930) Division and conjugation in *Euplotes patella* Ehrenberg with special reference to the nuclear phenomena. *Univ. Calif. Publ. Zool.*, 33: 193–258.

——— (1933) The external fibrillar system of *Euplotes* with notes on the neuromotor apparatus. *Biol. Bull.*, 64: 53–66.

——— (1937) Studies on the ciliate *Tillina canalifera* n. sp. *Trans. Amer. micr. Soc.*, 56: 447–456.

——— (1940) Cytoplasmic inclusions in the ciliate *Tillina canalifera* Turner. *Arch. Protistenk.*, 93: 255–272.

——— (1941) Fertilization in protozoa. *In* Calkins, G. N. and F. M. Summers, editors, Protozoa in Biological Research, pp. 583–645. Columbia Univ. Press, New York.

UBISCH, M. VON (1913) Ein Beitrag zur Kenntnis der Gattung *Lagenophrys. Arch. Protistenk.*, 29: 39–77.

UHLIG, G. (1960) Entwicklungsphysiologische Untersuchungen zur Morphogenese von *Stentor coeruleus* Ehrbg. *Arch. Protistenk.*, 105: 1–109.

ULRICH, W. (1950) Begriff und Einteilung der Protozoen. *In* Moderne Biologie, Festschrift zum 60. Geburtstag von Hans Nachtsheim, Berlin, pp. 241–250.

UYEMURA, M. (1934) Über einige neue Ciliaten aus dem Darmkanal von japanischen Echinoideen (I). *Sci. Rep. Tokyo Bunrika Daigaku* (Sect. B), 1: 181–191.

UZMANN, J. R. and A. P. STICKNEY (1954) *Trichodina myicola* n. sp., a peritrichous ciliate from the marine bivalve *Mya arenaria* L. *J. Protozool.*, 1: 149–155.

VAN WAGTENDONK, W. J. (1955) Encystment and excystment of protozoa. *In* Hutner, S. H. and A. Lwoff, editors, Biochemistry and Physiology of Protozoa, Vol. II, pp. 85–90. Academic Press, New York.

VAN WAGTENDONK, W. J., SIMONSEN, D. H., and L. P. ZILL (1952) The use of electromigration techniques in washing and concentrating cultures of *Paramecium aurelia. Physiol. Zoöl.*, 25: 312–317.

VERSCHAFFELT, F. (1930) Bijtrage tot de kennis der nederlandsche soet-en brakwater protozoen. *Bot. Jaarb.*, 21: 1–198. [In Flemish]

VERWORN, M. (1889) Psycho-physiologische Protisten-Studien. Experimentelle Untersuchungen. G. Fischer, Jena. 227 pp.

VIAUD, G. and N. BONAVENTURE (1956) Recherches expérimentales sur le galvanotropisme des paramécies. *Bull. biol. France Belg.*, 90: 287–319.

VIEWEGER, T. (1912) Recherches sur la sensibilité des infusoires (alcaliooxytaxisme), les réflexes locomoteurs, l'action des sels. *Arch. Biol., Paris*, 27: 723–799.

VILLENEUVE-BRACHON, S. (1940) Recherches sur le ciliés hétérotriches. *Arch. Zool. exp. gén.*, 82: 1–180.

VISSCHER, J. P. (1923) Feeding reactions in the ciliate, *Dileptus gigas*, with special reference to the function of trichocysts. *Biol. Bull.*, 45: 113–143.

——— (1927) Conjugation in the ciliated protozoan, *Dileptus gigas*, with special reference to the nuclear phenomena. *J. Morph.*, 44: 383–415.

VIVIER, É. (1955) Contribution à l'étude de la conjugaison chez *Paramecium caudatum. Bull. Soc. zool. Fr.*, 80: 163–170.

——— (1960) Cycle nucléolaire en rapport avec l'alimentation chez *Paramecium caudatum. C. R. Acad. Sci., Paris*, 250: 205–207.

Vojtek, J. (1957) Zur Kenntnis der Gattung *Trichodina* Ehrenberg 1830. *Mém. Soc. zool. tchécosl.*, 21: 173–180.

Vörösváry, B. (1950) Die Ciliaten des " Kalános "-Baches. *Ann. Biol. Univ. szeged.*, 1: 343–387. [In Hungarian with Russian and German summaries]

Wailes, G. H. (1943) Canadian Pacific Fauna. 1. Protozoa. 1f. Ciliata. 1g. Suctoria. Univ. Toronto Press, Toronto. 46 pp.

Walker, P. M. B. and J. M. Mitchison (1957) DNA synthesis in two ciliates. *Exp. Cell Res.*, 13: 167–170.

Wallengren, H. (1894) Studier öfver Ciliata infusorier. I. Slägtet *Licnophora* Claparède. *Acta Univ. lund.*, 48 pp. [In Swedish with German summary]

——— (1895) Studier öfver Ciliata infusorier. II. Slägtet *Heliochona* Plate, slägtet *Chilodochona* n. g., slägtet *Hemispeira* Fabre-Domergue. *Acta Univ. lund.*, 77 pp. [In Swedish with German summary]

——— (1897) Studier öfver Ciliata infusorier. III. Bidrag till Kännedomen om Fam. Urceolarina Stein. *Särt. fysiogr. sällsk. Handl.*, 8: 1–48. [In Swedish with German summary]

——— (1900) Zur Kenntnis der vergleichenden Morphologie der hypotrichen Infusorien. *Bih. svensk. VetenskAkad. Handl.*, 26: 1–31.

——— (1901) Zur Kenntniss der Neubildungs- und Resorptionsprozesses bei der Theilung der hypotrichen Infusorien. *Zool. Jb. (Abt. Anat. u. Ontog. Thiere)*, 15: 1–58.

——— (1902) Inanitionserscheinungen der Zelle. Untersuchungen an Protozoen. *Z. allg. Physiol.*, 1: 67–128.

Wang, C. C. (1925) Study of the protozoa of Nanking. I. *Contr. biol. Lab. Sci. Soc. China*, 1: 1–160.

——— (1928) Ecological studies of the seasonal distribution of protozoa in a fresh-water pond. *J. Morph.*, 46: 431–478.

——— (1940) Notes on some freshwater infusoria. *Sinensia*, 11: 11–32.

Wang, C. C. and D. Nie (1932) A survey of the marine protozoa of Amoy. *Contr. biol. Lab. Sci. Soc. China*, 8: 285–385.

——— (1933) Report on the rare and new species of freshwater infusoria. I. *Contr. biol. Lab. Sci. Soc. China*, 10: 1–99.

——— (1935) Report on the rare and new species of freshwater infusoria. II. *Sinensia*, 6: 399–524.

Watanabe, K. (1957a) Cytological studies on *Paramecium*. *Ochan. Igaku Zasshi*, 5: 455–472. [In Japanese with English summary]

——— (1957b) Variation in number of micronuclei in *Paramecium caudatum*. *Annot. zool. jap.*, 30: 211–216.

——— (1959) Effect of colchicine on binary fission and conjugation in *Paramecium caudatum*. *Annot. zool. jap.*, 32: 129–132.

Watanabe, K. and S. Tsuda (1957) The fine structure of pellicle and pharynx of *Paramecium* observed with electron microscope. *Zool. Mag.*, 66: 183–186. [In Japanese with English summary]

WATSON, J. M. (1940) Studies on the morphology and bionomics of a little-known holotrichous ciliate — *Balantiophorus minutus* Schew. I. Structure and relationships. *J. roy. micr. Soc.*, 60: 207–231.

———— (1944) Studies on the morphology and bionomics of a little-known holotrichous ciliate — *Balantiophorus minutus* Schew. II. The effect of environmental factors. *J. roy. micr. Soc.*, 64: 31–67.

———— (1945a) The identity of the ciliate *Balantidium minutum*, an alleged parasite of man. *Trans. roy. Soc. trop. Med. Hyg.*, 39: 151–160.

———— (1945b) A new ophryoscolecid ciliate, *Entodinium insolitum*, sp. n., from the Indian rhinoceros. *Proc. zool. Soc. Lond.*, 114: 507–522.

———— (1946a) Studies on the morphology and bionomics of a little-known holotrichous ciliate — *Balantiophorus minutus* Schew. III. Coprophilic habits and the effect of urine. *Parasitology*, 37: 138–151.

———— (1946b) The bionomics of coprophilic protozoa. *Biol. Revs.*, 21: 121–139.

WEATHERBY, J. H. (1929) Excretion of nitrogenous substances in protozoa. *Physiol. Zoöl.*, 2: 375–394.

WEBB, M. G. (1956) An ecological study of brackish water ciliates. *J. Anim. Ecol.*, 25: 148–175.

WEBER, G. (1912) Die Bewegung der Peristomcilien bei den heterotrichen Infusorien. *S. B. Akad. Wiss. Wien*, 121 (Abt. III): 3–48.

WEILL, R. (1946) *Ctenoctophrys chattoni* n. g., n. sp. infusoire planctonique octoradié, à caractère de méduse et de cténophore. *C. R. Acad. Sci., Paris*, 222: 683–685.

WEISZ, P. B. (1948) Regeneration in *Stentor* and the gradient theory. *J. exp. Zool.*, 109: 439–450.

———— (1949) The role of the macronucleus in the differentiation of *Blepharisma undulans*. *J. Morph.*, 85: 503–518.

———— (1950a) On the mitochondrial nature of the pigmented granules in *Stentor* and *Blepharisma*. *J. Morph.*, 86: 177–184.

———— (1950b) Multiconjugation in *Blepharisma*. *Biol. Bull.*, 98: 242–246.

———— (1950c) On the morphogenetic rôle of the macronucleus during conjugation in *Blepharisma undulans*. *J. exp. Zool.*, 114: 293–304.

———— (1951a) A general mechanism of differentiation based on morphogenetic studies in ciliates. *Amer. Nat.*, 85: 293–311.

———— (1951b) An experimental analysis of morphogenesis in *Stentor coeruleus*. *J. exp. Zool.*, 116: 231–258.

———— (1954) Morphogenesis in protozoa. *Quart. Rev. Biol.*, 29: 207–229.

———— (1955) Chemical inhibition of regeneration in *Stentor coeruleus*. *J. cell. comp. Physiol.*, 46: 517–528.

———— (1956) Experiments on the initiation of division in *Stentor coeruleus*. *J. exp. Zool.*, 131: 137–162.

WELLS, C. (1959) The differential survival of three interbreeding clones of *Tetrahymena pyriformis* after X-irradiation. (Abstr.) *J. Protozool.*, 6 (Suppl.): 18–19.

——— (1960a, b) [Please see p. 287]

WENRICH, D. H. (1926) The structure and division of *Paramecium trichium* Stokes. *J. Morph.*, 43: 81–103.

——— (1928a) *Paramecium woodruffi* n. sp. (Protozoa, Ciliata). *Trans. Amer. micr. Soc.*, 47: 256–261.

——— (1928b) Eight well-defined species of *Paramecium* (Protozoa, Ciliata). *Trans. Amer. micr. Soc.*, 47: 275–282.

——— (1929a) The structure and behavior of *Actinobolus vorax* n. sp. (Protozoa, Ciliata). *Biol. Bull.*, 56: 390–401.

——— (1929b) Observations on some freshwater ciliates (Protozoa). I. *Teuthophrys trisulca* Chatton and de Beauchamp and *Stokesia vernalis* n. g., n. sp. *Trans. Amer. micr. Soc.*, 48: 221–241.

——— (1929c) Observations on some freshwater ciliates (Protozoa). II. *Paradileptus*, n. gen. *Trans. Amer. micr. Soc.*, 48: 352–365.

———, editor (1954) Sex in Microorganisms. AAAS Pub., Washington, D. C. 362 pp.

WENRICH, D. H. and W. F. DILLER (1950) Methods of Protozoology. *In* Jones, R. McC., editor, McClung's Handbook of Microscopical Technique, pp. 432–474. 3rd ed. Hoeber, New York.

WENYON, C. M. (1926) Protozoology, A Manual for Medical Men, Veterinarians and Zoologists. Vols. I and II. Baillière, Tindall and Cox, London. 1,563 pp.

WENZEL, F. (1953) Die Ciliaten der Moosrasen trockner Standorte. *Arch. Protistenk.*, 99: 70–141.

——— (1955) Über eine Artentstehung innerhalb der Gattung *Spathidium* (Holotricha, Ciliata). [*S. ascendens* n. sp. und *S. polymorphum* n. sp.] *Arch. Protistenk.*, 100: 515–540.

WERMEL, E. M. (1928) Untersuchungen über *Chromidina elegans* (Foett.) Gond. *Arch. Protistenk.*, 64: 419–445.

WEST, L. S. (1953) Protozoa of the Upper Peninsula of Michigan. *Pap. Mich. Acad. Sci.*, 38 (yr. 1952): 269–284.

WETZEL, A. (1925) Vergleichend-cytologische Untersuchungen an Ciliaten. *Arch. Protistenk.*, 51: 209–304.

——— (1927) Über zwei unbekannte holotriche Ciliaten, *Frontoniella complanata* nov. gen. spec. und *Spathidium caudatum* n. sp. *Arch. Protistenk.*, 60: 130–141.

——— (1928) Der Faulschlamm und seine Ziliaten Leitformen. *Z. Morph. Ökol. Tiere*, 13: 179–328.

WESSENBERG, H. (1957) Studies on the life cycle and morphogenesis of *Opalina*. (Abstr.) *J. Protozool.*, 4 (Suppl.): 13.

WEYER, G. (1930) Untersuchungen über die Morphologie und Physiologie des Formwechsels der *Gastrostyla steinii* Engelmann. *Arch. Protistenk.*, 71: 139–228.

WHITELEY, A. H. (1960) [Please see p. 287]

WICHTERMAN, R. (1937) Division and conjugation in *Nyctotherus cordiformis* (Ehr.) Stein (Protozoa, Ciliata) with special reference to the nuclear phenomena. *J. Morph.*, 60: 563–611.

——— (1940) Cytogamy: a sexual process occurring in living joined pairs of *Paramecium caudatum* and its relation to other sexual phenomena. *J. Morph.*, 66: 423–451.

——— (1942) A new ciliate from a coral of Tortugas and its symbiotic zooxanthellae. *Pap. Tortugas Lab.*, 33: 105–111.

——— (1948) The biological effects of x-rays on mating types and conjugation of *Paramecium bursaria*. *Biol. Bull.*, 94: 113–127.

——— (1951) The ecology, cultivation, structural characteristics and mating types of *Paramecium calkinsi*. *Proc. Pa. Acad. Sci.*, 25: 51–65.

——— (1952) A method for obtaining abundant dividing stages of *Paramecium. Trans. Amer. micr. Soc.*, 71: 303–305.

——— (1953) The Biology of *Paramecium*. Blakiston, Philadelphia. 527 pp.

——— (1955) The usefulness of the one-celled animal, *Paramecium*, in studying the biological effects of high-dosage X-radiation. *Proc. Pa. Acad. Sci.*, 29: 78–93.

——— (1959) Mutation in the protozoan *Paramecium multimicronucleatum* as a result of X-irradiation. *Science*, 129: 207–208.

WILLIAMS, N. E. (1959) The formation of reproductive cysts by *Tetrahymena vorax*. (Abstr.) *J. Protozool.*, 6 (Suppl.): 14.

——— (1960a, b) [Please see p. 287)

WILLIAMS, N. E. and O. H. SCHERBAUM (1959) Morphogenetic events in normal and synchronously dividing *Tetrahymena*. *J. Embryol. exp. Morph.*, 7: 241–256.

WILLIS, A. G. (1942) Studies on *Lagenophrys tattersalli* sp. n. (Ciliata, Peritricha, Vorticellinac). Part I. Structure, asexual reproduction and metamorphosis. *Quart. J. micr. Sci.*, 83: 171–196.

——— (1945) On the structure and life-history of *Metephelota coronata* gen. nov., sp. nov. (Suctoria, Ephelotidae). *Trans. roy. Soc. Edinb.*, 61: 399–413.

——— (1948) Studies on *Lagenophrys tattersalli* (Ciliata, Peritricha, Vorticellinae). Part II. Observations on bionomics, conjugation, and apparent endomixis. *Quart. J. micr. Sci.*, 89: 385–400.

WILSON, E. B. (1928) The Cell in Development and Heredity. Macmillan, New York. 1,232 pp.

WINDSOR, D. A. (1959) *Colpoda steinii* and *Tetrahymena limacis* in several terrestrial pulmonate gastropods collected in Illinois. (Abstr.) *J. Protozool.*, 6: (Suppl.): 33.

——— (1960) [Please see p. 287]

WINKLER, R. H. and J. O. CORLISS (1961?) [Please see p. 287]

WITTNER, M. (1957a) Effects of temperature and pressure on oxygen poisoning of *Paramecium*. *J. Protozool.*, 4: 20–23.

—— (1957b) Inhibition and reversal of oxygen poisoning in *Paramecium*. *J. Protozool.*, 4: 24–29.

WOHLFARTH-BOTTERMANN, K. E. (1950) Funktion und Struktur der *Paramecium*-Trichocysten. *Naturwissenschaften*, 37: 562–563.

—— (1954) Cytologische Studien I. Zur sublichtmikroskopischen Struktur des Cytoplasmas und zum Nachweis seiner "Partikel-populationen." *Protoplasma*, 43: 347–381.

—— (1956) Protistenstudien VII. Die Feinstruktur der Mitochondrien von *Paramecium caudatum*. *Z. Naturforsch.*, 11b: 578–580.

—— (1957) Cytologische Studien IV. Die Entstehung, Vermehrung und Sekretabgabe der Mitochondrien von *Paramecium*. *Z. Naturforsch.*, 12b: 164–167.

—— (1958a) Cytologische Studien II. Die Feinstruktur des Cytoplasmas von *Paramecium*. *Protoplasma*, 49: 231–247.

—— (1958b) Cytologische Studien V. Feinstrukturveränderungen des Cytoplasmas und der Mitochondrien von *Paramecium* nach Einwirkung letaler Temperaturen und Röntgendosen. *Protoplasma*, 50: 82–92.

WOHLFARTH-BOTTERMANN, K. E. and G. PFEFFERKORN (1953) Protistenstudien I. Pro- und Nesselkapseltrichocysten der Ciliaten-Gattung *Prorodon*. *Z. wiss. Mikr.*, 61: 239–248.

WOODRUFF, L. L. (1905) An experimental study on the life-history of hypotrichous infusoria. *J. exp. Zool.*, 2: 585–632.

—— (1911) *Paramaecium aurelia* and *Paramaecium caudatum*. *J. Morph.*, 22: 223–237.

—— (1912) Observation on the origin and sequence of the protozoan fauna of hay infusions. *J. exp. Zool.*, 12: 203–264.

—— (1913) Cell size, nuclear size and the nucleo-cytoplasmic relation during the life of a pedigreed race of *Oxytricha fallax*. *J. exp. Zool.*, 15: 1–22.

—— (1921a) Micronucleate and amicronucleate races of infusoria. *J. exp. Zool.*, 34: 329–337.

—— (1921b) The structure, life history, and intrageneric relationships of *Paramecium calkinsi*, sp. nov. *Biol. Bull.*, 41: 171–180.

—— (1938) Philosophers in little things. *Univ. Okla. Bull.*, No. 739, pp. 21–33.

—— (1939a) Some pioneers in microscopy with special reference to protozoology. *Trans. N. Y. Acad. Sci.*, 1: 74–77.

—— (1939b) Microscopy before the nineteenth century. *Amer. Nat.*, 73: 485–516.

—— (1945) The early history of the genus *Paramecium* with special reference to *Paramecium aurelia* and *Paramecium caudatum*. *Trans. Conn. Acad. Arts Sci.*, 36: 517–531.

WOODRUFF, L. L. and R. ERDMANN (1914) A normal periodic reorganization process without cell fusion in *Paramecium*. *J. exp. Zool.*, 17: 425–518.

WOODRUFF, L. L. and H. SPENCER (1922) Studies on *Spathidium spathula*. I. The structure and behavior of *Spathidium* with special reference to the capture and ingestion of its prey. *J. exp. Zool.*, 35: 189–205.

—— (1924) Studies on *Spathidium spathula*. II. The significance of conjugation. *J. exp. Zool.*, 39: 133–196.

WORLEY, L. G. (1933) The intracellular fibre systems of *Paramecium*. *Proc. nat. Acad. Sci.*, *Wash.*, 19: 323–326.

—— (1934) Ciliary metachronism and reversal in *Paramecium*, *Spirostomum* and *Stentor*. *J. cell. comp. Physiol.*, 5: 53–72.

WRISBERG, H. A. (1765) Observationum de Animalculis Infusoriis Satura. Vendenhoeck, Goettingae. 110 pp.

WRZESNIOWSKI, A. (1870) Beobachtungen über Infusorien aus der Umgebung von Warschau. *Z. wiss. Zool.*, 20: 467–511.

—— (1877) Beiträge zur Naturgeschichte der Infusorien. *Z. wiss. Zool.*, 29: 267–323.

YAGIU, R. (1933) Studies on the ciliates from the intestine of *Anthocidaris crassispina* (A. Agassiz). I. *Cyclidium ozakii* sp. nov. and *Strobilidium rapulum* sp. nov. *J. Sci. Hiroshima Univ.* (B, 1), 2: 211–222.

—— (1940) The division, conjugation and nuclear reorganization of *Entorhipidium echini* Lynch. *J. Sci. Hiroshima Univ.* (B, 1), 7: 125–156.

—— (1956a) Studies on the morphogenesis in Ciliata. I. The regulation of the silver line system. *J. Sci. Hiroshima Univ.* (B, 1), 16: 53–59.

—— (1956b) Studies on the morphogenesis in Ciliata. II. The individuality of the macronucleus in maintenance of the peristome. *J. Sci. Hiroshima Univ.* (B, 1), 16: 61–72.

YAGIU, R. and A. NAKATA (1956) The behavior of the macronucleus and micronucleus of *Condylostoma spatiosum*. *J. Sci. Hiroshima Univ.* (B, 1), 16: 73–79.

YAGIU, R. and Y. SHIGENAKA (1956) A new marine ciliate *Blepharisma candidum* n. sp. *J. Sci. Hiroshima Univ.* (B, 1), 16: 81–86.

YAMASAKI, M. (1939) On some new ciliates living in the hind-gut of the roach, *Panesthia angustipennis* Illiger. *Annot. zool. jap.*, 18: 65–74.

YOCOM, H. B. (1918) The neuromotor apparatus of *Euplotes patella*. *Univ. Calif. Publ. Zool.*, 18: 337–396.

—— (1934) Observations on the experimental adaptation of certain fresh-water ciliates to sea water. *Biol. Bull.*, 67: 273–276.

YOUNG, D. (1939) Macronuclear reorganization in *Blepharisma undulans*. *J. Morph.*, 64: 297–353.

YOUNG, D. B. (1922) A contribution to the morphology and physiology of the genus *Uronychia*. *J. exp. Zool.*, 36: 353–395.

YOUNG, M. D. (1950) Attempts to transmit *Balantidium coli*. *Amer. J. trop. Med.*, 30: 71–72.

YOW, F. W. (1958) A study of the regeneration pattern of *Euplotes eurystomus*. *J. Protozool.*, 5: 84–88.

YUSA, A. (1957) The morphology and morphogenesis of the buccal organelles in *Paramecium* with particular reference to their systematic significance. *J. Protozool.*, 4: 128–142.

———— (1960a, b) [Please see additional reference section which commences below]

ZEBRUN, W. (1957) An electron microscopic investigation of nuclear and cytoplasmic structures in *Tetrahymena rostrata*. (Abstr.) *J. Protozool.*, 4 (Suppl.): 22.

ZEUTHEN, E. (1958) Artificial and induced periodicity in living cells. *Adv. biol. med. Physics*, 6: 37–73.

ZEUTHEN, E. and O. H. SCHERBAUM (1954) Synchronous divisions in mass cultures of the ciliate protozoon *Tetrahymena pyriformis*, as induced by temperature changes. *In* Kitching, J. A., editor, Cell Physiology, pp. 141–156. London.

ZICK, K. (1928) *Urceolaria korschelti* n. sp., eine neue marine Urceolarine, nebst einen Überblick über die Urceolarinen. *Z. wiss. Zool.*, 132: 355–403.

ZINGER, J. A. (1929) Beiträge zur Morphologie und Cytologie der Süsswasserinfusorien. *Arch. russes Protist.*, 8: 51–90. [In Russian with German summary]

ZWEIBAUM, J. (1912) La conjugaison et la différenciation sexuelle chez les infusoires (Enriques et Zweibaum). V. Les conditions nécessaires et suffisantes pour la conjugaison du *Paramaecium caudatum*. *Arch. Protistenk.*, 26: 275–393.

ADDITIONAL REFERENCES

[I am indebted to Pergamon Press Ltd. for kindly permitting me, at the late time of reading final page-proofs, to include here the following complete references to several papers not available at earlier dates and to insert brief notices or citations of them in appropriate places in the text of this book and in their proper alphabetical order in preceding pages of the present reference section.]

ADAM, K. M. G. (1951) The quantity and distribution of the ciliate protozoa in the large intestine of the horse. *Parasitology*, 41: 301–311.

———— (1953) *In vivo* observations on the ciliate protozoa inhabiting the large intestine of the horse. *J. gen. Microbiol.*, 9: 376–384.

BARTHELMES, D. (1960) *Tetrahymena parasitica* (Penard 1922) Corliss 1952 als Parasit in Larven vom *Chironomus plumosus*-Typ. *Z. Fischerei*, 9: 273–280.

BEADLE, L. C. and J. R. NILSSON (1959) The effect of anaerobic conditions on two heterotrich ciliate protozoa from papyrus swamps. *J. exp. Biol.*, 36: 583–589.

BEALE, G. H. and A. JURAND (1960) Structure of the mate-killer (mu) particles in *Paramecium aurelia*, stock 540. *J. gen. Microbiol.*, 23: 243–252.

BERGER, J. (1961b?) Systematic studies on the entocommensal ciliates of echinoids. I. A new genus and family of carnivorous ciliates from strongylocentrotid sea urchins. (Ciliata: Trichostomatida). [In preparation]

—— (1961c?) Systematic studies on the entocommensal ciliates of echinoids. II. A revision of the " trichostome " genus *Entodiscus* (Ciliata: Hymenostomatida). [In preparation]

BOCK, K. J. (1952a) Über einige holo- und spirotriche Ciliaten aus den marinen Sandgebieten der Kieler Bucht. *Zool. Anz.*, 149: 107–115.

—— (1952b) Zur Ökologie der Ciliaten des marinen Sandgrundes der Kieler Bucht I. *Kieler Meeresforsch.*, 9: 77–89.

—— (1953) Zur Ökologie der Ciliaten des marinen Sandgrundes der Kieler Bucht II. *Kieler Meeresforsch.*, 9: 252–256.

BOVEE, E. C. (1960) Protozoa of the Mountain Lake region, Giles County, Virginia. *J. Protozool.*, 7: 352–361.

BRETSCHNEIDER, L. H. (1959) Die submikroskopische Struktur der Pellikula von *Epidinium ecaudatum* (Ophryoscolecidae). *Proc. Acad. Sci. Amst.* (ser. C), 62: 542–555.

BUHSE, H. E., Jr. (1960) Some properties of *Tetrahymena paravorax* Corliss, 1957, strain RP. (Abstr.) *J. Protozool.*, 7 (Suppl.): 9–10.

CORLISS, J. O. (1961a) Natural infection of tropical mosquitoes by ciliated protozoa of the genus *Tetrahymena*. *Trans. roy. Soc. trop. Med. Hyg.*, 55. [In press]

—— (1961b) Fixing and Staining of Protozoa. Chapter 36 *in* Lacy, D. and S. O. Palay, editors, The Microtomist's Vade-Mecum (Bolles Lee). 12th ed. Churchill, London. [In press]

CORLISS, J. O. and M. P. DYSART (1960) Evidence of " clonal decline " in *Tetrahymena rostrata* and the apparent effect of autogamy upon this decline. (Abstr.) *J. Protozool.*, 7 (Suppl.): 18.

DE TERRA, N. (1960a) The effect of enucleation on restoration of the interphase rate of ^{32}P uptake after cell division in *Stentor coeruleus*. *Exp. Cell Res.*, 21: 34–40.

—— (1960b) A study of nucleo-cytoplasmic interactions during cell division in *Stentor coeruleus*. *Exp. Cell Res.*, 21: 41–48.

DRAGESCO, J. (1960) Ciliés mésopsammiques littoraux. Systématique, morphologie, écologie. *Trav. Sta. biol. Roscoff* (N.S.), 12: 1–356.

DYSART, M. P. (1960) Study of macronuclear chromatin extrusion in *Tetrahymena limacis* using tritiated thymidine. (Abstr.) *J. Protozool.*, 7 (Suppl.): 10–11.

DYSART, M. P. and J. O. CORLISS (1960) Effect of colchicine and colcemide on fission rate and macronuclear structure in *Tetrahymena limacis*. (Abstr.) *J. Protozool.*, 7 (Suppl.): 10.

EHRET, C. F. (1959b) Photobiology and biochemistry of circadian rhythms in non-photosynthesizing cells. *Fed. Proc.*, 18: 1232–1240.

——— (1960) Organelle systems and biological organization. *Science*, 132: 115–123.

ELLIOTT, A. M., ADDISON, M. A., and S. E. CAREY (1960) *Tetrahymena* from Europe and a new variety from England. (Abstr.) *J. Protozool.*, 7 (Suppl.): 20.

FRANKEL, J. (1960a) Morphogenesis in *Glaucoma chattoni*. *J. Protozool.*, 7: 362–376.

——— (1960b) Effects of localized damage on morphogenesis and cell division in a ciliate, *Glaucoma chattoni*. *J. exp. Zool.*, 143: 175–193.

GRIMSTONE, A. V. (1961) Fine structure and morphogenesis in protozoa. *Biol. Rev.*, 36: 97–150.

GUTTES, E. and S. GUTTES (1960) Incorporation of tritium-labeled thymidine into the macronucleus of *Stentor coeruleus*. *Exp. Cell. Res*, 19: 626–628.

NOIROT-TIMOTHÉE, C. (1959) *Diplodinium moucheti* n. sp. (infusoire cilié). Remarques sur l'évolution des Ophrysocolecidae en Afrique. *Ann. Sci. nat., Zool.* (sér. 12), 1: 331–337.

——— (1960) Étude d'une famille de ciliés: les Ophryoscolecidae. Structures et ultrastructures. *Ann. Sci. nat., Zool.* (sér. 12), 2: 527–718.

SCHERBAUM, O. H. (1960) Synchronous division of micro-organisms. *Ann. Rev. Microbiol.*, 14: 283–310.

SEAMAN, G. R. (1959) Cytochemical evidence for urease activity in *Tetrahymena*. *J. Protozool.*, 6: 331–333.

——— (1960) Large-scale isolation of kinetosomes from the ciliated protozoan *Tetrahymena pyriformis*. *Exp. Cell Res.*, 21: 292–302.

SIMPSON, G. G. (1961) Principles of Animal Taxonomy. Columbia Univ. Press, New York. 247 pp.

SLEIGH, M. A. (1957) Further observations on co-ordination and the determination of frequency in the peristomial cilia of *Stentor*. *J. exp. Biol.*, 34: 106–115.

——— (1960) The form of beat in cilia of *Stentor* and *Opalina*. *J. exp. Biol.*, 37: 1–10.

SMALL, E. B. and R. J. PROFANT (1960a) A reevaluation of the morphology of the hymenostome ciliate *Frontonia leucas* Ehrenberg, 1838, with emphasis on the buccal organization. (Abstr.) *J. Protozool.*, 7 (Suppl.): 9.

——— (1960b) Stomatogenesis as a part of cell division in the hymenostome ciliate *Frontonia leucas* Ehrenberg, 1838. (Abstr.) *J. Protozool.*, 7 (Suppl.): 9.

SONNEBORN, T. M. (1960) The gene and cell differentiation. *Proc. nat. Acad. Sci., Wash.*, 46: 149–165.

Sonneborn, T. M. and R. V. Dippell (1960) The genetic basis of the difference between single and double *Paramecium aurelia*. (Abstr.) *J. Protozool.*, 7 (Suppl.): 26.

Wells, C. (1960a) Identification of free and bound amino acids in three strains of *Tetrahymena pyriformis* using paper chromatography. *J. Protozool.*, 7: 7–10.

——— (1960b) The response of *Tetrahymena pyriformis* to ionizing radiation: strain specific radiosensitivities. *J. cell. comp. Physiol.*, 55: 207–219.

Whiteley, A. H. (1960) Interactions of nucleus and cytoplasm in controlling respiratory patterns in regenerating *Stentor coeruleus*. *Compt. rend. trav. Lab. Carlsberg*, 32: 49–62.

Williams, N. E. (1960a) The polymorphic life history of *Tetrahymena patula*. *J. Protozool.*, 7: 10–17.

——— (1960b) Three sublines of *Tetrahymena vorax* strain V_2 with stable and significant differences. (Abstr.) *J. Protozool.*, 7 (Suppl.): 9.

Windsor, D. A. (1960) Morphological changes exhibited by *Tetrahymena limacis* upon isolation from three newly discovered hosts. (Abstr.) *J. Protozool.*, 7 (Suppl.): 27.

Winkler, R. H. and J. O. Corliss (1961?) Notes on the rarely described green colonial protozoon *Ophrydium versatile* (O.F.M.) (Ciliophora, Peritrichida). [In preparation]

Yusa, A. (1960a) Effects of repetitive electroshock treatment on incorporation of labelled amino acids in *Paramecium*. (Abstr.) *J. Protozool.*, 7 (Suppl.): 27–28.

——— (1960b) Observations on the fine structure of unextruded " resting " trichocysts. (Abstr.) *J. Protozool.*, 7 (Suppl.): 28.

SYSTEMATIC
INDEX

SYSTEMATIC INDEX

INCLUDED here are some 1,400 supraspecific names of ciliates or ciliate-groups. Page references to the classificational section of Part II are given in regular type; all other page references are in *italics*. Names treated as junior *synonyms* or *homonyms*, at any taxonomic level, are *italicized:* there are nearly 400 of these. Names which are considered valid appear as follows: generic, in standard Roman type; familial, in **boldface;** subordinal, ordinal, subclass, class, and subphylum in LARGE AND SMALL capital letters. Plate and figure numbers are included for those genera which have been illustrated (page numbers of Plates are given on pp. vii–viii).